PRECIOUS MOMENTS

by ENESCO

FOURTH EDITION

Secondary Market Price Guide
& Collector Handbook

EDITORIAL

Managing Editor:	Jeff Mahony
Associate Editors:	Melissa A. Bennett
	Gia C. Manalio
	Mike Micciulla
	Paula Stuckart
Assistant Editors:	Heather N. Carreiro
	Jennifer Renk
	Joan C. Wheal
Editorial Assistants:	Timothy R. Affleck
	Beth Hackett
	Christina M. Sette
	Steven Shinkaruk

WEB
(CollectorsQuest.com)

Web Graphic Designer: Ryan Falis

PRODUCTION

Production Manager: Scott Sierakowski

ART

Creative Director:	Joe T. Nguyen
Assistant Art Director:	Lance Doyle
Senior Graphic Designers:	Marla B. Gladstone
	Susannah C. Judd
	David S. Maloney
	Carole Mattia-Slater
	David Ten Eyck
Graphic Designers:	Jennifer J. Bennett
	Sean-Ryan Dudley
	Kimberly Eastman
	Melani Gonzalez
	Jim MacLeod
	Jeremy Maendel
	Chery-Ann Poudrier

R&D

Product Development
Manager: Paul Rasid
R&D Specialist: Priscilla Berthiaume

ISBN 1-585-981-57-5

CheckerBee
PUBLISHING
306 Industrial Park Road
Middletown, CT 06457

CollectorsQuest
•com

Table Of Contents

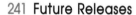

Foreword By Eugene Freedman

Dear Collectors,

It seems like yesterday that Sam Butcher, Yasuhei Fujioka and myself met for the first time to discuss transforming Sam's inspirational artwork of children with teardrop-shaped eyes into sculpted figurines. In reality, it's been 22 years – 22 glorious years. Not only did our friendship blossom during that time, but we've met such extraordinary people,  like you, along the way. It is the PRECIOUS MOMENTS collectors and club members who have made our journey so special.

The year 2000 was an incredible year. As I wrap up the "Around the World With Gene Freedman Tour" to 55 cities worldwide, I fondly remember all the wonderful people I've met at each stop. The hugs, kisses and good wishes bestowed upon me were so special, and your support of Easter Seals was quite generous. Altogether, the PRECIOUS MOMENTS collectors raised more than $25,000 – a true testament to the "loving, caring, sharing" people that you are. I am confident that you will continue your tireless efforts in 2001 for each of the different philanthropies that the PRECIOUS MOMENTS collection supports.

On behalf of Sam and Fujioka-san, I extend my gratitude and love to you, our valued collectors, for your continuous support of the PRECIOUS MOMENTS collection. We've been together for the past 22 years, and I look forward to the next 22 years, because as you know, for PRECIOUS MOMENTS, "the best is yet to come."

God Bless,

Eugene Freedman

Founding Chairman
Enesco Group, Inc.

Introducing The Collector's Value Guide™

For over two decades, the Enesco PRECIOUS MOMENTS® line of collectibles has provided its fans with enjoyment. With its start as a small line of inspirational figurines, the collection has since grown to contain over 2,000 pieces. Therefore, it stands to reason, that it is no easy task to keep track of your collection. So our *Collector's Value Guide™ to PRECIOUS MOMENTS® by Enesco* is here to help! The Value Guide is the perfect resource to help you keep track of which figurines you own and to record their current values on the secondary market.

In the Value Guide, you will find up-to-date information on each PRECIOUS MOMENTS piece. Each piece appears with information on its release date, retail status and original retail price. You will also find an easy-to-use production mark chart that will show you all of the years the piece was produced, as well as a secondary market value for each mark. In addition to the large, full-color pictures of each piece, the Value Guide contains great information on all aspects of this adorable line of collectibles; from an in-depth biography of Sam Butcher, the artist whose drawings bring each and every beloved PRECIOUS MOMENTS piece to life, to a look at the ten most valuable pieces in the PRECIOUS MOMENTS collection. And that's not all – in our guide you'll also find:

* *New introductions for 2001!*
* *A tour of the PRECIOUS MOMENTS® Chapel!*
* *A spotlight on Sam Butcher's new collection, Saminals!*
* *Fun and easy ways to display and enjoy your PRECIOUS MOMENTS® collection!*
* *Tips on how to shop the secondary market!*
* *A look at the PRECIOUS MOMENTS® Care-A-Van!*
* *And much, much more!*

The PRECIOUS MOMENTS® Story

It's been over 20 years since Sam Butcher and Enesco brought the PRECIOUS MOMENTS collection and its message of "loving, caring and sharing" to the world. Today, the message continues to reach thousands of people each year as they discover the joy and fun of collecting PRECIOUS MOMENTS.

The Beginning . . .

It all began back in 1974 when an artist named Sam Butcher and his friend Bill Biel formed an inspirational greeting card company called "Jonathan and David." Butcher named the line of greeting cards, which featured inspirational messages and drawings of teardrop-eyed children, "Precious Moments" because they were "messengers of love, caring and sharing." In 1978, at a trade show in Los  Angeles, Eugene Freedman, then CEO and Chairman of Enesco, spotted Butcher's cards and immediately realized the potential of the artist's renderings. He offered to turn the cards into a line of collectible figurines, but Butcher was hesitant, fearing that commercialization of his product would diminish its meaning.

 Undeterred, Freedman brought one of the cards to his longtime friend, Master Sculptor Yasuhei Fujioka and asked him to create a porcelain bisque figurine of the drawing. When Butcher saw the finished product, he was so in awe of the perfect translation of his message that he wept with joy. It was then that the PRECIOUS MOMENTS collection was born.

In the fall of 1978, the "Original 21" figurines, which included "Love One Another" (the first figurine sculpted by Fujioka), made their debut at a trade show in Chicago. The pieces were an immediate hit with retailers and collectors alike. Freedman, Butcher and Fujioka then formed the team that has since brought approximately 2,000 PRECIOUS MOMENTS pieces to the world. The PRECIOUS MOMENTS collection has now expanded from just

figurines to include bells, ornaments, plates, hinged boxes, thimbles and more and has become one of the most popular collectible lines in the world.

Enesco, which produces PRECIOUS MOMENTS, is one of the world's leading producers of fine collectibles with a product line that encompasses more than 10,000 giftware, collectible and home accent items. The PRECIOUS MOMENTS collection is one of their most popular lines among collectors and industry professionals alike. The company has won several awards for PRECIOUS MOMENTS through the years, including The National Association of Limited Edition Dealers' (NALED) "Collectible Of The Year" award in 1992 and "Figurine Of The Year" in 1994. Enesco was also recognized with the "Ornament Of The Year" award in 1994, 1995 and 1996.

Precious Collectibles

As the PRECIOUS MOMENTS collection has grown, Enesco has had to periodically retire or suspend pieces to make room for new figurines. When a piece is retired, the mold is broken and that piece will never be produced again. Suspended production, however, means that a figurine may be reintroduced at a future date. Retirements and suspensions also carry the added benefit of helping to keep collectors excited about the line. The thrill of obtaining a piece just before it is retired is one of the many joys that comes along with being a PRECIOUS MOMENTS collector.

The molds of retired Enesco PRECIOUS MOMENTS figurines being broken by a bulldozer during a collector event.

Other PRECIOUS MOMENTS figurines are sometimes limited by time or production quantity. Annuals are pieces which are marked with the year they were produced and are available only for that year. A number of ornaments are produced in this manner. Both annuals and limited edition pieces are considered "closed" after their production run has ended. Another exciting aspect of collecting is the hunt for store and catalog exclusives. These pieces are often the most difficult to obtain, since they are only available through a limited number of outlets and often sell out very quickly.

To collectors, one of the most important aspects of PRECIOUS MOMENTS pieces are the production marks which are found on the bottom of the figurines. Production marks have been used since 1981 and serve as a classification system to help collectors determine the year in which their pieces were produced. Figurines created prior to 1981 are referred to as "no mark" pieces, while pieces produced after 1981 in which the mark has been left off are considered "unmarked." (See the *Production Mark Chart* on page 29 for more information.)

A PRECIOUS MOMENTS figurine stamped with a 1989 production mark.

The PRECIOUS MOMENTS® Community

Another important dimension was added to the collection in 1981, as well. For the first time, a PRECIOUS MOMENTS collectors' club was formed, giving collectors a new way to share their love of PRECIOUS MOMENTS figurines. By the end of its first year, nearly

The cover of an issue of the quarterly "GOODNEWSLETTER" publication.

70,000 collectors had joined the club. Each year, all of the members of The PRECIOUS MOMENTS *Collectors' Club* receive the "GOODNEWSLETTER" publication which keeps them informed of PRECIOUS MOMENTS news, as well as serves as a place to share stories, inspiration and even decorating tips. Members also have the opportunity to purchase special "members only" figurines and gifts. Since 1981, two other clubs have been introduced to the delight of fans of the line. The Enesco PRECIOUS MOMENTS *Birthday Club*® was established in 1995 for younger PRECIOUS MOMENTS collectors, but is no longer in existence. In 1999 the *Birthday Club* was replaced in by The PRECIOUS MOMENTS *Fun Club*®, which offers its own fun, colorful newsletter and special offers.

In keeping with the principles of compassion and love that PRECIOUS MOMENTS promote, Enesco serves as a corporate sponsor to several charities and organizations, including Easter Seals, the Boys & Girls Clubs Of America, the National Alliance of Breast Cancer Organizations, and The Special Olympics. Enesco often offers special pieces whose proceeds go to help these charities or organizations. For instance, $2.00 of the proceeds of every sale of the figurine "A Winning Spirit Comes From Within" are donated to benefit The Special Olympics.

Enesco also sponsors several activities and programs which help to spread the PRECIOUS MOMENTS message around the country. The Care-A-Van program was initiated in 1998 to help celebrate the PRECIOUS MOMENTS collection's 20th anniversary. The colorfully decorated traveling museum is filled with a variety of special PRECIOUS MOMENTS pieces. In fact, it proved to be so popular that it has continued to travel the country ever since. In 2000, the Care-A-Van sported a new look as it traveled the land with the mission of honoring

The interior of the PRECIOUS MOMENTS Care-A-Van.

our men and women in the military, as well as Special Olympics athletes. The van made stops at five Special Olympics events, 35 military bases and the International Collectible Expositions held in Georgia and Illinois.

Another exciting event in 2000 was Enesco Founding Chairman Eugene Freedman's 75th birthday on March 9. In order to honor his special day, Sam Butcher designed his first mustachioed figure, titled, "Precious Moments Will Last Forever." Freedman then embarked on a worldwide tour of 55 Century Circle Retailers to meet collectors and sign the special tour figurine. Enesco partnered with Easter Seals for the entire tour and raised money for the charity through generous collector donations.

More Moments

Although the success of PRECIOUS MOMENTS has been phenomenal, Sam Butcher and Enesco have never been content to rest on their laurels. In 1996, Butcher created LITTLE MOMENTS®, a line of smaller versions of the teardrop-eyed figurines. In 1998, he invited collectors to take a walk down COUNTRY LANE™, a collection Butcher created based on his memories of time spent on his Grandma Ethel's farm. TENDER TAILS, a collection of plush beanbags, was introduced in 1997, and finally, a line of miniature teardrop-eyed resin animals, called *Saminals*, were introduced in 2000.

The Future ...

In 1984, Sam Butcher began work on The PRECIOUS MOMENTS® Chapel, with the intent of providing people with a place of worship, comfort and peace. Inspired by a visit to the Sistine Chapel, Butcher painted a mural on the ceiling of the Chapel that covers more than 1,400 square feet. Although Butcher feels that his work on the Chapel will never be complete, the grounds currently cover over 2,000 acres and include a wedding chapel, a gallery museum and the breathtaking Fountain of Angels.

What's next is anyone's guess, but collectors hope Sam Butcher and his inspirational creations will be around for many years to come.

Enesco And Precious Moments®, Inc. Biographies

Enesco Group, Inc., one of the world's leading manufacturers of collectible and giftware lines, originated in 1958 as the import gifts division of the N. Shure Company. Upon disbanding

The Enesco headquarters located in Itasca, Illinois.

from N. Shure, Enesco adopted its unique name, derived from the phonetic pronunciation of its parent company's initials (N.S. Co.). Eugene Freedman has been with the company since its early days, and is responsible for bringing PRECIOUS MOMENTS into the Enesco fold in 1978. The production of the first collection of PRECIOUS MOMENTS pieces in 1978 has been cited as the primary factor in Enesco's explosive growth and success.

In 1983, Enesco was purchased by Stanhome Inc. – a move that helped the company expand its operations globally. Today, Enesco is based in Itasca, Illinois and has over 18 branches worldwide with distribution of its products in more than 30 countries. In addition to PRECIOUS MOMENTS, the company handles many other fine collectible and giftware lines, including Cherished Teddies®, Harry Potter™, Lilliput Lane® and Mary's Moo Moos®.

PRECIOUS MOMENTS®, Inc. was formed in 1991 in response to the overwhelming demand for PRECIOUS MOMENTS products. PMI oversees the licensing and product approvals for the PRECIOUS MOMENTS collection, making certain that only the highest quality products are produced. PMI has a library of over 3,500 PRECIOUS MOMENTS images as well as a research and development center, which it makes available to licensees. Sam Butcher's eldest son, Jon, holds the position of C.E.O. of the St. Charles, Illinois-based company, while Sara Pilafas occupies the position of company president.

Eugene Freedman Biography

As the Founding Chairman and a director of Enesco Group, Inc., Eugene Freedman has been with the company since its inception in 1958 and has been a crucial force in guiding Enesco to its current status as a worldwide leader in the collectible and giftware industry.

Freedman was raised in Milwaukee and attended college at Northwestern University and the California Institute of Technology. He also served in the South Pacific during World War II, and received his naval officer's commission from Notre Dame upon his return.

In the early 1950s, Freedman returned to Milwaukee and took a job as salesman for a gifts and novelty company. The lure of opening his own business was strong, however, and he left to open a plastics and decorative figurine manufacturing plant in 1958. Finding himself still unsatisfied, he soon sold his shares in that company and went in search of a new adventure.

Freedman found his destiny in the form of the N. Shure Company, which had just opened an import gifts branch called Enesco. Freedman pooled his money with six others to buy the branch and took over the job of buying giftware from Europe and Asia.

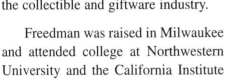

Some 20 years later, while on a flight layover, he happened upon Sam Butcher's artwork. He immediately saw the possibilities for transforming the teardrop-eyed children into figurines, and the PRECIOUS MOMENTS collection was born. Today, Freedman still holds the line close to his heart, and works to spread the tenets of "loving, caring and sharing" all over the world.

Yasuhei Fujioka Biography

Master Sculptor Yasuhei Fujioka has spent a lifetime perfecting his art. The man with the "magical hands" has been responsible for transforming artist Sam Butcher's two-dimensional drawings into life-like porcelain bisque figurines ever since creating the very first PRECIOUS MOMENTS prototype in 1978.

Fujioka was born into a family of artisans in 1921 in Nagoya, Japan. He learned at a young age to love his family's craft and went on to study advanced ceramics in college. In 1955, after 10 years in the ceramics field, he opened his own design studio, where he has worked ever since. Since opening the studio, Master Sculptor Fujioka has been on a mission to make the best porcelain and giftware sculptures in the industry.

Fujioka and Enesco's Eugene Freedman met in 1960 and soon became friends, as well as business associates. Freedman turned to Fujioka when he needed a prototype sculpture made of Sam Butcher's drawings. The result was the first PRECIOUS MOMENTS piece, called "Love One Another." When Butcher saw Fujioka's rendering of his drawing he was so impressed that he asked to meet the sculptor. Butcher knew immediately that Fujioka was the right one to "breathe life" into his artwork.

In 1995, Fujioka handed over the job of President of the Design Studio to his son, Shuhei Fujioka, though he still serves as Master Sculptor and oversees the studio's 10 to 15 artisans. In his spare time, Fujioka conceived and created two of his own lines for Enesco – Coral Kingdom and Heavenly Kingdom.

Sam Butcher Biography

Artists often seem more sensitive than the rest of us and Sam Butcher, the multi-talented artist and creator of the beloved PRECIOUS MOMENTS line, is no different. Over the past 20-odd years he has touched the lives of millions of people with his heart-warming depictions of teardrop-eyed children and his messages of "loving, caring and sharing."

Born in Jackson, Michigan on New Year's Day in 1939, Butcher was the third of five children born to an English-Irish mechanic and his Lebanese-Syrian wife. His love of art was apparent early on and his artistic nature separated him somewhat from his more practical working-class family members. He would spend long hours entertaining himself by making up stories and drawing pictures to illustrate them. By the time he entered kindergarten, Butcher knew that he wanted to become an artist. As his family was poor, Butcher would often scour area garbage dumps looking for scraps of paper and other materials on which to draw.

At the age of 10, Butcher's family moved to northern California. There, he began to receive encouragement in his artistic endeavors. Although Butcher had to travel 60 miles to attend the nearest school, he began to find solace as his teachers noticed his talent and encouraged the budding artist. Although his father stressed the importance of getting a job over getting an education, young Butcher was not to be deterred. His hard work was rewarded in 1957 during his senior year of high school when he was awarded a scholarship to attend the College of Arts and Crafts in Berkeley, California.

During his first year in Berkeley, Butcher met his future wife, Katie Cushman. The two were married two years later and baby Jon,

their first child, was born in 1962. In order to support his young wife and child, Butcher left school to find a full-time job. He held a variety of jobs to support his family, including working as a janitor, a dishwasher and a short order cook. In 1963, after their second child Philip was born, the Butchers began attending a small local church. As Butcher began to study the Bible, his devotion to God grew and he soon gave over his life to the Lord. This newfound faith led Butcher to accept a job as a "chalkboard minister" where he would use chalk illustrations to teach children about the Lord and to restore faith and comfort to adults who were going through difficult times.

Through church contacts, Butcher found a position as a staff artist with the International Child Evangelism Fellowship in Grand Rapids, Michigan. This job enabled him to showcase his work in a variety of mediums, including a weekly television program.

By 1974, the Butcher family had grown to include seven children and Sam continued to supplement his income with janitorial work. In his spare time, Butcher had been making inspirational greeting cards to give to friends and family members which featured the now-famous teardrop-eyed children. His friend Bill Biel saw that Butcher's artwork was truly a gift and should be shared with the public. Together, they formed a company called "Jonathan and David" (named for the Biblical friendship of David and Prince Jonathan) and began selling the cards to Christian bookstores.

Fate stepped in soon when Enesco chairman and CEO Eugene Freedman spotted the cards at a Los Angeles trade show in 1978. He was impressed with what he saw and approached Butcher about creating a figurine line. Butcher was hesitant at first, fearing that commercialization of the product would take away from its meaning, but he relented after seeing sculptor Yasuhei Fujioka's rendition of one of his drawings. Butcher reportedly fell to his knees and wept with joy at the sight of the piece and signed an agreement with Enesco. Thus, the now famous "Original 21" PRECIOUS MOMENTS figurines were born.

Since then, Butcher has designed over 2,000 figurines. As his fan base has grown, so has recognition of his talents. Through the years, Butcher has been honored with numerous industry awards, including NALED's prestigious "Artist of the Year" award in both 1992 and 1995.

Butcher, now the proud grandfather to over 16 children, insists that his family has always come first in his life and that his work is more a ministry than a business. The artist has said he feels blessed that he has been able to share God's message with so many. And collectors are surely greatful as well, as they continue to look forward to more inspirational figurines from Sam Butcher for years to come.

A smiling young fan greets a PRECIOUS MOMENTS character on the grounds of the chapel.

What's New For PRECIOUS MOMENTS®

The following section takes a look at the newest additions to the PRECIOUS MOMENTS line of collectibles. Most of the pieces will be hitting store shelves in the early part of the year, but look carefully, there are a few fall/winter 2001 previews on the list!

General Figurines

Blessed With A Loving Godmother . . . A godmother's loving instruction and advice will last a lifetime. Don't forget her on Mother's Day!

Cherish Every Step . . . A baby's first steps are always precious. This beautiful piece commemorates a mother's joy in seeing her young child grow.

A Godchild Close To My Heart (3 assorted) . . . These little ones are passing on all the lessons taught to them by their godmother to their eager friends!

Giving My Heart Freely . . . There's no charge for these hearts as this little girl cheerfully gives out some loving and caring!

I'll Never Let You Down . . . These two friends promise to always work together and they seem to balance each other perfectly!

I'm Completely Suspended With Love . . . In his bowtie and suspenders, this little gentleman is ready to show off his love for you.

It's A Banner Day, Congratulations . . . This little one is waiting to proclaim your achievements, whatever they may be!

Life's Beary Precious With You . . . Holding her teddy bear, no one can deny that this little girl treasures her friends!

The Lord Bless You And Keep You (Bridal Party Series, 10 assorted) . . . These precious figurines are the perfect way to commemorate both weddings and anniversaries.

The Lord Can Dew Anything . . . Fresh morning dew always holds the promise of a new day and no day is better than one during which we remember that nothing is impossible with the Lord.

O-Fish-Aly Friends For A Lifetime . . . These two best friends have put on their fishing gear and reeled in basketfuls of fish. But the real treasure, however, is their vow to be friends forever!

Take Thyme For Yourself . . . This little girl donned her woven gardening hat and picked some fresh herbs just for you.

To The Sweetest Girl In The Cast . . . This little actress is the perfect way to say "Break A Leg!" to the thespian in your life!

Wait Patiently On The Lord . . . This boy may be looking at his watch, but he knows that good things come to those who wait!

Wishing You A Birthday Full Of Surprises . . . Guess who popped out of this special birthday package! Wearing his party hat and ready to blow his horn for his new best friend, this puppy is sure to bring happiness and cheer whenever he wags his tail!

You Are Always In My Heart (2 assorted) . . . Just in time for Valentine's Day, these pieces will perfectly illustrate to your loved ones that you are always thinking of them and that they occupy a special place in your heart.

You Are The Queen Of My Heart . . . Show that extra-special lady in your life that she will always reign as the queen of your heart by giving her this symbol of your love.

You Are The Wind Beneath My Wings . . . This little clown just might be able to fly as long as his best friend continues to help him along the way.

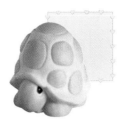

You Can't Hide From God ... Sometimes we all want to hide under a shell, but this turtle is learning that even his sturdy exterior isn't enough to make him invisible from God's grace!

You Will Always Be Mine ... This little boy is hard at work in the mines to prove that he'll always be there for you!

You're A Dandy Mom And I'm Not Lion ... Either a bunch of dandelions that you pick yourself or this adorable keepsake can show Mom just how much you care about her!

You're A Honey ... Don't worry – this bee can't sting! But it can add just the right dose of sweetness to your collection!

You're As Sweet As Apple Pie ... This all-American little boy is enjoying his apple pie from the inside out!

Annual Christmas Figurines

The Future Is In Our Hands ... This figurine encourages us to look to the future for exciting opportunities in the new millennium. This piece was created with a cardinal, as well as a blue bird!

Annual Christmas Ornaments

The Future Is In Our Hands ... This little girl is the perfect reminder of the new beginnings that come with the holiday season and the new year. Like the figurine that shares its name, this piece was also created with a variation.

COUNTRY LANE

Life Would Be The Pits Without Friends ...
You can never have too many friends to lean on, or so they say. But in this case, one more critter might mean bad news for this group of buddies!

Commemorative Figurines

Love One Another ... This is the first double figurine ever produced for Easter Seals and it completes the 9" Easter Seals collection. The two lovebirds in the piece sit cheek-to-cheek atop a stump carved with a symbol of their love for each other.

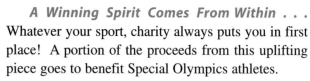

A Winning Spirit Comes From Within ...
Whatever your sport, charity always puts you in first place! A portion of the proceeds from this uplifting piece goes to benefit Special Olympics athletes.

You Have The Beary Best Heart ... This little girl knows that all teddy bears need hearts of their own and she's making sure that her bear has an extra special one!

You Tug On My Heart String . . . The commemorative Boys & Girls Clubs of America piece for 2001 depicts two youngsters playing tug-o'-war with a piece of string held together by a pink heart. Who will win? It doesn't matter who wins, as long as they work together!

LITTLE MOMENTS

Build Your Own Family Series (18 assorted) . . . Every family is beautiful and unique, and this new LITTLE MOMENTS series allows you to create a collection of figurines for every member of your family. And don't worry, you won't have to leave the family pets out, either!

Musicals

Bridal Arch Musical . . . This beautiful accessory, which plays "Mendohlsson's Wedding March," is the perfect complement to your *Bridal Party* collection.

I Give You My Love Forever True . . . This musical piece plays "Pachelbel's Cannon" and is a lovely way to remember weddings of both today and yesteryear.

Plush

***Loving, Caring And Sharing (set/3)* ...** These huggable bears are embroidered with the words "Loving, "Caring" or "Sharing." All three of the bears' paws lock together to create a circle of unity.

Be sure to stay tuned to *www.CollectorsQuest.com* for information and photos about upcoming 2001 PRECIOUS MOMENTS releases, including:

Figurines

All About Heaven
Celebrating His Arrival
Everything Is Beautiful In Its Own Way
Girl Festival Additions
I Give You My Heart
Life Is So Uplifting
Lord Let Our Friendship Bloom
May Your Christmas Begin With A Bang!
May Your Days Be Merry And Bright
Missing You
Oh, What A Wonder-fall Day
On A Scale From 1 To 10, You Are The Deerest
Our Friendship Was Made To Order
Roll Away, Roll Away, Roll Away
The Royal Budge Is Good For The Soul
Starsmith

Clocks

It's Almost Time For Santa

Ornaments

Baby's First Christmas
May Your Christmas Begin With A Bang
Our First Christmas Together
Sno-Ball Without You

Recent Retirements And Suspensions

The year 2000 was exciting for PRECIOUS MOMENTS collectors with the announcement of the first-ever PRECIOUS MOMENTS "Collectors' Choice" retirement of figurines. Collectors had the opportunity to cast their votes based on a list of 50 figurines. The lucky 15 chosen to be honored with retirement were announced on July 7, 2000. Several other figurines were also retired throughout the year, along with a gaggle of TENDER TAILS critters.

Retired Figurines

❏ Friends From The Very
   Beginning (#261068, 1997)

❏ Friends Never Drift Apart
   (#100250, 1986)
❏ Friendship Hits The Spot
   (#520748, 1989)
❏ From The First Time I
   Spotted You, I Knew We'd
   Be Friends (*Birthday Series*,
   #260940, 1997)
❏ God Blessed Our Year
   Together With So Much
   Love And Happiness
   (#E2854, 1984)
❏ Hallelujah Country
   (#105821, 1988)

Retired Figurines, cont.

❏ I Will Love You All Ways
   (#679704, 1999)
❏ I'm Sending You A White
   Christmas (#E2829, 1984)
❏ Isn't He Precious (*Nativity
   Series*, #E5379, 1984)
❏ Jesus Loves Me
   (#E9279, 1983)
❏ Love Never Fails
   (#12300, 1985)
❏ Make A Joyful Noise
   (#E1374G, 1979)
❏ Meowie Christmas
   (#109800, 1988)

Retired Figurines, cont.

❏ Peas Pass The Carrots
(*COUNTRY LANE*,
    #307076, 1998)

❏ A Prince Of A Guy
    (#526037, 1996)
❏ Sending You My Love
    (#109967, 1987)
❏ That's What Friends Are For
    (#521183, 1990)
❏ Time Heals (#523739, 1990)
❏ You Are Always On My
    Mind (#306967, 1998)
❏ You Are My Once In A
    Lifetime (#531030, 1998)
❏ You're A Lifesaver To Me
    (#204854, 1997)
❏ Waiting For A Merry
    Christmas (#527637, 2000)
❏ Walking By Faith
    (#E3117, 1980)

Retired TENDER TAILS

❏ Bee (#464295, 1999)
❏ Billy Goat (*COUNTRY
    LANE*, #476102, 1998)
❏ Brown Cow (*COUNTRY
    LANE*, #540560, 1998)

Retired TENDER TAILS, cont.

❏ Butterfly (#482234, 1999)
❏ Goose (#473952, 1999)
❏ Hippo (#475912, 1998)
❏ Horse (*COUNTRY LANE*,
    #540609, 1998)
❏ Lamb (#477192, 1999)
❏ Valentine Bear
    (#670200, 1999)
❏ Monkey (#475939, 1998)
❏ Peach Pig (*COUNTRY LANE*,
    #540579, 1998)
❏ Penguin (#471917, 1998)
❏ Rooster (*COUNTRY LANE*,
    #540617, 1998)
❏ White Duck (*COUNTRY
    LANE*, #540587, 1998)

Suspended Musicals

❏ The Lord Bless You And
    Keep You (#E7180, 1982)

PRECIOUS MOMENTS® Top Ten

This section highlights the ten most valuable pieces in the PRECIOUS MOMENTS line as determined by their value on the secondary market. Please note that in order to qualify for the list, a piece must show a significant percentage increase in value from its retail price at time of issue.

God Loveth A Cheerful Giver
Figurine • #E1378
Issued: 1979 • Retired: 1981
Issue Price: $9.50 • Value: NM – $1,000

But Love Goes On Forever
Retailer's Dome • #E7350
Issued: 1984 • Closed: 1984
Issue Price: N/A • Value: ✝ – $855

Good Friends Are Forever
Special Event Figurine • #525049
Issued: 1990 • Closed: 1990
Issue Price: N/A • Value: ✐ – $730

Friends Never Drift Apart (LE-1993)
Medallion • #529079
Issued: 1993 • Closed: 1993
Issue Price: N/A • Value: UM – $655

Tammy (LE-5,000)
Doll • #E7267G
Issued: 1982 • Closed: 1982
Issue Price: $300 • Value: UM – $565

Nobody's Perfect
Figurine • #E9268
Issued: 1983 • Retired: 1990
Issue Price: $21
Value: Smile Variation – $557

Sailabration Cruise (LE-1995)
Figurine • #150061
Issued: 1995 • Closed: 1995
Issue Price: N/A • Value: ☞ – $550

Cubby (LE-5,000)
Doll • #E7267B
Issued: 1982 • Closed: 1982
Issue Price: $200 • Value: UM – $480

Hello Lord, It's Me Again
Members' Only Figurine • #PM811
Issued: 1981 • Closed: 1981
Issue Price: $25 • Value: ▲ – $455

Jesus Is Born
Figurine • #E2801
Issued: 1980 • Suspended: 1984
Issue Price: $37 • Value: NM – $405

PRECIOUS MOMENTS®
Production Marks

Since 1981, each Enesco PRECIOUS MOMENTS piece from the porcelain bisque line of collectibles has had a special symbol inscribed into its base. The symbol, which holds a special significance to artist Sam Butcher, is used to denote the year the piece was produced. Often times, pieces can also be found with either the preceding year's symbol or with a symbol from the year following the end of its production.

Pre-1981	**1990**	**2000**
NM No Mark	Flame	Egg
1981	**1991**	**2001**
Triangle	Vessel	Sandal
1982	**1992**	**Other**
Hourglass	Clef	UM Unmarked
1983	**1993**	**Other**
Fish	Butterfly	Diamond[1]
1984	**1994**	**Other**
Cross	Trumpet	Flag[2]
1985	**1995**	**Other**
Dove	Ship	Flag with Star[3]
1986	**1996**	**Other**
Olive Branch	Heart	Rosebud[4]
1987	**1997**	
Cedar Tree	Sword	
1988	**1998**	
Flower	Eyeglasses	
1989	**1999**	
Bow and Arrow	Star	

[1] appears only on piece #103004

[2] appears only on "Bless Those Who Serve Their Country" figurines produced in 1991

[3] appears only on "Bless Those Who Serve Their Country" figurines produced in 1992

[4] appears only on piece #525049

How To Use Your Collector's Value Guide™

1. Locate your piece in the Value Guide. Figurine series are listed first, followed by general figurines and LITTLE MOMENTS. Next are the series and general ornaments, followed by other PRECIOUS MOMENTS collectibles (bells, boxes, musicals, etc.). TENDER TAILS, *Chapel Exclusives* and *Club* pieces conclude the

1

Values ↑ $46
      ↓ $43

Wishing You A Merry
Christmas (Dated 1984)
#E5383
Issued: 1984 • Closed: 1984
Retail Price: $17

Value Guide. Most of the pieces are listed alphabetically by their inspirational title, however, in annual groupings, pieces are listed in chronological order. Alphabetical and numerical indexes are found in the back of the book to help you locate your pieces.

2. Find the market value of your piece. To do this, look at the bottom or back of your piece to find the production marking. Next, find your piece's production mark in the "Values" chart on the right side of the picture box.

3. Record both the price you paid and the secondary market value in the corresponding boxes at the bottom of the page. Each piece's picture box contains a "Retail Price" line which shows the price of the piece when it was first issued. If there is a second price, that indicates that it is either the piece's current retail price, or the last

Annual Christmas Figurines	
Price Paid	Value
1. **$17**	**$46**
2.	
3.	
4.	
5.	
6.	
7.	
	$46
Totals	

suggested retail price (if the piece is no longer available in stores).

4. Calculate the value for the page by adding all of the boxes in each column. Use a pencil so you can change the totals as your collection grows.

5. Transfer the total for each page to the "Total Value Of My Collection" worksheets which begin on page 243.

6. Add all of the totals from the Value Guide pages together to determine the overall value of your collection.

Figurine Series

Many pieces were added to various figurine series in 2001. Among them, "May Your Christmas Begin With A Bang!" was added to the annual figurine collection, and two new COUNTRY LANE pieces joined the line as well. The final piece in the 9" Easter Seals collection was also released and is limited to 1,500 pieces, so get it while you can!

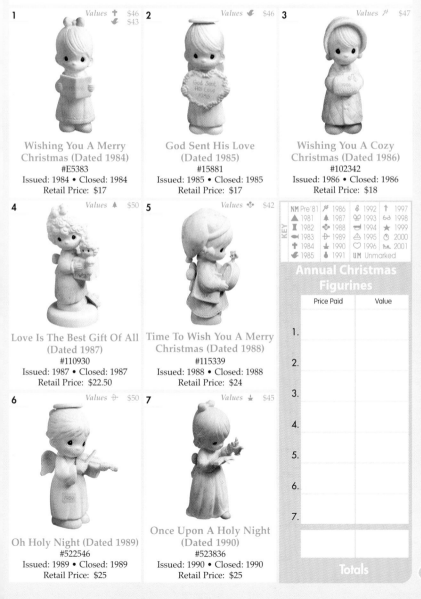

1   Values † $46
                        $43

Wishing You A Merry Christmas (Dated 1984)
#E5383
Issued: 1984 • Closed: 1984
Retail Price: $17

2   Values $46

God Sent His Love (Dated 1985)
#15881
Issued: 1985 • Closed: 1985
Retail Price: $17

3   Values $47

Wishing You A Cozy Christmas (Dated 1986)
#102342
Issued: 1986 • Closed: 1986
Retail Price: $18

4   Values ♣ $50

Love Is The Best Gift Of All (Dated 1987)
#110930
Issued: 1987 • Closed: 1987
Retail Price: $22.50

5   Values $42

Time To Wish You A Merry Christmas (Dated 1988)
#115339
Issued: 1988 • Closed: 1988
Retail Price: $24

6   Values $50

Oh Holy Night (Dated 1989)
#522546
Issued: 1989 • Closed: 1989
Retail Price: $25

7   Values $45

Once Upon A Holy Night (Dated 1990)
#523836
Issued: 1990 • Closed: 1990
Retail Price: $25

KEY					
NM Pre'81		1986		1992	† 1997
▲ 1981	▲	1987		1993	1998
I 1982		1988		1994	★ 1999
1983		1989		1995	2000
† 1984		1990	♡	1996	2001
1985		1991	UM	Unmarked	

Annual Christmas Figurines

	Price Paid	Value
1.		
2.		
3.		
4.		
5.		
6.		
7.		
Totals		

31

1 Values 🔥 $38

May Your Christmas Be Merry (Dated 1991)
#524166
Issued: 1991 • Closed: 1991
Retail Price: $27.50

2 Values 🔥 $35
      UM $40

But The Greatest Of These Is Love (Dated 1992)
#527688
Issued: 1992 • Closed: 1992
Retail Price: $27.50

3 Values ✿ $46

Wishing You The Sweetest Christmas (Dated 1993)
#530166
Issued: 1993 • Closed: 1993
Retail Price: $27.50

4 Values ➳ $42

You're As Pretty As A Christmas Tree (Dated 1994)
#530425
Issued: 1994 • Closed: 1994
Retail Price: $27.50

5 Values △ $42

He Covers The Earth With His Beauty (Dated 1995)
#142654
Issued: 1995 • Closed: 1995
Retail Price: $30

6 Values ♡ $37

Peace On Earth . . . Anyway (Dated 1996)
#183342
Issued: 1996 • Closed: 1996
Retail Price: $32.50

KEY					
NM Pre'81	♪ 1986	⚘ 1992	† 1997
▲ 1981	▲ 1987	✿ 1993	6∂ 1998
✗ 1982	⬥ 1988	➳ 1994	★ 1999
⬛ 1983	⊕ 1989	△ 1995	⊙ 2000
✝ 1984	★ 1990	♡ 1996	≈ 2001
✦ 1985	🔥 1991	UM Unmarked	

7 Values † $35

Cane You Join Us For A Merry Christmas (Dated 1997)
#272671
Issued: 1997 • Closed: 1997
Retail Price: $30

8 Values 6∂ $32

I'm Sending You A Merry Christmas (Dated 1998)
#455601
Issued: 1998 • Closed: 1998
Retail Price: $30

9 Values ★ N/E

Slide Into The Next Millennium With Joy (Dated 1999)
#587761
Issued: 1999 • Closed: 1999
Retail Price: $35

1

Values ☼ $32

The Future Is In Our Hands (Dated 2000)
#730068
Issued: 2000 • Closed: 2000
Retail Price: $30
Variation: With red bird – $45

2

New

Values ❧ $19

May Your Christmas Begin
With A Bang! (Dated 2001)
#877441
Issued: 2001 • To Be Closed: 2001
Retail Price: $19

3

Values † $32
🔔 $32
★ $30
☼ $30
❧ $30

Friendship Hits The Spot
#306916
Issued: 1998 • Open
Retail Price: $30

4

Values ♡ $26
† $26
🔔 $26

God Loveth A
Cheerful Giver
#272477
Issued: 1997 • Retired: 1998
Retail Price: $25

5

Values ♡ $32
† $32
🔔 $32
★ $30
☼ $30
❧ $30

Good Friends Are Forever
#272422
Issued: 1997 • Open
Retail Price: $30

6

Values † $25
🔔 $25
★ $25
☼ $25
❧ $25

He Cleansed My Soul
#306940
Issued: 1998 • Open
Retail Price: $25

7

Values ♡ $26
† $26
🔔 $26
★ $25
☼ $25
❧ $25

I Believe In Miracles
#272469
Issued: 1997 • Open
Retail Price: $25

8

Values ♡ $26
† $26
🔔 $26
★ $26
☼ $25
❧ $25

Love Is Sharing
#272493
Issued: 1997 • Open
Retail Price: $25

9

Values ♡ $32
† $32
🔔 $32
★ $32
☼ $30
❧ $30

Love One Another
#272507
Issued: 1997 • Open
Retail Price: $30

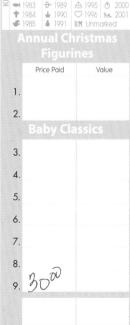

KEY					
NM Pre'81	❀ 1986	✿ 1992	† 1997
▲ 1981	▲ 1987	♈ 1993	❧ 1998
◫ 1982	✣ 1988	⬢ 1994	★ 1999
1983	Ð 1989	⬡ 1995	☼ 2000
† 1984	♦ 1990	♡ 1996	❧ 2001
☙ 1985	♦ 1991	UM Unmarked	

Annual Christmas Figurines

	Price Paid	Value
1.		
2.		

Baby Classics

3.		
4.		
5.		
6.		
7.		
8.		
9.	30⁰⁰	

Totals

1

Values	
†	$27
6d	$27
★	$25
☾	$25
⅛	$25

Loving You Dear Valentine
#306932
Issued: 1998 • Open
Retail Price: $25

2

Values	
♡	$30
†	$30
6d	$30
★	$30
☾	$30
⅛	$30

Make A Joyful Noise
#272450
Issued: 1997 • Open
Retail Price: $30

3

Values	
♡	$25
†	$25
6d	$25
★	$25
☾	$25
⅛	$25

We Are God's Workmanship
#272434
Issued: 1997 • Open
Retail Price: $25

4

Values	
♡	$26
†	$26
6d	$26
★	$25
☾	$25
⅛	$25

You Have Touched So
Many Hearts
#272485
Issued: 1997 • Open
Retail Price: $25

5

Values	
▲	$48
⅋	$44
Ð	$42
✦	$38
⅃	$36
⅋	$33
♈	$31

Brighten Someone's Day
#105953
Issued: 1987 • Susp.: 1993
Retail Price: $12.50 – $15

6

Values	
⅃	$27
⅋	$24
♈	$21
⊒	$18
△	$18
♡	$18
†	$18
6d	$18
★	$18

Can't Be Without You
#524492
Issued: 1991 • Retired: 1999
Retail Price: $16 – $17.50

Baby Classics

	Price Paid	Value
1.		
2.		
3.		
4.		

Birthday Series

5.		
6.		
7.		
8.		
9.		
10.		

Totals

7

Values	
⅌	$46
Ð	$40
✦	$38
⅃	$35
⅃	$33
♈	$30
UM	$65

Friends To The End
#104418
Issued: 1988 • Susp.: 1993
Retail Price: $15 – $18.50

8

Values	
♡	$26
†	$22
6d	$22
★	$22
☾	$22

From The First Time
I Spotted You I Knew
We'd Be Friends
#260940
Issued: 1997 • Retired: 2000
Retail Price: $20

9

Values	
⅃	$33
♈	$30
⊒	$30
△	$26
♡	$24

Happy Birdie
#527343
Issued: 1992 • Susp.: 1996
Retail Price: $16 – $17.50

10

Values	
⅌	$28
Ð	$24
✦	$22
⅃	$20
⅃	$20
♈	$18
⊒	$18
△	$18
♡	$18
†	$18
6d	$18
★	$18

Hello World
#521175
Issued: 1989 • Retired: 1999
Retail Price: $13.50 – $17.50

1

Values 🎀 $33
　　　▤ $30
　　　▱ $26

Hope You're Over
The Hump
#521671
Issued: 1993 • Susp.: 1996
Retail Price: $17.50 – $18.50

2

Values 🌢 $28
　　　& $22
　　　♀ $20
　　　▤ $18
　　　△ $18
　　　♡ $17.50
　　　† $17.50
　　　63 $17.50
　　　★ $17.50
　　　🕙 $17.50
　　　🐚 $17.50

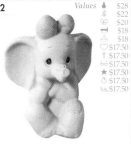

How Can I Ever Forget You
#526924
Issued: 1991 • Open
Retail Price: $15 – $17.50

3

Values △ $18
　　　♡ $14
　　　† $14
　　　63 $13.50
　　　★ $13.50
　　　🕙 $13.50
　　　🐚 $13.50

I Haven't Seen Much
Of You Lately
#531057
Issued: 1996 • Open
Retail Price: $13.50

4

Values & $25
　　　♀ $21
　　　▤ $19
　　　△ $18
　　　♡ $18
　　　† $18
　　　63 $18

I Only Have Arms For You
#527769
Issued: 1993 • Retired: 1998
Retail Price: $15 – $17.50

5

Values 🌢 $39
　　　& $35
　　　♀ $33
　　　▤ $30
　　　△ $28
　　　♡ $26

Let's Be Friends
#527270
Issued: 1992 • Retired: 1996
Retail Price: $15 – $17.50

6

Values † $20
　　　63 $17
　　　★ $15
　　　🕙 $15
　　　🐚 $15

My World's Upside Down
Without You
#531014
Issued: 1998 • Open
Retail Price: $15

7

Values ⚓ $42
　　　▲ $38
　　　& $36
　　　🔆 $33
　　　▤ $32

Not A Creature Was
Stirring (set/2)
#524484
Issued: 1990 • Susp.: 1994
Retail Price: $17

8

Values ▤ $20
　　　△ $17
　　　△ $16
　　　♡ $15
　　　† $15
　　　63 $15
　　　★ $15
　　　🕙 $15

Oinky Birthday
#524506
Issued: 1994 • Retired: 1999
Retail Price: $13.50 – $15

KEY							
NM	Pre '81	✷	1986	&	1992	†	1997
▲	1981	▲	1987	♀	1993	63	1998
▥	1982	✦	1988	▤	1994	★	1999
✝	1983	▱	1989	△	1995	🕙	2000
✝	1984	▲	1990	♡	1996	🐚	2001
✝	1985	🌢	1991	**UM**	Unmarked		

Birthday Series

	Price Paid	Value
1.		
2.		
3.		
4.		
5.		
6.		
7.		
8.		
9.		
10.		

Totals

9

Values ♣ $57
　　　⚜ $50
　　　▱ $45
　　　⚓ $41
　　　🌢 $38
　　　& $36
　　　♀ $36

Showers Of Blessings
#105945
Issued: 1987 • Retired: 1993
Retail Price: $16 – $20

10

Values ▱ $58
　　　⚓ $52
　　　🌢 $50
　　　& $46
　　　♀ $44
　　　▤ $42

To Be With You Is Uplifting
#522260
Issued: 1989 • Retired: 1994
Retail Price: $20 – $22.50

1

Values	
ᗞ	$56
⭐	$42
⬥	$38
⑂	$36
❀	$35

To My Favorite Fan
#521043
Issued: 1990 • Susp.: 1993
Retail Price: $16

2

Values	
⬗	$48
△	$43
♡	$40

Wishing You A Happy Bear Hug
#520659
Issued: 1995 • Susp.: 1996
Retail Price: $27.50

3

Values	
✿	$43
♫	$30
▲	$28
⬥	$26
ᗞ	$26
⭐	$25
⬥	$25
⑂	$24
❀	$23
⬗	$23
△	$23
♡	$22.50
†	$22.50
6∂	$22.50
★	$22.50
⏾	$22.50
⩙	$22.50

Bless The Days Of Our Youth
#16004
Issued: 1985 • Open
Retail Price: $15 – $22.50

4

Values	
✿	$43
♫	$27
▲	$23
⬥	$20
ᗞ	$20
⭐	$20
⬥	$18
⑂	$18
❀	$16
⬗	$16
♡	$15
†	$15
6∂	$15
★	$15
⏾	$15
⩙	$15

May Your Birthday Be Warm (Baby)
#15938
Issued: 1985 • Open
Retail Price: $10 – $15

5

Values	
✿	$46
♫	$30
▲	$26
⬥	$23
ᗞ	$22
⭐	$20
⬥	$20
⑂	$20
❀	$18
⬗	$18
♡	$15
†	$15
6∂	$15
★	$15
⏾	$15
⩙	$15

Happy Birthday Little Lamb (Age 1)
#15946
Issued: 1985 • Open
Retail Price: $10 – $15

6

Values	
✿	$48
♫	$34
▲	$32
⬥	$29
ᗞ	$29
⭐	$26
⬥	$24
⑂	$22
❀	$20
⬗	$20
△	$18
♡	$18
†	$17.50
6∂	$17.50
★	$17.50
⏾	$17.50
⩙	$17.50

God Bless You On Your Birthday (Age 2)
#15962
Issued: 1985 • Open
Retail Price: $11 – $17.50

KEY					
NM Pre'81	♫ 1986	⑂ 1992	† 1997		
▲ 1981	▲ 1987	❀ 1993	6∂ 1998		
⌶ 1982	⬥ 1988	⬗ 1994	★ 1999		
† 1983	ᗞ 1989	△ 1995	⏾ 2000		
† 1984	⭐ 1990	♡ 1996	⩙ 2001		
✿ 1985	⬥ 1991	**UM** Unmarked			

Birthday Series

	Price Paid	Value
1.		
2.		

Birthday Train

3.		
4.		
5.		
6.		
7.		
8.		
9.		
10.		

Totals

7

Values	
✿	$42
♫	$29
▲	$26
⬥	$24
ᗞ	$22
⭐	$22
⬥	$22
⑂	$20
❀	$19
⬗	$18
△	$17.50
♡	$17.50
†	$17.50
6∂	$17.50
★	$17.50
⩙	$17.50

Heaven Bless Your Special Day (Age 3)
#15954
Issued: 1985 • Open
Retail Price: $11 – $17.50

8

Values	
✿	$45
♫	$33
▲	$28
⬥	$24
ᗞ	$23
⭐	$23
⬥	$22
⑂	$22
❀	$20
⬗	$20
△	$20
♡	$20
†	$20
6∂	$20
★	$20
⩙	$20

May Your Birthday Be Gigantic (Age 4)
#15970
Issued: 1985 • Open
Retail Price: $12.50 – $20

9

Values	
✿	$40
♫	$30
▲	$26
⬥	$25
ᗞ	$25
⭐	$23
⬥	$23
⑂	$22.50
❀	$22.50
⬗	$22.50
♡	$22.50
†	$22.50
6∂	$22.50
★	$22.50
⏾	$22.50
⩙	$22.50

This Day Is Something To Roar About (Age 5)
#15989
Issued: 1985 • Open
Retail Price: $13.50 – $22.50

10

Values	
✿	$42
♫	$34
▲	$29
⬥	$29
ᗞ	$29
⭐	$26
⬥	$26
⑂	$24
❀	$23
⬗	$22.50
△	$22.50
♡	$22.50
†	$22.50
6∂	$22.50
★	$22.50
⏾	$22.50
⩙	$22.50

Keep Looking Up (Age 6)
#15997
Issued: 1985 • Open
Retail Price: $13.50 – $22.50

1

Values
▲ $38
⊹ $34
⊕ $28
⚓ $26
♦ $24
ξ $24
ℛℛ $22.50
➤ $22.50
△ $22.50
♡ $22.50
✝ $22.50
ᏭᏭ $22.50
★ $22.50
◔ $22.50
ᏰᏰ $22.50

Wishing You
Grr-eatness (Age 7)
#109479
Issued: 1988 • Open
Retail Price: $18.50 – $22.50

2

Values
▲ $38
❖ $34
⊕ $30
⚓ $27
ξ $25
ℛℛ $22.50
➤ $22.50
△ $22.50
♡ $22.50
✝ $22.50
ᏭᏭ $22.50
★ $22.50
◔ $22.50
ᏰᏰ $22.50

Isn't Eight Just
Great (Age 8)
#109460
Issued: 1988 • Open
Retail Price: $18.50 – $22.50

3

Values
ξ $34
ℛℛ $30
➤ $28
△ $25
♡ $25
✝ $25
ᏭᏭ $25
★ $25
◔ $25
ᏰᏰ $25

Being Nine Is Just
Divine (Age 9)
#521833
Issued: 1992 • Open
Retail Price: $25

4

Values
ξ $34
ℛℛ $30
➤ $28
△ $25
♡ $25
✝ $25
ᏭᏭ $25
★ $25
◔ $25
ᏰᏰ $25

May Your Birthday Be
Mammoth (Age 10)
#521825
Issued: 1992 • Open
Retail Price: $25

5

Values
ᏭᏭ $25
★ $25
◔ $25
ᏰᏰ $25

Take Your Time It's Your
Birthday (Age 11)
#488003
Issued: 1999 • Open
Retail Price: $25

6

Values
◔ $25
ᏰᏰ $25

Give A Grin And Let The
Fun Begin (Age 12)
#488011
Issued: 2000 • Open
Retail Price: $25

7

Values
◔ $25
ᏰᏰ $25

You Mean The Moose To
Me (Age 13)
#488038
Issued: 2000 • Open
Retail Price: $25

8

Values
★ $50
◔ $50
ᏰᏰ $50

Dear Jon, I Will Never
Leave You – Jesus
#588091
Issued: 1999 • Open
Retail Price: $50

9

Values
★ $25
◔ $25
ᏰᏰ $25

Eat Ham
#587842
Issued: 1999 • Open
Retail Price: $25

10

Values
◔ $25
ᏰᏰ $25

Eat Turkey
#763225
Issued: 2000 • Open
Retail Price: $25

KEY					
NM Pre'81	⚒ 1986	ξ 1992	✝ 1997		
▲ 1981	▲ 1987	ℛℛ 1993	ᏭᏭ 1998		
Ⅰ 1982	❖ 1988	➤ 1994	★ 1999		
➤ 1983	⊕ 1989	△ 1995	◔ 2000		
✝ 1984	⚓ 1990	♡ 1996	ᏰᏰ 2001		
⚓ 1985	♦ 1991	℧Ⓜ Unmarked			

Birthday Train

	Price Paid	Value
1.		
2.		
3.		
4.		
5.		
6.		
7.		

COUNTRY LANE

8.		
9.		
10.		

Totals

37

1

Values 😊 $50
★ $50
🕐 $45
🔔 $45

**Fork Over Those
Blessings To Others**
#307033
Issued: 1998 • Open
Retail Price: $45

2

Values ★ $45
🕐 $45
🔔 $45

Hay Good Lookin'
#649732
Issued: 2000 • Open
Retail Price: $45

3

Values 😊 $50
★ $50
🕐 $50
🔔 $50

Hogs & Kisses
#261106
Issued: 1999 • Open
Retail Price: $50

4

Values 😊 $51
★ $51

I'll Never Tire Of You
#307068
Issued: 1998 • Retired: 1999
Retail Price: $50

5
New

Values 🕐 $40
🔔 $40

**Life Would Be The Pits
Without Friends**
#795356
Issued: 2001 • Open
Retail Price: $40

6

Values 😊 $66
★ $66

**Nobody Likes To
Be Dumped**
#307041
Issued: 1998 • Retired: 1999
Retail Price: $65

KEY					
NM Pre'81		𝄞 1986		𝄢 1992	✝ 1997
▲ 1981		▲ 1987		🍐 1993	😊 1998
Ⅱ 1982		🔧 1988		🔨 1994	★ 1999
◄ 1983		Ð 1989		🔺 1995	🕐 2000
✝ 1984		★ 1990		♡ 1996	🔔 2001
🔥 1985		🔥 1991		∐M Unmarked	

	Price Paid	Value
1.		
2.		
3.		
4.		
5.		
6.		
7.		
8.		
9.		
10.		

Totals

7
New

Values 🔔 $37.50

*Photo
Unavailable*

**Oh, What A
Wonder-Fall Day**
#879096
Issued: 2001 • Open
Retail Price: $37.50

8

Values 😊 $55
★ $55
🕐 $55
🔔 $55

**Oh Taste And See That
The Lord Is Good**
#307025
Issued: 1998 • Open
Retail Price: $55

9

Values 😊 $45
★ $43
🕐 $37

Peas Pass The Carrots
#307076
Issued: 1998 • Retired: 2000
Retail Price: $35

10

Values ★ $40
🕐 $40
🔔 $40

**Shear Happiness And
Hare Cuts**
#539910
Issued: 1999 • Open
Retail Price: $40

1   Values ★ $60
   ⊘ $60
   ⚏ $60

Wishing You A Moo-ie Christmas
#455865
Issued: 1999 • Open
Retail Price: $60

2   Values ★ $55
   ⊘ $55
   ⚏ $55

You Brighten My Field Of Dreams
#587850
Issued: 1999 • Open
Retail Price: $55

3   Values ᤢ $45
   ★ $45
   ⊘ $45
   ⚏ $45

You're Just As Sweet As Pie
#307017
Issued: 1998 • Open
Retail Price: $45

4   Values ℱ $67
   ▲ $52

He Walks With Me (LE-1987)
#107999
Issued: 1987 • Closed: 1987
Retail Price: $25

5   Values ▲ $40
   ⬥ $33

Blessed Are They That Overcome (LE-1988)
#115479
Issued: 1988 • Closed: 1988
Retail Price: $27.50

6   Values ⬥ $62
   ⸭ $52

His Love Will Shine On You (LE-1989)
#522376
Issued: 1989 • Closed: 1989
Retail Price: $30

7   Values ⸭ $52
   ⬩ $46

Always In His Care (LE-1990)
#524522
Issued: 1990 • Closed: 1990
Retail Price: $30

8   Values ⬩ $70
   ⬥ $62

Sharing A Gift Of Love (LE-1991)
#527114
Issued: 1991 • Closed: 1991
Retail Price: $30

KEY			
NM Pre'81	ℱ 1986	∮ 1992	✝ 1997
▲ 1981	▲ 1987	9𝒫 1993	ᤢ 1998
✠ 1982	⬥ 1988	⊞ 1994	★ 1999
⬤ 1983	⸭ 1989	⬠ 1995	⊘ 2000
✝ 1984	⬩ 1990	♡ 1996	⚏ 2001
⬥ 1985	⬤ 1991	UM Unmarked	

COUNTRY LANE

	Price Paid	Value
1.		
2.		
3.		

Easter Seals Commemorative Figurines

4.		
5.		
6.		
7.		
8.		

Totals

1

Values 🔹 $112
🔸 $102

A Universal Love (LE-1992)
#527173
Issued: 1992 • Closed: 1992
Retail Price: $32.50

2

Values 🔹 $60
🔹 $52

You're My Number One
Friend (LE-1993)
#530026
Issued: 1993 • Closed: 1993
Retail Price: $30

3

Values 🔹 $53
🔹 $46

It Is No Secret What God
Can Do (LE-1994)
#531111
Issued: 1994 • Closed: 1994
Retail Price: $30

4

Values 🔹 $45
🔹 $40

Take Time To Smell The
Flowers (LE-1995)
#524387
Issued: 1995 • Closed: 1995
Retail Price: $30

5

Values 🔹 $38
🔹 $35

You Can Always Count On
Me (1996 Limited Edition)
#526827
Issued: 1995 • Closed: 1996
Retail Price: $30

6

Values ♡ $37
✝ $35

Give Ability A Chance
(1997 Limited Edition)
#192368
Issued: 1996 • Closed: 1997
Retail Price: $30

KEY						
NM Pre '81	🎷 1986	🔹 1992	✝ 1997		
▲ 1981	♠ 1987	🔹 1993	🔹 1998		
🗓 1982	🔹 1988	🔹 1994	★ 1999		
🔹 1983	⊅ 1989	🔺 1995	⊙ 2000		
✝ 1984	★ 1990	♡ 1996	🔹 2001		
🔹 1985	🔹 1991	∪M Unmarked			

**Easter Seals
Commemorative Figurines**

	Price Paid	Value
1.		
2.		
3.		
4.		
5.		
6.		
7.		
8.		
9.		
10.		
Totals		

7

Values ✝ $46
🔹 $43

Somebody Cares
(1998 Limited Edition)
#522325
Issued: 1997 • Closed: 1998
Retail Price: $40

8

Values 🔹 $39
★ $37

Heaven Bless You Easter
Seal (1999 Limited Edition)
#456314
Issued: 1998 • Closed: 1999
Retail Price: $35

9

Values ★ $32
⊙ $32

Give Your Whole Heart
(2000 Limited Edition)
#490245
Issued: 1999 • Closed: 2000
Retail Price: $30

10

Values ⊙ N/E
🔹 N/E

Jesus Loves Me
(2001 Limited Edition)
#745766
Issued: 2000 • To Be Closed: 2001
Retail Price: N/A

1 Values ♠ $1900 ♣ $1600

Jesus Loves Me (LE-1,000)
#104531
Issued: 1988 • Closed: 1988
Retail Price: $500

2 Values ₱ $900

Make A Joyful Noise
(LE-1,500)
#520322
Issued: 1989 • Closed: 1989
Retail Price: $500

3 Values ₱ $650 ♦ $585

You Have Touched So Many
Hearts (LE-2,000)
#523283
Issued: 1990 • Closed: 1990
Retail Price: $500

4 Values ♦ $725 ♦ $675

We Are God's
Workmanship (LE-2,000)
#523879
Issued: 1991 • Closed: 1991
Retail Price: $500

5 Values ♦ $650 ♦ $600

You Are Such A Purr-fect
Friend (LE-2,000)
#526010
Issued: 1992 • Closed: 1992
Retail Price: $500

6 Values ♦ $630 ♀ $585

Gather Your Dreams
(LE-2,000)
#529680
Issued: 1993 • Closed: 1993
Retail Price: $500

7 Values ♀ $580 ⊶ $550

You Are The Rose Of His
Creation (LE-2,000)
#531243
Issued: 1994 • Closed: 1994
Retail Price: $500

8 Values ⊶ $610 ⚠ $560

He's Got The Whole World
In His Hands (LE-2,000)
#526886
Issued: 1995 • Closed: 1995
Retail Price: $500

9 Values ⚠ $580 ♡ $560

He Loves Me (LE-2,000)
#152277
Issued: 1995 • Closed: 1996
Retail Price: $500

KEY			
NM Pre'81	✗ 1986	♦ 1992	✝ 1997
▲ 1981	♠ 1987	♀ 1993	⊶ 1998
✗ 1982	♣ 1988	⊶ 1994	★ 1999
⊶ 1983	₱ 1989	⚠ 1995	◉ 2000
✝ 1984	♦ 1990	♡ 1996	⊷ 2001
⊷ 1985	♦ 1991	UM Unmarked	

**Limited Edition 9"
Easter Seals Figurines**

	Price Paid	Value
1.		
2.		
3.		
4.		
5.		
6.		
7.		
8.		
9.		
Totals		

1

Values ♡ $550
† $530

Love Is Universal (LE-2,000)
#192376
Issued: 1996 • Closed: 1997
Retail Price: $500

2

Values † $550
6ᴅ $530

Love Grows Here (LE-2,000)
#272981
Issued: 1997 • Closed: 1998
Retail Price: $500

3

Values 6ᴅ $550
★ $530

We Are All Precious In His Sight (LE-2,000)
#475068
Issued: 1998 • Closed: 1999
Retail Price: $500

4

Values ★ $520
⏲ $520

Jesus Loves Me (LE-1,500)
#634735
Issued: 1999 • Retired: 2000
Retail Price: $500

5
New

Values ≋ $500

Love One Another (LE-1,500)
N/A
Issued: 2001 • Open
Retail Price: $500

6

Values ⛪ $30
♡ $24
† $22.50
6ᴅ $22.50
★ $22.50
⏲ $22.50
≋ $22.50

It's A Girl
#136204
Issued: 1995 • Open
Retail Price: $22.50

Limited Edition 9" Easter Seals Figurines

	Price Paid	Value
1.		
2.		
3.		
4.		
5.		

Growing In Grace

6.		
7.		
8.		
9.		
10.		
Totals		

7

Values ⛪ $33
♡ $25
† $25
6ᴅ $25
★ $25
⏲ $25
≋ $25

Age 1
#136190
Issued: 1995 • Open
Retail Price: $25

8

Values ⛪ $32
♡ $25
† $25
6ᴅ $25
★ $25
⏲ $25
≋ $25

Age 2
#136212
Issued: 1995 • Open
Retail Price: $25

9

Values ⛪ $32
♡ $25
† $25
6ᴅ $25
★ $25
⏲ $25
≋ $25

Age 3
#136220
Issued: 1995 • Open
Retail Price: $25

10

Values ⛪ $36
♡ $28
† $27.50
6ᴅ $27.50
★ $27.50
⏲ $27.50
≋ $27.50

Age 4
#136239
Issued: 1995 • Open
Retail Price: $27.50

1

Values ⚘ $35
♡ $28
† $27.50
6⅁ $27.50
★ $27.50
① $27.50
≥≈ $27.50

Age 5
#136247
Issued: 1995 • Open
Retail Price: $27.50

2

Values ⚘ $37
♡ $32
† $32
6⅁ $30
★ $30
① $30
≥≈ $30

Age 6
#136255
Issued: 1995 • Open
Retail Price: $30

3

Values ⚘ $38
♡ $33
† $32.50
6⅁ $32.50
★ $32.50
① $32.50
≥≈ $32.50

Age 7
#163740
Issued: 1996 • Open
Retail Price: $32.50

4

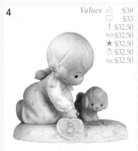

Values ⚘ $38
♡ $33
† $32.50
6⅁ $32.50
★ $32.50
① $32.50
≥≈ $32.50

Age 8
#163759
Issued: 1996 • Open
Retail Price: $32.50

5

Values ♡ $35
† $33
6⅁ $30
★ $30
① $30
≥≈ $30

Age 9
#183865
Issued: 1996 • Open
Retail Price: $30

6

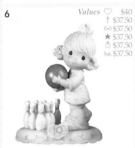

Values ♡ $40
† $37.50
6⅁ $37.50
★ $37.50
① $37.50
≥≈ $37.50

Age 10
#183873
Issued: 1996 • Open
Retail Price: $37.50

7

Values † $42
$38
6⅁ $37.50
★ $37.50
① $37.50
≥≈ $37.50

Age 11
#260924
Issued: 1997 • Open
Retail Price: $37.50

8

Values ♡ $42
† $38
6⅁ $37.50
★ $37.50
① $37.50
≥≈ $37.50

Age 12
#260932
Issued: 1997 • Open
Retail Price: $37.50

9

Values † $42
6⅁ $42
★ $42
① $40
≥≈ $40

Age 13
#272647
Issued: 1997 • Open
Retail Price: $40

10

Values † $37
6⅁ $37
★ $37
① $35
≥≈ $35

Age 14
#272655
Issued: 1997 • Open
Retail Price: $35

KEY		
NM Pre'81	⚘ 1986	♨ 1992	† 1997
▲ 1981	▲ 1987	♋ 1993	6⅁ 1998
☲ 1982	❖ 1988	◆ 1994	★ 1999
➳ 1983	⅁ 1989	⚘ 1995	① 2000
✝ 1984	★ 1990	♡ 1996	≥≈ 2001
➳ 1985	♦ 1991	UM Unmarked	

1

Values † $42
6ð $42
★ $42
🕐 $40
🔙 $40

Age 15
#272663
Issued: 1997 • Open
Retail Price: $40

2

Values 🔺 $55
♡ $50
† $48
6ð $45
★ $45
🕐 $45
🔙 $45

Age 16
#136263
Issued: 1995 • Open
Retail Price: $45

3

Values 🕐 $32.50
🔙 $32.50

I'm Proud To Be
An American
#588105
Issued: 2000 • Open
Retail Price: $32.50

4

Values 🕐 $32.50
🔙 $32.50

I'm Proud To Be
An American
#588113
Issued: 2000 • Open
Retail Price: $32.50

5

Values 🕐 $32.50
🔙 $32.50

I'm Proud To Be
An American
#588121
Issued: 2000 • Open
Retail Price: $32.50

6

Values 🕐 $32.50
🔙 $32.50

I'm Proud To Be
An American
#588148
Issued: 2000 • Open
Retail Price: $32.50

KEY			
NM Pre'81	✐ 1986	🖊 1992	† 1997
▲ 1981	▲ 1987	✤ 1993	6ð 1998
⚓ 1982	✤ 1988	⟆ 1994	★ 1999
✦ 1983	⟆ 1989	🔺 1995	🕐 2000
✝ 1984	★ 1990	♡ 1996	🔙 2001
✦ 1985	♦ 1991	UM Unmarked	

Growing In Grace

	Price Paid	Value
1.		
2.		

I'm Proud To Be An American

3.		
4.		
5.		
6.		
7.		
8.		
9.		
10.		

Totals

7

Values 🕐 $32.50
🔙 $32.50

I'm Proud To Be
An American
#588156
Issued: 2000 • Open
Retail Price: $32.50

8

Values 🕐 $32.50
🔙 $32.50

I'm Proud To Be
An American
#729876
Issued: 2000 • Open
Retail Price: $32.50

9

Values 🕐 $32.50
🔙 $32.50

I'm Proud To Be
An American
#729884
Issued: 2000 • Open
Retail Price: $32.50

10

Values 🕐 $32.50
🔙 $32.50

I'm Proud To Be
An American
#729892
Issued: 2000 • Open
Retail Price: $32.50

1 *Values* ☀ $32.50 ♨ $32.50

I'm Proud To Be
An American
#729906
Issued: 2000 • Open
Retail Price: $32.50

2 *Values* ☀ $32.50 ♨ $32.50

I'm Proud To Be
An American
#729914
Issued: 2000 • Open
Retail Price: $32.50

3 *Values* ☀ $32.50 ♨ $32.50

I'm Proud To Be
An American
#729922
Issued: 2000 • Open
Retail Price: $32.50

4 *Values* ☀ $32.50 ♨ $32.50

I'm Proud To Be
An American
#729930
Issued: 2000 • Open
Retail Price: $32.50

5 *Values* ☀ $32.50 ♨ $32.50

I'm Proud To Be
An American
#729949
Issued: 2000 • Open
Retail Price: $32.50

6 *Values* ☀ $32.50 ♨ $32.50

I'm Proud To Be
An American
#729957
Issued: 2000 • Open
Retail Price: $32.50

7 *Values* ☀ $32.50 ♨ $32.50

I'm Proud To Be
An American
#729965
Issued: 2000 • Open
Retail Price: $32.50

8 *Values* ☀ $32.50 ♨ $32.50

I'm Proud To Be
An American
#729973
Issued: 2000 • Open
Retail Price: $32.50

9 *Values* ☀ $32.50 ♨ $32.50

I'm Proud To Be
An American
#730009
Issued: 2000 • Open
Retail Price: $32.50

10 *Values* ☀ $32.50 ♨ $32.50

I'm Proud To Be
An American
#730017
Issued: 2000 • Open
Retail Price: $32.50

KEY			
NM Pre'81	✐ 1986	✿ 1992	✝ 1997
▲ 1981	♠ 1987	9❂ 1993	ϭ➔ 1998
☰ 1982	✤ 1988	⊟ 1994	★ 1999
◀ 1983	⅁ 1989	△ 1995	☀ 2000
✝ 1984	★ 1990	♡ 1996	⅏ 2001
✍ 1985	♣ 1991	ᴜᴍ Unmarked	

I'm Proud To Be An American

	Price Paid	Value
1.		
2.		
3.		
4.		
5.		
6.		
7.		
8.		
9.		
10.		
Totals		

1

Values ☽ $32.50
🔖 $32.50

I'm Proud To Be
An American
#730025
Issued: 2000 • Open
Retail Price: $32.50

2

Values ☽ $32.50
🔖 $32.50

I'm Proud To Be
An American
#730033
Issued: 2000 • Open
Retail Price: $32.50

3
New
Values 🔖 $20

Photo
Unavailable

All About Heaven
#525952
Issued: 2001 • Open
Retail Price: $20

4
Values † $19
6ð $18.50
★ $18.50
☽ $18.50
🔖 $18.50

Cats With Kitten
#291293
Issued: 1997 • Open
Retail Price: $18.50

5
Variation
Values ✗ $175
← $160
† $155
🐟 $150
♫ $150
▲ $145
⚜ $142
Ð $142
⚓ $142
♡ $140
§ $140
⚘ $140
△ $140
♡ $140
† $140
6ð $140
★ $140
☽ $140
🔖 $140

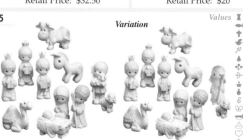

Come Let Us Adore Him (set/11)
#E2395
Issued: 1982 • Open
Retail Price: $80 – $140
Variation: Shepherd w/turban set – $240

KEY				
NM Pre '81	♫ 1986	§ 1992	† 1997	
▲ 1981	▲ 1987	⚘ 1993	6ð 1998	
✗ 1982	⚜ 1988	⚓ 1994	★ 1999	
← 1983	Ð 1989	△ 1995	☽ 2000	
† 1984	⚓ 1990	♡ 1996	🔖 2001	
🐟 1985	⚓ 1991	UM Unmarked		

**I'm Proud To Be
An American**

	Price Paid	Value
1.		
2.		

Miniature Nativity

3.		
4.		
5.		
6.		
7.		
8.		
9.		

Totals

6
Values △ $42
♡ $37
† $35
6ð $35
★ $35
☽ $35
🔖 $35

Come Let Us Adore
Him (set/3)
#142743
Issued: 1995 • Open
Retail Price: $35

7
Values † $30
← $30
★ $30
☽ $30
🔖 $30

Donkey, Camel And
Cow (set/3)
#279323
Issued: 1997 • Open
Retail Price: $30

8
Values † $19
6ð $17.50
★ $17.50
☽ $17.50
🔖 $17.50

For An Angel You're So
Down To Earth
#283444
Issued: 1997 • Open
Retail Price: $17.50

9
Values 6ð $17.50
★ $17.50
☽ $17.50
🔖 $17.50

Hang On To That
Holiday Feeling
#455962
Issued: 1998 • Open
Retail Price: $17.50

1

Values
🎀	$28
🗝	$23
♡	$20
†	$20
👓	$20
★	$20

Happy Birthday Jesus
#530492
Issued: 1993 • Retired: 1999
Retail Price: $20

2

Values
⬤	$22
🔺	$18.50
♡	$18.50
†	$18.50
👓	$18.50
★	$18.50

Have I Got News For You
#528137
Issued: 1994 • Retired: 1999
Retail Price: $16 – $18.50

3

Values
†	$37
♣	$33
✈	$28
♠	$28
✤	$26
⊖	$24
⬤	$22
♦	$20
⊗	$18.50
🎀	$18.50
🗝	$18.50
🔺	$18.50
♡	$18.50
†	$18.50
★	$18.50
🕐	$18.50
⚓	$18.50
UM	$38

**I'll Play My Drum
For Him**
#E5384
Issued: 1984 • Open
Retail Price: $10 – $18.50

4

Values
⊖	$38
★	$35
♠	$33
⊗	$33
🎀	$30

Isn't He Precious
#522988
Issued: 1989 • Susp.: 1993
Retail Price: $15 – $16.50

5

Values
⬤	$28
⊗	$22
🎀	$20
🗝	$18.50
🔺	$18.50
♡	$18.50
†	$18.50
👓	$18.50
★	$18.50

It's A Perfect Boy
#525286
Issued: 1991 • Retired: 1999
Retail Price: $16.50 – $18.50

6

Values
♡	$23
🔺	$18.50
👓	$18.50
★	$18.50
🕐	$18.50

**Making A Trail To
Bethlehem**
#184004
Issued: 1996 • Open
Retail Price: $18.50

7

Values
✈	$40
♣	$35
✤	$35
⊖	$35
♦	$33
♠	$33
⊗	$33

Mini Animals (set/3)
#102296
Issued: 1986 • Susp.: 1992
Retail Price: $13.50 – $19

8

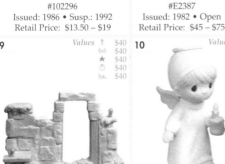

Values
🗡	$138
†	$118
🔔	$112
✈	$102
♣	$102
♠	$95
✤	$90
⊖	$80
★	$80
♦	$80
⊗	$77
🎀	$77
🗝	$77
🔺	$77
♡	$77
†	$75
👓	$75
★	$75
🕐	$75
⚓	$75

**Nativity Buildings
And Tree (set/4)**
#E2387
Issued: 1982 • Open
Retail Price: $45 – $75

<table>
<tr><td rowspan="5">KEY</td><td>NM Pre'81</td><td>🗡 1986</td><td>⊗ 1992</td><td>† 1997</td></tr>
<tr><td>🔺 1981</td><td>♠ 1987</td><td>🎀 1993</td><td>👓 1998</td></tr>
<tr><td>🗡 1982</td><td>✤ 1988</td><td>🗝 1994</td><td>★ 1999</td></tr>
<tr><td>† 1983</td><td>⊖ 1989</td><td>🔺 1995</td><td>🕐 2000</td></tr>
<tr><td>✈ 1984</td><td>⬤ 1990</td><td>♡ 1996</td><td>⚓ 2001</td></tr>
<tr><td></td><td>♣ 1985</td><td>♦ 1991</td><td>UM Unmarked</td><td></td></tr>
</table>

Miniature Nativity

	Price Paid	Value
1.		
2.		
3.		
4.		
5.		
6.		
7.		
8.		
9.		
10.		

Totals

9

Values
†	$40
👓	$40
★	$40
🕐	$40
⚓	$40

Nativity Wall
#283436
Issued: 1997 • Open
Retail Price: $40

10

Values
†	$68
✈	$59
✈	$53

Oh Worship The Lord
#E5385
Issued: 1984 • Susp.: 1986
Retail Price: $10

1

Values ✝ $72
🕊 $64
♫ $58

Oh Worship The Lord
#E5386
Issued: 1984 • Susp.: 1986
Retail Price: $10

2

Values ✿ $35
🕊 $27
⚓ $24
🍼 $22
🐚 $20
🐝 $18.50
🕊 $18.50
🔔 $18.50
♡ $18.50
✝ $18.50
★ $18.50
⏰ $18.50
🌿 $18.50

Rejoice O Earth
#520268
Issued: 1988 • Open
Retail Price: $13 – $18.50

3

Values ✝ $22.50
6ᵈ $22.50
★ $22.50
⏰ $22.50
🌿 $22.50

Shepherd And Sheep (set/2)
#213616
Issued: 1997 • Open
Retail Price: $22.50

4

Values 🎵 $33
▲ $23
✿ $20
🕊 $20
⚓ $20
🍼 $20
🐝 $18.50
🕊 $18.50
🔔 $18.50
♡ $18.50
✝ $18.50
6ᵈ $18.50
★ $18.50
⏰ $18.50
🌿 $18.50

Shepherd Of Love
#102261
Issued: 1986 • Open
Retail Price: $10 – $18.50

5

Values ⚓ $40
🍼 $37
🐝 $33
🐚 $30

Some Bunny's Sleeping
#522996
Issued: 1990 • Susp.: 1993
Retail Price: $12

6

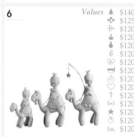

Values ▲ $140
✿ $125
🕊 $120
⚓ $120
🍼 $120
🐝 $120
🐚 $120
🕊 $120
🔔 $120
♡ $120
✝ $120
6ᵈ $120
★ $120
⏰ $120
🌿 $120

They Followed The Star (set/3)
#108243
Issued: 1987 • Open
Retail Price: $75 – $120

KEY			
NM Pre'81	🎵 1986	🐝 1992	✝ 1997
▲ 1981	▲ 1987	🐚 1993	6ᵈ 1998
ⅈ 1982	✿ 1988	🔔 1994	★ 1999
🕊 1983	🕊 1989	🔺 1995	⏰ 2000
✝ 1984	⚓ 1990	♡ 1996	🌿 2001
🕊 1985	🍼 1991	UM Unmarked	

Miniature Nativity

	Price Paid	Value
1.		
2.		
3.		
4.		
5.		
6.		
7.		
8.		
9.		

Nativity

10.		

Totals

7

Values 🐝 $18
🐚 $14
🔔 $12
🔺 $10
♡ $10
✝ $10
6ᵈ $10
★ $10

Tubby's First Christmas
#525278
Issued: 1992 • Retired: 1999
Retail Price: $10

8

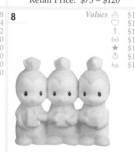

Values 🔺 $16
♡ $12
✝ $12
6ᵈ $12
★ $12
⏰ $12
🌿 $12

We Have Come From Afar
#530913
Issued: 1995 • Open
Retail Price: $12

9

Values ♡ $55
✝ $55
6ᵈ $55
★ $55
⏰ $55
🌿 $55

Wee Three Kings (set/3)
#213624
Issued: 1996 • Open
Retail Price: $55

10

Values ♡ $32.50
✝ $32.50
6ᵈ $32.50
★ $32.50
⏰ $32.50
🌿 $32.50

All Sing His Praises
#184012
Issued: 1996 • Open
Retail Price: $32.50

1

And You Shall See A Star
#272787
Issued: 1997 • Open
Retail Price: $32.50

2

Behold The Lamb Of God
#588164
Issued: 1999 • Open
Retail Price: $45

3

Behold The Lord (set/3)
#737607
Issued: 2000 • Open
Retail Price: $25

4

**Bringing God's Blessing
To You**
#E0509
Issued: 1983 • Susp.: 1987
Retail Price: $35 – $38.50

5

Camel
#E2363
Issued: 1982 • Open
Retail Price: $20 – $35

6

**Christmas Is A Time
To Share**
#E2802
Issued: 1980 • Susp.: 1984
Retail Price: $20 – $27.50

7

Come Let Us Adore Him (set/9)
#E2800
Issued: 1980 • Susp.: 1986
Retail Price: $60 – $90

8

Come Let Us Adore Him
#E5619
Issued: 1981 • Susp.: 1985
Retail Price: $10 – $11

Nativity

	Price Paid	Value
1.		
2.		
3.		
4.		
5.		
6.		
7.		
8.		

Totals

1

Values
🍃 $150
🎋 $145
♠ $145
🔱 $145
➗ $145
⚓ $142
🕯 $142
⚜ $142
🎗 $142
➖ $142
🔺 $142
♡ $142
† $140
🔗 $140
★ $140
🕐 $140
🐚 $140

Come Let Us Adore Him (set/9)
#104000
Issued: 1986 • Open
Retail Price: $95 – $140

2

Values
🔺 $57
♡ $50
† $50
🔗 $50
★ $50
🕐 $50
🐚 $50

Come Let Us Adore Him (set/3)
#142735
Issued: 1995 • Open
Retail Price: $50

3

Values
† $47
🍃 $45
🎋 $42
♠ $42
🔱 $40
➗ $36
⚓ $36
⚜ $32.50
🎗 $32.50
➖ $32.50
🔺 $32.50
♡ $32.50
† $32.50
🔗 $32.50
★ $32.50
🕐 $32.50
🐚 $32.50
UM $55

Cow With Bell
#E5638
Issued: 1981 • Open
Retail Price: $16 – $32.50

4

Values
NM $115
🔺 $110
I $90
➖ $83
† $82
🍃 $78

Crown Him Lord Of All
#E2803
Issued: 1980 • Susp.: 1984
Retail Price: $20 – $27.50

5

Values
† $25
🍃 $23
🎋 $20
♠ $20
🔱 $20
➗ $18
⚓ $18
⚜ $18
🎗 $18
➖ $18
🔺 $15
♡ $15
† $15
🔗 $15
★ $15
🕐 $15
🐚 $15
UM $35

Donkey
#E5621
Issued: 1981 • Open
Retail Price: $6 – $15

Nativity

	Price Paid	Value
1.		
2.		
3.		
4.		
5.		
6.		
7.		
8.		
9.		

Totals

6

Values
I $80
➖ $75
† $72
UM $75

The First Noël
#E2365
Issued: 1982 • Susp.: 1984
Retail Price: $16 – $17

7

Values
I $82
➖ $77
† $70
UM $75

The First Noël
#E2366
Issued: 1982 • Susp.: 1984
Retail Price: $16 – $17

8

Values
† $152
➖ $130
🎋 $120

For God So Loved The World (set/4)
#E5382
Issued: 1984 • Susp.: 1986
Retail Price: $70

9

Values
I $72
➖ $68
† $65
🍃 $62
🎋 $55
♠ $55
🔱 $52
➗ $48
UM $78

Goat
#E2364
Issued: 1982 • Susp.: 1989
Retail Price: $10 – $15

1   *Values* ⚓ $39
       🕯 $32
       🐚 $26
       🌸 $25

Happy Birthday Dear Jesus
#524875
Issued: 1990 • Susp.: 1993
Retail Price: $13.50

2   *Values* ▲ $68
       ❖ $60
       ⊕ $53
       ⚓ $49
       🕯 $49

Have I Got News For You
#105635
Issued: 1987 • Susp.: 1991
Retail Price: $22.50 – $30

3   *Values* NM $155
       ▲ $132
       I $122
       ◄ $112
       † $104

He Careth For You
#E1377B
Issued: 1979 • Susp.: 1984
Retail Price: $9 – $20

4   *Values* NM $150
       ▲ $130
       I $115
       ◄ $105
       † $98

He Leadeth Me
#E1377A
Issued: 1979 • Susp.: 1984
Retail Price: $9 – $20

5   *Values* 👓 $27

He Leadeth Me
Special Event Figurine
#E1377R
Issued: 1998 • Closed: 1998
Retail Price: $9

6   *Values* NM $82
       ▲ $71
       I $60
       ◄ $51
       † $46
       ✈ $40
       ❀ $40
       ▲ $38
       ❖ $36
       ⊕ $35
       ⚓ $33
       🕯 $33
       ♫ $33
       9P $32.50
       ▬ $32.50
       △ $32.50
       † $32.50
       👓 $32.50
       ★ $32.50
       ⊙ $32.50
       ⋙ $32.50

The Heavenly Light
#E5637
Issued: 1981 • Open
Retail Price: $15 – $32.50

7   *Values* † $127
       ◄ $116
       ♫ $105
       ▲ $105

His Name Is Jesus
#E5381
Issued: 1984 • Susp.: 1987
Retail Price: $45 – $50

8   *Values* I $86
       ◄ $80
       † $75
       UM $116

His Sheep Am I
#E7161
Issued: 1982 • Susp.: 1984
Retail Price: $25 – $27.50

KEY

NM Pre '81	♫ 1986	♫ 1992	† 1997
▲ 1981	▲ 1987	9P 1993	👓 1998
I 1982	❖ 1988	▬ 1994	★ 1999
◄ 1983	⊕ 1989	△ 1995	⊙ 2000
† 1984	★ 1990	♡ 1996	⋙ 2001
✦ 1985	🕯 1991	UM Unmarked	

Nativity

	Price Paid	Value
1.		
2.		
3.		
4.		
5.		
6.		
7.		
8.		
9.		
10.		

Totals

9   *Values* ✈ $38
       ♫ $33
       ▲ $30
       ❖ $30
       ⊕ $27
       ⚓ $27
       🕯 $25
       ♫ $25
       9P $23
       ▬ $20
       △ $20
       ♡ $20
       † $20
       👓 $20
       ★ $20
       ⊙ $20
       ⋙ $20

Honk If You Love
Jesus (set/2)
#15490
Issued: 1985 • Open
Retail Price: $13 – $20

10   *Values* I $120
       ◄ $92
       † $85
       ✦ $79

I'll Play My Drum For Him
#E2356
Issued: 1982 • Susp.: 1985
Retail Price: $30 – $33

1

Values

I	$53
✝	$46
⬧	$40
⬧	$40
ℐ	$37
▲	$34
⬧	$34
⬧	$34
✦	$32
⬧	$32
⬧	$30
⬧	$30
⬧	$27.50
⬧	$27.50
✝	$27.50
★	$27.50
☀	$27.50
⬧	$27.50

I'll Play My Drum
For Him
#E2360
Issued: 1982 • Open
Retail Price: $16 – $27.50

2

Values

✝	$50
⬧	$43
⬧	$43
▲	$38
⬧	$35
⬧	$35
✦	$33
⬧	$33
⬧	$33
⬧	$33
⬧	$33
⬧	$33
♡	$32.50
✝	$32.50
⬧	$32.50
★	$32.50
☀	$32.50

Isn't He Precious
#E5379
Issued: 1984 • Retired: 2000
Retail Price: $20 – $32.50

3

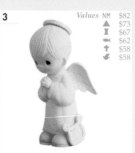

Values NM $82

▲	$73
I	$67
⬧	$62
✝	$58
⬧	$58

Isn't He Wonderful
#E5639
Issued: 1981 • Susp.: 1985
Retail Price: $12 – $17

4

Values NM $85

▲	$80
I	$73
⬧	$70
✝	$65
⬧	$62

Isn't He Wonderful
#E5640
Issued: 1981 • Susp.: 1985
Retail Price: $12 – $17

5

Values ⬧ $80

✝	$74
⬧	$68
ℐ	$68
▲	$65
⬧	$65
⬧	$65
✦	$63

It's A Perfect Boy
#E0512
Issued: 1983 • Susp.: 1990
Retail Price: $18.50 – $27.50

6

Values ℐ $57

▲	$52
⬧	$52
⬧	$50

It's The Birthday Of A King
#102962
Issued: 1986 • Susp.: 1989
Retail Price: $19 – $25

Nativity

	Price Paid	Value
1.		
2.		
3.		
4.		
5.		
6.		
7.		
8.		
9.		
10.		

Totals

7

Values NM $155

▲	$148
I	$140
⬧	$124
✝	$120

Jesus Is Born
#E2012
Issued: 1979 • Susp.: 1984
Retail Price: $12 – $25

8

Values NM $405

▲	$370
I	$345
⬧	$330
✝	$310

Jesus Is Born
#E2801
Issued: 1980 • Susp.: 1984
Retail Price: $37 – $55

9

Values ⬧ $52

✦	$48
⬧	$44
⬧	$40
⬧	$38

Jesus Is The Sweetest
Name I Know
#523097
Issued: 1989 • Susp.: 1993
Retail Price: $22.50 – $25

10

Values ⬧ $68

⬧	$57
✦	$52
⬧	$48
⬧	$46
⬧	$45

Jesus The Savior Is Born
#520357
Issued: 1988 • Susp.: 1993
Retail Price: $25 – $32.50

1

Values † $63
    ❦ $60
    🎯 $56
    ⚶ $56
    ✤ $54
    ♄ $52

Joy To The World
#E5378
Issued: 1984 • Susp.: 1989
Retail Price: $18 – $25

2

Values 🌣 $30
    ★ $30
    ◷ $30
    🎋 $30

The Light Of The World Is Jesus
#455954
Issued: 1998 • Open
Retail Price: $30

3

Values † $100
    🌣 $100
    ★ $100
    ◷ $100
    🎋 $100

Lighted Inn
#283428
Issued: 1997 • Open
Retail Price: $100

4

Values 🜊 $37
    ♡ $34
    † $34
    🌣 $34

Making A Trail To Bethlehem
#142751
Issued: 1995 • Retired: 1998
Retail Price: $30 – $32.50

5

Values † $92
    🜊 $86
    🎯 $82

A Monarch Is Born
#E5380
Issued: 1984 • Susp.: 1986
Retail Price: $33

6

Values 🗝 $22
    🜊 $18.50
    ♡ $18.50
    † $18.50
    🌣 $18.50
    ★ $18.50
    ◷ $18.50
    🎋 $18.50

Nativity Cart
#528072
Issued: 1994 • Open
Retail Price: $18.50

7

Values UM $24

Nativity Displayer
#PMA077
Issued: 1993 • Open
Retail Price: $18 – $24

8

Values NM $165
    ▲ $160
    Ⅱ $148
    ➡ $140
    † $135
    🎯 $132
    🎯 $130
    ▲ $130
    ✤ $125
    ♄ $125
    ⚶ $125
    ⚶ $125
    ♌ $120
    🗝 $120
    🜊 $120
    ♡ $120
    † $120
    🌣 $120
    ★ $120
    ◷ $120
    🎋 $120

Nativity Wall (set/2)
#E5644
Issued: 1981 • Open
Retail Price: $60 – $120

9

Values † $60
    🌣 $60
    ★ $60
    ◷ $60
    🎋 $60

Palm Trees, Hay Bale And Baby Food (set/4)
#272582
Issued: 1997 • Open
Retail Price: $60

10

Values ➡ $177
    † $157
    🎯 $150
    🎯 $145

Prepare Ye The Way Of The Lord (set/6)
#E0508
Issued: 1983 • Susp.: 1986
Retail Price: $75

Nativity

	Price Paid	Value
1.		
2.		
3.		
4.		
5.		
6.		
7.		
8.		
9.		
10.		

Totals

1

Values	NM	$85
	▲	$77
	✗	$62
		$54
		$50
	✝	$45
		$42
		$42
	✤	$37
	⅁	$35
		$35
		$34
		$34
		$34
		$34
		$34
		$34
	✝	$33
	ᏖᏖ	$33
		$33

Rejoice O Earth
#E5636
Issued: 1981 • Retired: 1999
Retail Price: $15 – $32.50

2

Values	❀	$58
		$48
		$35
	♡	$32
	✝	$32

Ring Out The Good News
#529966
Issued: 1993 • Retired: 1997
Retail Price: $27.50 – $30

3

New

Photo
Unavailable

| Values | ᏖᏖ | $45 |

The Royal Budge Is Good
For The Soul
#878987
Issued: 2001 • Open
Retail Price: $45

4

Values	♡	$42
	✝	$42
	ᏖᏖ	$40
	★	$40
	◐	$40
	ᏖᏖ	$40

Shepherd With Lambs (set/3)
#183954
Issued: 1996 • Open
Retail Price: $40

5

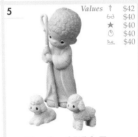

Values	✝	$42
	ᏖᏖ	$40
	★	$40
	◐	$40
	ᏖᏖ	$40

Shepherd With Two
Lambs (set/3)
#183962
Issued: 1997 • Open
Retail Price: $40

6

Values	✤	$46
	⅁	$39
		$36
		$36
		$34
	❀	$33
		$30
		$30
	♡	$30

Some Bunny's Sleeping
#115274
Issued: 1988 • Susp.: 1996
Retail Price: $15 – $18.50

KEY							
NM	Pre'81	✗	1986	⅁	1992	✝	1997
▲	1981	✤	1987	❀	1993	ᏖᏖ	1998
✗	1982	✤	1988	❀	1994	★	1999
	1983	⅁	1989		1995	◐	2000
✝	1984	★	1990	♡	1996	ᏖᏖ	2001
	1985	⅁	1991	**UM**	Unmarked		

Nativity

	Price Paid	Value
1.		
2.		
3.		
4.		
5.		
6.		
7.		
8.		
9.		
10.		

Totals

7

Values	NM	$350
	✗	$305
	✗	$265
	✝	$250
		$240
		$240
	▲	$240
	✤	$240
	⅁	$240
		$235
		$230
	⅁	$225
	❀	$225
		$225
		$225
	♡	$225
	✝	$225
	ᏖᏖ	$225
	★	$225
	◐	$225
	ᏖᏖ	$225

They Followed The
Star (set/3)
#E5624
Issued: 1981 • Open
Retail Price: $130 – $225

8

Values	NM	$260
	▲	$250
	✗	$235
		$215
	✝	$200
		$195

They Followed The Star
#E5641
Issued: 1981 • Susp.: 1985
Retail Price: $75 – $100

9

Values	✝	$53
		$42
		$40
		$40
	▲	$38
	✤	$38
	⅁	$38
		$35
		$35
	⅁	$32
		$30

Tubby's First Christmas
#E0511
Issued: 1983 • Susp.: 1993
Retail Price: $12 – $16.50

10

Values	⅁	$34
	⅁	$30
	❀	$26
		$22

We Have Come From Afar
#526959
Issued: 1991 • Susp.: 1994
Retail Price: $17.50

1

Values	NM	$123
	▲	$115
	Ⅱ	$96
	↔	$92
	✝	$86

We Have Seen His Star
#E2010
Issued: 1979 • Susp.: 1984
Retail Price: $8 – $19

2

Values	NM	$160
	▲	$138
	Ⅱ	$118
	✝	$100
	✦	$97
	🦅	$92
	ⅉ	$85
	♠	$85
	✤	$83
	⊕	$83
	↓	$80
	♪	$77
	⅋	$77
	⚲	$75
	☖	$75
	♡	$75
	✝	$75
	69	$75
	★	$75
	◐	$75
	ﯤ	$75

We Three Kings
(set/3)
#E5635
Issued: 1981 • Open
Retail Price: $40 – $75

3

Values	✝	$30
	69	$30
	★	$30
	◐	$30
	ﯤ	$30

Wishing Well
#292753
Issued: 1997 • Open
Retail Price: $30

4

Values	♪	$40
	⅋	$33
	◀	$33
	☖	$33
	♡	$33
	✝	$33
	69	$33
	★	$33

**Wishing You A Comfy
Christmas**
#527750
Issued: 1992 • Retired: 1999
Retail Price: $27.50 – $30

5

Values	ⅉ	$530

Come Let Us Adore Him (Dealers' Only, set/9)
#104523
Issued: 1986 • Closed: 1986
Retail Price: $400

6

Values	♠	$260
	✤	$235
	⊕	$230
	↓	$230
	🦅	$230

**O Come Let Us Adore
Him (set/4)**
#111333
Issued: 1987 • Susp.: 1991
Retail Price: $200 – $220

KEY			
NM Pre'81	ⅉ 1986	♪ 1992	✝ 1997
▲ 1981	♠ 1987	⅋ 1993	69 1998
Ⅱ 1982	✤ 1988	⚲ 1994	★ 1999
☖ 1983	⊕ 1989	◀ 1995	◐ 2000
✝ 1984	↓ 1990	♡ 1996	ﯤ 2001
🦅 1985	🦅 1991	UM Unmarked	

Nativity

	Price Paid	Value
1.		
2.		
3.		
4.		

9" Nativity

5.		
6.		

Totals

1   *Values* ❀ $110
    🗑 $100
    ⚜ $93
    ♡ $93

Circus Tent Night-Light
#528196
Issued: 1994 • Susp.: 1996
Retail Price: $90

2   *Values* ❀ $32
    🗑 $28
    ⚜ $24
    ♡ $22

Collin
#529214
Issued: 1994 • Susp.: 1996
Retail Price: $20

3   *Values* ❀ $32
    🗑 $28
    ⚜ $25
    ♡ $25

Dusty
#529176
Issued: 1994 • Susp.: 1996
Retail Price: $22.50

4   *Values* ⚜ $30
    ♡ $25

Jennifer (set/2)
#163708
Issued: 1996 • Susp.: 1996
Retail Price: $20

5   *Values* 🗑 $32
    ⚜ $26
    ♡ $23

Jordan (set/2)
#529168
Issued: 1995 • Susp.: 1996
Retail Price: $20

6   *Values* ❀ $33
    🗑 $26
    ⚜ $22
    ♡ $19

Katie
#529184
Issued: 1994 • Susp.: 1996
Retail Price: $17

KEY			
NM Pre'81	✣ 1986	✦ 1992	✝ 1997
▲ 1981	✤ 1987	❀ 1993	1998
✕ 1982	✤ 1988	🗑 1994	★ 1999
◄ 1983	Ð 1989	⚜ 1995	◎ 2000
✝ 1984	☀ 1990	♡ 1996	► 2001
✦ 1985	☀ 1991	UM Unmarked	

Sammy's Circus

	Price Paid	Value
1.		
2.		
3.		
4.		
5.		
6.		
7.		
8.		
9.		

Totals

7   *Values* ❀ $30
    🗑 $24
    ⚜ $22
    ♡ $20

Markie
#528099
Issued: 1994 • Susp.: 1996
Retail Price: $18.50

8   *Values* ❀ $52
    🗑 $35

Sammy (LE-1994)
#529222
Issued: 1994 • Closed: 1994
Retail Price: $20

9   *Values* UM $24

Sammy's Circus Displayer
#PMB015
Issued: 1994 • Discontinued: 1997
Retail Price: $18 – $24

1 *Values* ✿ $22
🍴 $19
👑 $15
♡ $14

Tippy
#529192
Issued: 1994 • Susp.: 1996
Retail Price: $12

2 *Values* ✿ $300
🍴 $260

Sammy's Circus (set/7, *includes* 528099, 528196, 529176,
529184, 529192, 529214 & 529222)
#604070
Issued: 1994 • Closed: 1994
Retail Price: $200

3 *Values* UM $22

Accessories (set/8)
#212725
Issued: 1997 • Retired: 1997
Retail Price: $20

4 *Values* † $32

Aunt Bulah And Uncle Sam
#272825
Issued: 1997 • Retired: 1997
Retail Price: $22.50

5 *Values* † $26

Aunt Cleo
#272817
Issued: 1997 • Retired: 1997
Retail Price: $18.50

6 *Values* ♻ $50
✿ $42
🍴 $36

Aunt Ruth And
Aunt Dorothy
#529486
Issued: 1992 • Retired: 1994
Retail Price: $20

KEY			
NM Pre'81	♫ 1986	♨ 1992	† 1997
▲ 1981	▲ 1987	✿ 1993	6↩ 1998
▮ 1982	✤ 1988	♨ 1994	★ 1999
◄ 1983	✛ 1989	△ 1995	⊙ 2000
✝ 1984	✦ 1990	♡ 1996	☘ 2001
✦ 1985	● 1991	UM Unmarked	

Sammy's Circus

	Price Paid	Value
1.		
2.		

Sugar Town

3.		
4.		
5.		
6.		
7.		
8.		

Totals

7 *Values* † $22

Bike Rack
#272906
Issued: 1997 • Retired: 1997
Retail Price: $15

8 *Values* △ $18
♡ $14
† $12

Bird Bath
#150223
Issued: 1995 • Retired: 1997
Retail Price: $8.50

1 *Values* ♡ $20 / † $16

Bonfire
#184152
Issued: 1996 • Retired: 1997
Retail Price: $10

2 *Values* † $13

Bunnies
#531804
Issued: 1997 • Retired: 1997
Retail Price: $10

3 *Values* ⬠ $18 / ♡ $13 / † $13

Bus Stop
#150207
Issued: 1995 • Retired: 1997
Retail Price: $8.50

4 *Values* † $36

Chuck (LE-1997)
#272809
Issued: 1997 • Closed: 1997
Retail Price: $22.50

5 *Values* ⬟ $33 / ⬠ $24 / ♡ $24 / † $22

Cobblestone Bridge
#533203
Issued: 1994 • Retired: 1997
Retail Price: $17

6 *Values* ♡ $20 / † $13

Cocoa
#184063
Issued: 1996 • Retired: 1997
Retail Price: $7.50

Sugar Town

	Price Paid	Value
1.		
2.		
3.		
4.		
5.		
6.		
7.		
8.		
9.		
10.		
Totals		

7 *Values* ⬟ $23 / ⬠ $17 / ♡ $15 / † $15

Curved Sidewalk
#533149
Issued: 1994 • Retired: 1997
Retail Price: $10

8 *Values* ⬟ $105 / ⬠ $97 / ♡ $92 / † $92

Doctor's Office Night-Light
#529869
Issued: 1994 • Retired: 1997
Retail Price: $80 – $85

9 *Values* ⬟ $36 / ♡ $32 / † $28

Donny
#531871
Issued: 1995 • Retired: 1997
Retail Price: $22.50

10 *Values* ⬟ $25 / ⬠ $16 / ♡ $16 / † $16

Double Tree
#533181
Issued: 1994 • Retired: 1997
Retail Price: $10

1 Values 🗑 $38 ⊿ $26 ♡ $23 ✝ $20

Dr. Sam Sugar
#529850
Issued: 1994 • Retired: 1997
Retail Price: $17

2 Values 🐝 $35 🎩 $30 ⚓ $26 ♡ $23 ✝ $23

Dusty
#529435
Issued: 1993 • Retired: 1997
Retail Price: $17

3 Values 🔔 $42 🐝 $36 🗑 $33

Evergreen Tree
#528684
Issued: 1992 • Retired: 1994
Retail Price: $15

4 Values ⊿ $15 ♡ $9 ✝ $9

Fire Hydrant
#150215
Issued: 1995 • Retired: 1997
Retail Price: $5

5 Values ♡ $22 ✝ $19

Flag Pole
#184136
Issued: 1996 • Retired: 1997
Retail Price: $15

6 Values 🗑 $30 ⊿ $25 ♡ $22 ✝ $20

Free Christmas Puppies
#528064
Issued: 1994 • Retired: 1997
Retail Price: $12.50

7 Values ✝ $26

Garbage Can
#272914
Issued: 1997 • Retired: 1997
Retail Price: $20

8 Values 🔔 $42 🐝 $33 🗑 $30

Grandfather
#529516
Issued: 1992 • Retired: 1994
Retail Price: $15

KEY			
NM Pre'81	ℳ 1986	🔔 1992	✝ 1997
▲ 1981	♠ 1987	🐝 1993	1998
Ⅱ 1982	⬧ 1988	🗑 1994	★ 1999
🔷 1983	ⅅ 1989	⊿ 1995	⏰ 2000
✝ 1984	★ 1990	♡ 1996	⚓ 2001
⬥ 1985	♦ 1991	UM Unmarked	

Sugar Town

	Price Paid	Value
1.		
2.		
3.		
4.		
5.		
6.		
7.		
8.		
9.		
10.		
Totals		

9 Values ♡ $35 ✝ $30

Hank And Sharon
#184098
Issued: 1996 • Retired: 1997
Retail Price: $25

10 Values ✝ $28

Heather
#272833
Issued: 1997 • Retired: 1997
Retail Price: $20

1

Values ♡ $21
† $18

Hot Cocoa Stand
#184144
Issued: 1996 • Retired: 1997
Retail Price: $15

2

Values ⌐ $37
△ $31
♡ $27
† $23

Jan
#529826
Issued: 1994 • Retired: 1997
Retail Price: $17

3

Values ✿ $42
⌐ $34
△ $33
♡ $27
† $26

Katy Lynne
#529524
Issued: 1993 • Retired: 1997
Retail Price: $20

4

Values ⌐ $17
♡ $14
♡ $12
† $12

Lamp Post
#529559
Issued: 1994 • Retired: 1997
Retail Price: $8

5

Values ⌐ $37
△ $30
♡ $30
† $25

Leon And Evelyn Mae
#529818
Issued: 1994 • Retired: 1997
Retail Price: $20

6

Values ♡ $28
† $24

Leroy
#184071
Issued: 1996 • Retired: 1997
Retail Price: $18.50

KEY			
NM Pre'81	✸ 1986	⅋ 1992	† 1997
▲ 1981	▲ 1987	❀ 1993	ଚ 1998
⊞ 1982	❖ 1988	⌐ 1994	★ 1999
◄ 1983	ꝺ 1989	△ 1995	☾ 2000
† 1984	⬥ 1990	♡ 1996	੩ 2001
◀ 1985	◉ 1991	**UM** Unmarked	

Sugar Town

	Price Paid	Value
1.		
2.		
3.		
4.		
5.		
6.		
7.		
8.		
9.		
10.		

Totals

7

Values ♡ $67
† $58

Lighted Tree
#184039
Issued: 1996 • Retired: 1997
Retail Price: $45

8

Values △ $24
♡ $18
† $17

Luggage Cart
#150185
Issued: 1995 • Retired: 1997
Retail Price: $13

9

Values ⌐ $17
△ $13
♡ $9
† $9

Mailbox
#531847
Issued: 1994 • Retired: 1997
Retail Price: $5

10

Values ♡ $34
† $28

Mazie
#184055
Issued: 1996 • Retired: 1997
Retail Price: $18.50

1 *Values* † $28

Merry Go Round
#272841
Issued: 1997 • Retired: 1997
Retail Price: $20

2 *Values* $ $58
⚘ $50
⚑ $45

Nativity
#529508
Issued: 1992 • Retired: 1994
Retail Price: $20

3 *Values* ⬠ $24
♡ $18
† $18

Park Bench
#529540
Issued: 1995 • Retired: 1997
Retail Price: $13

4 *Values* $ $45
⚘ $40
⚑ $33

Philip
#529494
Issued: 1992 • Retired: 1994
Retail Price: $17

5 *Values* ⬠ $22
♡ $17
† $17

Railroad Crossing Sign
#150177
Issued: 1995 • Retired: 1997
Retail Price: $12

6 *Values* ⬠ $52
♡ $36

Sam (LE-1995)
#150169
Issued: 1995 • Closed: 1995
Retail Price: $20

7 *Values* $ $220

Sam Butcher (LE-1992)
#529567
Issued: 1992 • Closed: 1992
Retail Price: $22.50

8 *Values* ⚘ $70

Sam Butcher With Sugar
Town Population Sign
(LE-1993)
#529842
Issued: 1993 • Closed: 1993
Retail Price: $22.50

KEY					
NM Pre'81	⚙ 1986	$ 1992	† 1997
▲ 1981	⚘ 1987	⚘ 1993	⚑ 1998
▮ 1982	⚜ 1988	⚑ 1994	★ 1999
◄ 1983	⚒ 1989	⬠ 1995	☉ 2000
✝ 1984	⚑ 1990	♡ 1996	⚑ 2001
⚑ 1985	⚑ 1991	UM Unmarked	

Sugar Town

	Price Paid	Value
1.		
2.		
3.		
4.		
5.		
6.		
7.		
8.		
9.		
10.		

Totals

9 *Values* ⚘ $40
⚑ $33
⬠ $33
♡ $30
† $27

Sam's Car
#529443
Issued: 1993 • Retired: 1997
Retail Price: $22.50

10 *Values* ⬠ $115
⚑ $98
⬠ $95
♡ $92
† $90

Sam's House Night-Light
#529605
Issued: 1993 • Retired: 1997
Retail Price: $80 – $85

1

Values 🎀 $40 · 🔫 $32 · ⛵ $25 · ♡ $23 · † $23

Sammy
#528668
Issued: 1993 • Retired: 1997
Retail Price: $17

2

Values † $105

School House Night-Light (also available with Canadian flag)
#272795
Issued: 1997 • Retired: 1997
Retail Price: $80

3

Values 🔫 $22 · ⛵ $14 · ♡ $12 · † $12

Single Tree
#533173
Issued: 1994 • Retired: 1997
Retail Price: $10

4

Values 🔫 $55

Stork With Baby Sam (LE-1994)
#529788
Issued: 1994 • Closed: 1994
Retail Price: $22.50

5

Values 🔫 $20 · ⛵ $16 · ♡ $13 · † $13

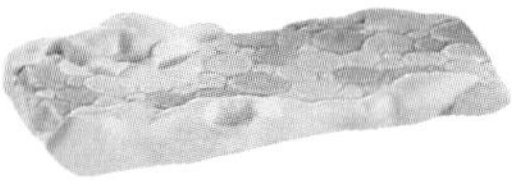

Straight Sidewalk
#533157
Issued: 1994 • Retired: 1997
Retail Price: $10

6

Values ⛵ $21 · ♡ $15 · † $15

Street Sign
#532185
Issued: 1995 • Retired: 1997
Retail Price: $10

KEY

NM Pre'81	🌾 1986	𝄞 1992	† 1997
▲ 1981	🌲 1987	🎀 1993	👓 1998
⌶ 1982	✤ 1988	🔫 1994	★ 1999
🐟 1983	⊕ 1989	⛵ 1995	⌚ 2000
✝ 1984	★ 1990	♡ 1996	🚣 2001
🕊 1985	🔥 1991	UM Unmarked	

Sugar Town

	Price Paid	Value
1.		
2.		
3.		
4.		
5.		
6.		
7.		
8.		
9.		
10.		
Totals		

7

Values 🔫 $33 · ⛵ $30 · ♡ $28 · † $24

Sugar And Her Doghouse (set/2)
#533165
Issued: 1994 • Retired: 1997
Retail Price: $20

8

Values UM $34

Sugar Town Cargo Car (LE-1997)
#273007
Issued: 1997 • Closed: 1997
Retail Price: $27.50

9

Values 𝄞 $155 · 🎀 $140 · 🔫 $130

Sugar Town Chapel Night-Light
#529621
Issued: 1992 • Retired: 1994
Retail Price: $85

10

Values 🎀 $38

Sugar Town Chapel Ornament (LE-1993)
#530484
Issued: 1993 • Closed: 1993
Retail Price: $17.50

1   *Values* ŪM $24

Sugar Town Displayer
#PMB007
Issued: 1993 • Retired: 1997
Retail Price: $18 – $24

2   *Values* △ $30

**Sugar Town Doctor's
Office Ornament (LE-1995)**
#530441
Issued: 1995 • Closed: 1995
Retail Price: $17.50 – $20

3   *Values* ŪM $90

Sugar Town Express (set/3)
♪Christmas Medley
#152595
Issued: 1995 • Retired: 1997
Retail Price: $75

4   *Values* ◊ $20
     △ $15
     △ $15
     ♡ $12
     † $12

Sugar Town Fence
#529796
Issued: 1993 • Retired: 1997
Retail Price: $10

5   *Values* ŪM $32

**Sugar Town Passenger Car
(LE-1996)**
#192406
Issued: 1996 • Closed: 1996
Retail Price: $27.50

6   *Values* ◄ $32
     △ $24

**Sugar Town Sam's House
Ornament (LE-1994)**
#530468
Issued: 1994 • Closed: 1994
Retail Price: $17.50

7   *Values* ♡ $56
     † $50

Sugar Town Skating Pond
#184047
Issued: 1996 • Retired: 1997
Retail Price: $40

8   *Values* ♡ $36
     † $28

**Sugar Town Skating Sign
(LE-1996)**
#184020
Issued: 1996 • Closed: 1996
Retail Price: $15

KEY			
NM Pre'81	✻ 1986	✵ 1992	† 1997
▲ 1981	▲ 1987	✻✻ 1993	6♂ 1998
▮ 1982	✤ 1988	◄ 1994	★ 1999
◄ 1983	Ð 1989	△ 1995	◐ 2000
✝ 1984	♣ 1990	♡ 1996	≈ 2001
◢ 1985	♠ 1991	ŪM Unmarked	

Sugar Town

	Price Paid	Value
1.		
2.		
3.		
4.		
5.		
6.		
7.		
8.		
9.		

Totals

9   *Values* ◄ $115
     △ $95
     ♡ $90
     † $90

Sugar Town Square Clock
#532908
Issued: 1994 • Retired: 1997
Retail Price: $80 – $85

1

Values ♡ $27
† $22

Sugar Town Train Station Ornament (LE-1996)
#184101
Issued: 1996 • Closed: 1996
Retail Price: $18.50

2

Values ⬧ $35
♡ $32
† $28

Tammy And Debbie
#531812
Issued: 1995 • Retired: 1997
Retail Price: $22.50

3

Values ⬧ $130
♡ $120
† $110

Train Station Night-Light
#150150
Issued: 1995 • Retired: 1997
Retail Price: $100

4

Values ♡ $72
† $66

Warming Hut Night-Light
#192341
Issued: 1996 • Retired: 1997
Retail Price: $60

5

Values ⬐ $290
⬧ $251
♡ $231
† $214

Sugar Town Doctor's Office Collector's Set (set/6, includes 528064, 529818, 529826, 529850, 529869 & 533165)
#184187
Issued: 1996 • Retired: 1997
Retail Price: $170

KEY			
NM Pre'81	🐾 1986	♨ 1992	† 1997
▲ 1981	▲ 1987	🐝 1993	🐚 1998
I 1982	⬥ 1988	⬐ 1994	★ 1999
⬅ 1983	Ð 1989	△ 1995	Ø 2000
✝ 1984	★ 1990	♡ 1996	⬑ 2001
✦ 1985	⬧ 1991	UM Unmarked	

Sugar Town

	Price Paid	Value
1.		
2.		
3.		
4.		
5.		
6.		
7.		
8.		

Totals

6

Values ⬐ $343

Sugar Town Doctor's Office Collector's Set (set/7, LE-1994, includes 528064, 529788, 529818, 529826, 529850, 529869 & 533165)
#529281
Issued: 1994 • Closed: 1994
Retail Price: $189

7

Values ⬧ $90
♡ $61
† $61

Sugar Town Enhancement Set (set/5, includes 150207, 150215, 150223, 529540 & 532185)
#152269
Issued: 1995 • Retired: 1997
Retail Price: $45

8

Values ♡ $59
† $51

Sugar Town Enhancement Set (set/3, includes 184136, 184144 & 184152)
#184160
Issued: 1996 • Retired: 1997
Retail Price: $40

1

Values † $53

Sugar Town Enhancement
Set (set/3, *includes*
272906, 272914 & 531804)
#273015
Issued: 1997 • Retired: 1997
Retail Price: $45

2

Values 6ð $260

Sugar Town Post Office Collector's Set (set/8, LE-1998)
#456217
Issued: 1998 • Closed: 1998   •

3

Values ℘ $283
≈ $242
△ $223
♡ $209
† $203

Sugar Town Sam's House Collector's Set
(set/6, *includes* 528668, 529435, 529443, 529524, 529605 & 529796)
#184195
Issued: 1996 • Retired: 1997
Retail Price: $170

4

Values ℘ $351

KEY			
NM Pre'81	⅋ 1986	⅄ 1992	† 1997
▲ 1981	▲ 1987	℘ 1993	6ð 1998
Ⅱ 1982	✦ 1988	✾ 1994	★ 1999
◄ 1983	⌖ 1989	△ 1995	☽ 2000
† 1984	✦ 1990	♡ 1996	⅏ 2001
✦ 1985	♦ 1991	ⅡM Unmarked	

Sugar Town Sam's House Collector's Set
(set/7, LE-1993, *includes* 528668, 529435, 529443, 529524,
529605, 529796 & 529842)
#531774
Issued: 1993 • Closed: 1993
Retail Price: $189

5

Values † $249

Sugar Town School House Collector's Set
(set/6, LE-1997, *includes* 272795, 272809, 272817, 272825,
272833 & 272841, also available with Canadian flag)
#272876
Issued: 1997 • Closed: 1997
Retail Price: $183.50

Sugar Town

	Price Paid	Value
1.		
2.		
3.		
4.		
5.		

Totals

1

Values ♡ $263
† $231

Sugar Town Skating Pond Collector's Set
(set/7, LE-1996, *includes* 184020, 184047, 184055, 184063, 184071, 184098 & 192341)
#184128
Issued: 1996 • Closed: 1996
Retail Price: $184.50

2

Values ♡ $231
† $204

Sugar Town Skating Pond Collector's Set
(set/6, *includes* 184047, 184055, 184063, 184071, 184098 & 192341)
#272930
Issued: 1997 • Retired: 1997
Retail Price: $169.50

KEY			
NM Pre'81	✒ 1986	✿ 1992	† 1997
▲ 1981	♠ 1987	⁹⁰ 1993	⬥ 1998
Ⅱ 1982	✦ 1988	☞ 1994	★ 1999
◀ 1983	Ⴆ 1989	△ 1995	☯ 2000
✝ 1984	✦ 1990	♡ 1996	≊ 2001
✤ 1985	♠ 1991	**UM** Unmarked	

Sugar Town

	Price Paid	Value
1.		
2.		
3.		
4.		

Totals

3

Values △ $275
♡ $241

Sugar Town Train Station Collector's Set (set/6, LE-1995,
includes 150150, 150169, 150177, 150185, 531812 & 531871)
#150193
Issued: 1995 • Closed: 1995
Retail Price: $190

4

Values △ $230
♡ $208
† $193

Sugar Town Train Station Collector's Set
(set/5, *includes* 150150, 150177, 150185, 531812 & 531871)
#184179
Issued: 1996 • Retired: 1997
Retail Price: $170

1 Values 💑 $18
                   ➡ $12
                   ⚓ $10
                   ♡ $9
                   ✝ $9
                   👓 $9
                   ★ $9
                   🕐 $9
                   🐚 $9

Bunnies
#530123
Issued: 1993 • Open
Retail Price: $9

2 Values ⚓ $22
                   ♡ $15
                   ✝ $15
                   👓 $15
                   ★ $15
                   🕐 $15
                   🐚 $15

Congratulations, You Earned Your Stripes
#127809
Issued: 1995 • Open
Retail Price: $15

3 Values 💑 $27
                   ➡ $20
                   ⚓ $18
                   ♡ $18
                   ✝ $18
                   👓 $18
                   ★ $18
                   🕐 $18
                   🐚 $18

Elephants
#530131
Issued: 1993 • Open
Retail Price: $18

4 Values 💑 $24
                   ♡ $19
                   ⚓ $16
                   ♡ $16
                   ✝ $16
                   👓 $16
                   ★ $16
                   🕐 $16
                   🐚 $16

Giraffes
#530115
Issued: 1993 • Open
Retail Price: $16

5 Values ⚓ $16
                   ♡ $16
                   ✝ $10
                   👓 $10
                   ★ $10
                   🕐 $10
                   🐚 $10

I'd Goat Anywhere With You
#163694
Issued: 1996 • Open
Retail Price: $10

6 Values ➡ $22
                   ♡ $17
                   ✝ $15
                   ♡ $15
                   👓 $15
                   ★ $15
                   🕐 $15
                   🐚 $15

Llamas
#531375
Issued: 1994 • Open
Retail Price: $15

7 Values 💑 $145
                   ➡ $134
                   ⚓ $125
                   ♡ $125
                   ✝ $125
                   👓 $125
                   ★ $125
                   🕐 $125
                   🐚 $125

Noah's Ark Night-Light (set/3)
#530042
Issued: 1993 • Open
Retail Price: $125

8 Values 💑 $20
                   ➡ $16
                   ⚓ $14
                   ♡ $12
                   ✝ $12
                   👓 $12
                   ★ $12
                   🕐 $12
                   🐚 $12

Pigs
#530085
Issued: 1993 • Open
Retail Price: $12

KEY					
NM Pre'81	💥 1986	🔔 1992	✝ 1997
▲ 1981	▲ 1987	💑 1993	👓 1998
🍷 1982	✣ 1988	➡ 1994	★ 1999
➡ 1983	� 1989	⚓ 1995	🕐 2000
✝ 1984	♦ 1990	♡ 1996	🐚 2001
🌿 1985	♦ 1991	UM Unmarked	

Two By Two

	Price Paid	Value
1.		
2.		
3.		
4.		
5.		
6.		
7.		
8.		

Totals

1

Values
🐑 $16
🎄 $13
△ $10
♡ $10
† $10
👓 $10
★ $10
🕐 $10
🔔 $10

Sheep
#530077
Issued: 1993 • Open
Retail Price: $10

2

Values
★ $20
🕐 $20
🔔 $20

A Tail Of Love
#679976
Issued: 2000 • Open
Retail Price: $20

3

Values ∪M $24

Two By Two Displayer
#PMA022
Issued: 1993 • Discontinued: 1993
Retail Price: $24

4

Values
🐑 $245
🎄 $212
△ $195
♡ $190
† $190
👓 $190
★ $190
🕐 $190
🔔 $190

Two By Two Collector's Set
(set/8, *includes* 530042, 530077, 530085, 530115, 530123 & 530131)
#530948
Issued: 1993 • Open
Retail Price: $190

KEY							
NM	Pre'81	🎗	1986	⚓	1992	†	1997
▲	1981	♠	1987	🐑	1993	👓	1998
Ⅱ	1982	✿	1988	🎄	1994	★	1999
◀	1983	♦	1989	△	1995	🕐	2000
†	1984	✚	1990	♡	1996	🔔	2001
♨	1985	🔔	1991	∪M	Unmarked		

Two By Two

	Price Paid	Value
1.		
2.		
3.		
4.		
Totals		

General Figurines

It's hard to believe that when the PRECIOUS MOMENTS collection debuted, there were only 21 figurines in the line. Today, there are hundreds of PRECIOUS MOMENTS figurines for collectors to choose from, including limited edition, exclusive and charity pieces. Though many of these wonderful figurines have been retired or suspended, each year delights collectors with the addition of new pieces.

1
Values 🌂 $36
★ $36
🕐 $35
🔔 $35

Alaska Once More, How's Yer Christmas?
#455784
Issued: 1998 • Open
Retail Price: $35

2
Values 🌂 $60
★ $60
🕐 $60
🔔 $60

All Girls Are Beautiful (set/5)
#481661
Issued: 1999 • Open
Retail Price: $60

3
Values ★ $30
🕐 $30
🔔 $30

Alleluia, He Is Risen
#692409
Issued: 2000 • Open
Retail Price: $30

4
Values 🌂 $26
★ $26
🕐 $25
🔔 $25

Always Listen To Your Heart
#488356
Issued: 1999 • Open
Retail Price: $25

5
Values 🔔 $59
🔔 $53

America You're Beautiful (LE-1993)
National Day Of Prayer Figurine
#528862
Issued: 1993 • Closed: 1993
Retail Price: $35

KEY			
NM Pre'81	🎋 1986	🔔 1992	† 1997
▲ 1981	▲ 1987	♋ 1993	🌂 1998
Ⅱ 1982	⬩ 1988	⊟ 1994	★ 1999
◄ 1983	⊕ 1989	△ 1995	🕐 2000
† 1984	⬩ 1990	♡ 1996	🔔 2001
🍀 1985	🍴 1991	UM Unmarked	

6
Values ♡ $56
† $56
🌂 $55
★ $55
🕐 $55
🔔 $55

And A Child Shall Lead Them
#E9287R
Issued: 1997 • Open
Retail Price: $50 – $55

7
Values 🎋 $55
▲ $45
⬩ $40
⊕ $37
⬩ $35
🍴 $35
🔔 $35
♋ $33
⊟ $33
△ $32.50
♡ $32.50
† $32.50
🌂 $32.50
★ $32.50
🕐 $32.50
🔔 $32.50

Angel Of Mercy
#102482
Issued: 1986 • Open
Retail Price: $20 – $32.50

General Figurines

	Price Paid	Value
1.		
2.		
3.		
4.		
5.		
6.		
7.		

Totals

1

Values	
♡	$47
†	$47
👓	$45
★	$45
☾	$45
🐞	$45

Angels On Earth
#183776
Issued: 1996 • Open
Retail Price: $40 – $45

2

Values	
♦	$96
⚘	$88
♀	$84
�	$82
△	$80
♡	$78

**Angels We Have
Heard On High**
#524921
Issued: 1991 • Retired: 1996
Retail Price: $60 – $70

3

Values	
⟷	$32
†	$29
💨	$29
💱	$25
▲	$24
⬥	$24
⅁	$24
🡇	$22
🍶	$22
UM	$34

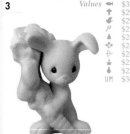

Animal Collection – Bunny
#E9267C
Issued: 1983 • Susp.: 1991
Retail Price: $6.50 – $11

4

Values	
⟷	$32
†	$29
💨	$29
💱	$25
▲	$24
⬥	$24
⅁	$24
🡇	$22
🍶	$22
UM	$34

Animal Collection – Dog
#E9267B
Issued: 1983 • Susp.: 1991
Retail Price: $6.50 – $11

5

Values	
⟷	$32
†	$29
💨	$29
💱	$25
▲	$24
⬥	$24
⅁	$24
🡇	$22
🍶	$22
UM	$34

Animal Collection – Kitten
#E9267D
Issued: 1983 • Susp.: 1991
Retail Price: $6.50 – $11

6

Values	
⟷	$32
†	$29
💨	$29
💱	$25
▲	$24
⬥	$24
⅁	$24
🡇	$22
🍶	$22
UM	$34

Animal Collection – Lamb
#E9267E
Issued: 1983 • Susp.: 1991
Retail Price: $6.50 – $11

KEY					
NM Pre'81	💨 1986	⚘ 1992	† 1997		
▲ 1981	▲ 1987	♀ 1993	🔄 1998		
⅄ 1982	⬥ 1988	⟷ 1994	★ 1999		
⟷ 1983	⅁ 1989	△ 1995	☾ 2000		
† 1984	🡇 1990	♡ 1996	🐞 2001		
💨 1985	🍶 1991	UM Unmarked			

General Figurines

	Price Paid	Value
1.		
2.		
3.		
4.		
5.		
6.		
7.		
8.		
9.		

Totals

7

Values	
⟷	$32
†	$29
💨	$29
💱	$25
▲	$24
⬥	$24
⅁	$24
🡇	$22
🍶	$22
UM	$34

Animal Collection – Pig
#E9267F
Issued: 1983 • Susp.: 1991
Retail Price: $6.50 – $11

8

Values	
⟷	$32
†	$29
💨	$29
💱	$25
▲	$24
⬥	$24
⅁	$24
🡇	$22
🍶	$22
UM	$34

Animal Collection – Teddy
#E9267A
Issued: 1983 • Susp.: 1991
Retail Price: $6.50 – $11

9

Values	
⟷	$28
△	$21
♡	$18.50
†	$18.50
👓	$18.50
★	$18.50
☾	$18.50
🐞	$18.50

**Another Year And
More Grey Hares**
#128686
Issued: 1995 • Open
Retail Price: $17.50 – $18.50

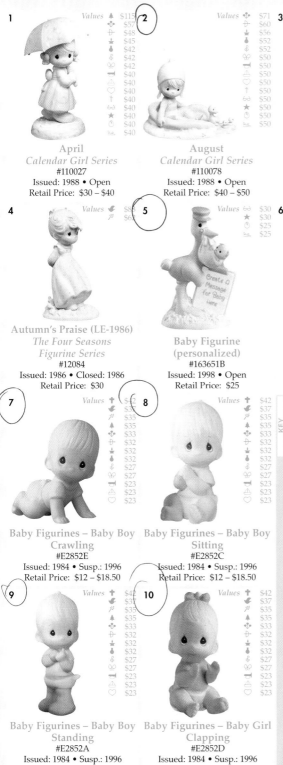

1 Values ▲ $115 / $57 / $48 / $45 / $42 / $42 / $40 / $40 / $40 / $40 / $40 / $40 / $40 / $40

April
Calendar Girl Series
#110027
Issued: 1988 • Open
Retail Price: $30 – $40

2 Values $71 / $60 / $56 / $52 / $52 / $50 / $50 / $50 / $50 / $50 / $50 / $50 / $50

August
Calendar Girl Series
#110078
Issued: 1988 • Open
Retail Price: $40 – $50

3 Values ⏲ $40 / $40

Auntie, You Make Beauty Blossom
#737623
Issued: 2000 • Open
Retail Price: $40

4 Values $85 / $65

Autumn's Praise (LE-1986)
The Four Seasons Figurine Series
#12084
Issued: 1986 • Closed: 1986
Retail Price: $30

5 Values $30 / $30 / $25 / $25

Baby Figurine (personalized)
#163651B
Issued: 1998 • Open
Retail Price: $25

6 Values $30 / $30 / $25 / $25

Baby Figurine (personalized)
#163651G
Issued: 1998 • Open
Retail Price: $25

KEY			
NM Pre'81	♪ 1986	♣ 1992	✝ 1997
▲ 1981	♣ 1987	♋ 1993	⌘ 1998
✕ 1982	✧ 1988	▱ 1994	★ 1999
⊡ 1983	⊕ 1989	△ 1995	⏲ 2000
✝ 1984	♦ 1990	♡ 1996	⊿ 2001
♪ 1985	♦ 1991	UM Unmarked	

7 Values ✝ $42 / $37 / $35 / $35 / $33 / $32 / $32 / $32 / $27 / $27 / $23 / $23 / $23

Baby Figurines – Baby Boy Crawling
#E2852E
Issued: 1984 • Susp.: 1996
Retail Price: $12 – $18.50

8 Values ✝ $42 / $37 / $35 / $35 / $33 / $32 / $32 / $32 / $27 / $27 / $23 / $23 / $23

Baby Figurines – Baby Boy Sitting
#E2852C
Issued: 1984 • Susp.: 1996
Retail Price: $12 – $18.50

9 Values ✝ $42 / $37 / $35 / $35 / $33 / $32 / $32 / $32 / $27 / $27 / $23 / $23 / $23

Baby Figurines – Baby Boy Standing
#E2852A
Issued: 1984 • Susp.: 1996
Retail Price: $12 – $18.50

10 Values ✝ $42 / $37 / $35 / $35 / $33 / $32 / $32 / $32 / $27 / $27 / $23 / $23 / $23

Baby Figurines – Baby Girl Clapping
#E2852D
Issued: 1984 • Susp.: 1996
Retail Price: $12 – $18.50

General Figurines

	Price Paid	Value
1.		
2.	40.50	
3.		
4.		
5.	25.00	
6.		
7.	12-18.50	
8.	"	
9.	"	
10.		

Totals

1 Values ✝ $42 / $37 / ❀ $35 / ♠ $35 / ⚓ $33 / ⚓ $32 / ⚘ $32 / ♣ $32 / $27 / $27 / $23 / ♡ $23

Baby Figurines – Baby Girl Lying Down
#E2852F
Issued: 1984 • Susp.: 1996
Retail Price: $12 – $18.50

2 Values ✝ $42 / $37 / ❀ $35 / ♠ $35 / ⚓ $33 / $32 / $32 / $32 / $27 / $27 / $23 / ♡ $23

Baby Figurines – Baby Girl Standing With Bow
#E2852B
Issued: 1984 • Susp.: 1996
Retail Price: $12 – $18.50

3 Values ♪ $37 / ❀ $29 / $26 / $25 / ♡ $25 / ✝ $25 / $25 / ★ $25 / $25 / $25

Baby's First Birthday
Baby's First Series
#524069
Issued: 1993 • Open
Retail Price: $25

4 Values $42

Baby's First Christmas (Dated 1985)
#15539
Issued: 1985 • Closed: 1985
Retail Price: $13

5 Values $42

Baby's First Christmas (Dated 1985)
#15547
Issued: 1985 • Closed: 1985
Retail Price: $13

6 Values $190 / $175 / ♠ $168

Baby's First Haircut
Baby's First Series
#12211
Issued: 1985 • Susp.: 1987
Retail Price: $32.50 – $40

General Figurines

	Price Paid	Value
1.		
2.		
3.		
4.		
5.		
6.		
7.		
8.		
9.		
10.		

Totals

7 Values $55 / $47 / ❀ $44 / $42 / ♡ $42 / ✝ $42 / 6∂ $42 / ★ $42

Baby's First Meal
Baby's First Series
#520077
Issued: 1991 • Retired: 1999
Retail Price: $35 – $40

8 Values ⚓ $90 / $82 / $78 / $72 / $70 / ❀ $67 / $65

Baby's First Pet
Baby's First Series
#520705
Issued: 1989 • Susp.: 1994
Retail Price: $45 – $50

9 Values ✝ $195 / $176 / $170

Baby's First Picture
Baby's First Series
#E2841
Issued: 1984 • Retired: 1986
Retail Price: $45

10 Values ✝ $104 / $100 / $96 / ♠ $92 / ⚓ $90

Baby's First Step
Baby's First Series
#E2840
Issued: 1984 • Susp.: 1988
Retail Price: $35 – $40

1

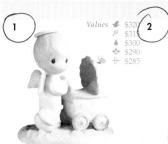

Values 🦋 $320
 ⚘ $315
 ▲ $300
 ♣ $290
 Ð $285

Baby's First Trip
Baby's First Series
#16012
Issued: 1986 • Susp.: 1989
Retail Price: $32.50 – $45

2

Values ♨ $36
 ♔ $30
 ▬ $28
 ♡ $26
 † $26
 ♋ $26
 ★ $26

Baby's First Word
Baby's First Series
#527238
Issued: 1992 • Retired: 1999
Retail Price: $25

3

Values ★ $50
 ☉ $50
 ≈ $50

Be Fruitful And Multiply
#524409
Issued: 2000 • Open
Retail Price: $50

4

Values NM $142
 ▲ $125
 ▮ $110
 ◄ $100
 † $94
 🦋 $88

Variation

Be Not Weary And Well Doing

Be Not Weary In Well Doing
#E3111
Issued: 1980 • Retired: 1985
Retail Price: $14 – $19
*Variation: "Be Not Weary **And** Well Doing"* – $220

5

Values NM $118
 ▲ $105
 ▮ $93
 ◄ $85
 † $83

**Bear Ye One
Another's Burdens**
#E5200
Issued: 1981 • Susp.: 1984
Retail Price: $20 – $25

6

Values ★ $50
 ☉ $50
 ≈ $50

**The Beauty Of God
Blooms Forever**
Four Seasons Series
#129143
Issued: 1999 • Open
Retail Price: $50

7

Values ♋ $37
 ★ $37
 ☉ $35
 ≈ $35

**Believe It Or Knot,
I Luv You**
#487910
Issued: 1999 • Open
Retail Price: $35

KEY					
NM Pre'81	♫ 1986	♨ 1992	† 1997
▲ 1981	♔ 1987	♔ 1993	♋ 1998
▮ 1982	♣ 1988	▬ 1994	★ 1999
◄ 1983	Ð 1989	⚘ 1995	☉ 2000
† 1984	★ 1990	♡ 1996	≈ 2001
🦋 1985	♦ 1991	UM Unmarked	

General Figurines

	Price Paid	Value
1.		
2.		
3.		
4.		
5.		
6.		
7.		
8.		
9.		

Totals

8

Values ▲ $105
 ♣ $86
 Ð $78
 ★ $74
 ♦ $70

Believe The Impossible
#109487
Issued: 1988 • Susp.: 1991
Retail Price: $35 – $45

9

Values ☉ $45
 ≈ $45

Believe The Impossible
Care-A-Van Exclusive
#109487R
Issued: 2000 • Open
Retail Price: $45

1

Values		
★	$50
○	$50
≈	$50

Beside The Still Waters
Four Seasons Series
#129127
Issued: 1999 • Open
Retail Price: $50

2

Values	
✝	$40
✦	$37
♫	$35
▲	$34
✧	$34
♁	$32
✦	$32
§	$30
♧	$30
♋	$28
⊐	$28
△	$27
♡	$25
✝	$25
👓	$25
★	$25
○	$25
≈	$25

Best Man
Bridal Party Series
#E2836
Issued: 1984 • Open
Retail Price: $13.50 – $25

3

Values		
👓	$40
★	$40
○	$35
≈	$35

Birthday Figurine
(personalized)
#163686
Issued: 1998 • Open
Retail Price: $35

4

Values		
★	$50
○	$50
≈	$50

Bless Be The Tie
That Binds
#520918
Issued: 2000 • Open
Retail Price: $50

5

Values	
✕	$285
◀	$246
✝	$232

Bless This House
#E7164
Issued: 1982 • Susp.: 1984
Retail Price: $45 – $50

6

Values	
⌐	$148
(*)	$132

Bless Those Who Serve
Their Country
#526568
Issued: 1991 • Susp.: 1992
Retail Price: $32.50

General Figurines

	Price Paid	Value
1.		
2.		
3.		
4.		
5.		
6.		
7.		
8.		
9.		
10.		

Totals

7

Values	
⌐	$50
(*)	$46

Bless Those Who Serve
Their Country
#526576
Issued: 1991 • Susp.: 1992
Retail Price: $32.50

8

Values	
⌐	$62
(*)	$57

Bless Those Who Serve
Their Country
#526584
Issued: 1991 • Susp.: 1992
Retail Price: $32.50

9

Values	
⌐	$48
(*)	$48

Bless Those Who Serve
Their Country
#527289
Issued: 1991 • Susp.: 1992
Retail Price: $32.50

10

Values	
⌐	$45
(*)	$45

Bless Those Who Serve
Their Country
#527297
Issued: 1991 • Susp.: 1992
Retail Price: $32.50

1 Values $70 / $70

Bless Those Who Serve Their Country
#527521
Issued: 1991 • Susp.: 1992
Retail Price: $32.50

2 Values ★ $25 / $25 / $25

Bless You
#679879
Issued: 2000 • Open
Retail Price: $25

3 Values $58 / $54 / $53 / $50 / $50 / $50 / $48 / $48 / $47 / $47 / $47 / $45 / $45 / $45 / $45 / $45 / $45 / $45

Bless You Two
#E9255
Issued: 1983 • Open
Retail Price: $21 – $45

4 Values $44 / $35 / $28 / $27.50 / $27.50 / $27.50 / $27.50 / $27.50

Bless Your Soul
#531162
Issued: 1995 • Open
Retail Price: $25 – $27.50

5 Values NM $130 / $110 / $93 / $83 / $79 / $73

Blessed Are The Peacemakers
#E3107
Issued: 1980 • Retired: 1985
Retail Price: $13 – $19

6 Values NM $63 / $55 / $53 / $53 / $47 / $47 / $42 / $42 / $42 / $38 / $38 / $38

Blessed Are The Pure In Heart
#E3104
Issued: 1980 • Susp.: 1991
Retail Price: $9 – $19

7 Values ★ $64

Blessed Are They With A Caring Heart
Century Circle Figurine
#163724
Issued: 1999 • Closed: 1999
Retail Price: $55

8 Values $220 / $200

Blessed Art Thou Amongst Women (LE-1999)
#261556
Issued: 1999 • Closed: 1999
Retail Price: $175

9 Values $40 / $40
New

Blessed With A Loving Godmother
#795348
Issued: 2001 • Open
Retail Price: $40

10 $120 / $108 / $102 / $95 / $89

Blessings From Above
#523747
Issued: 1990 • Retired: 1994
Retail Price: $45 – $50

KEY				
NM Pre'81	1986	1992	1997	
1981	1987	1993	1998	
1982	1988	1994	★ 1999	
1983	1989	1995	2000	
1984	1990	1996	2001	
1985	1991	UM Unmarked		

General Figurines

	Price Paid	Value
1.		
2.		
3.		
4.		
5.		
6.		
7.		
8.		
9.		
10.		

Totals

1

Values
- $92
- $85
- $82
- $79

Blessings From My House To Yours
#E0503
Issued: 1983 • Susp.: 1986
Retail Price: $27

2

Values
- $46
- $42
- $37
- $37
- $37
- $37
- $37

Bless-Um You
#527335
Issued: 1993 • Retired: 1998
Retail Price: $35

3

Values
- $148
- $136
- $126
- $120
- $112
- $112
- $110
- $110

Bon Voyage
#522201
Issued: 1989 • Susp.: 1996
Retail Price: $75 – $90

4

Values
- $40
- $40
- $40
- $40
- $40
- $40

A Bouquet From God's Garden Of Love
Growing In God's Garden Of Love Series
#184268
Issued: 1997 • Open
Retail Price: $37.50 – $40

5

Values
- $36
- $30
- $30
- $30
- $28
- $27.50
- $27.50
- $27.50
- $27.50
- $27.50
- $27.50
- $27.50
- $27.50
- $27.50
- $27.50

Bride
Bridal Party Series
#E2846
Issued: 1987 • Open
Retail Price: $18 – $27.50

6

Values
- $40
- $33
- $32
- $31
- $29
- $29
- $29
- $27
- $27
- $25
- $25
- $25
- $25
- $25
- $25
- $25
- $25

Bridesmaid
Bridal Party Series
#E2831
Issued: 1984 • Open
Retail Price: $13.50 – $25

KEY			
NM Pre'81	⅋ 1986	⚘ 1992	† 1997
▲ 1981	▲ 1987	⅋ 1993	6₰ 1998
�𝕀 1982	⚜ 1988	⊐ 1994	★ 1999
◀ 1983	Ð 1989	⚖ 1995	⊕ 2000
† 1984	⊏ 1990	♡ 1996	⋈ 2001
◀ 1985	♦ 1991	UM Unmarked	

General Figurines

	Price Paid	Value
1.		
2.		
3.		
4.		
5.		
6.		
7.		
8.		
9.		
10.		

Totals

7

Values
- $115
- $105
- $98
- $95
- $92
- $90
- $90
- $90
- $90
- $90
- $90

Bring The Little Ones To Jesus
Child Evangelism Fellowship Figurine
#527556
Issued: 1992 • Open
Retail Price: $90

8

Values
- $92
- $85
- $80

Bringing You A Merry Christmas
#527599
Issued: 1993 • Retired: 1995
Retail Price: $45

9

Values
- $108
- $97
- $90
- $86

Brotherly Love
#100544
Issued: 1986 • Susp.: 1989
Retail Price: $37 – $47.50

10

Values
- $135
- $110
- $97
- $94
- $89
- $89
- $89
- $86
- $86
- $84
- $84
- $81

Bundles Of Joy
#E2374
Issued: 1982 • Retired: 1993
Retail Price: $27.50 – $45

1

Values NM $110
▲ $83
I $65
✝ $58
❦ $55
✿ $50
♫ $48
♠ $48
⬥ $48
⊕ $44
✦ $42
✦ $42
❀ $42
& $42
♀ $42
✕ $42
♡ $40
✝ $40
★ $40
◷◷ $40
☼ $40
☽ $40

**But Love Goes
On Forever**
#E3115
Issued: 1980 • Open
Retail Price: $16.50 – $40

2

Values ✝ $855
UM $725

**But Love Goes On Forever
Retailer's Dome (Dealers'
Only, Gift To Centers)**
#E7350
Issued: 1984 • Closed: 1984
Retail Price: N/A

3

Values ◷◷ $30
★ $30
☼ $30
☽ $30

**Caught Up In Sweet
Thoughts Of You**
#521973
Issued: 1999 • Open
Retail Price: $30

4
New

Values ☽ $40

*Photo
Unavailable*

Celebrating His Arrival
#878952
Issued: 2001 • Open
Retail Price: $40

5

Values ◷◷ $58

Charity Begins In The Heart
Victorian Girls Series
#307009
Issued: 1998 • Retired: 1998
Retail Price: $50

6

Values ▲ $88
⬥ $80
⊕ $74
✦ $70
& $70
& $67
♀ $65
✕ $65
✝ $62
♡ $62

Cheers To The Leader
#104035
Issued: 1987 • Retired: 1997
Retail Price: $22.50 – $32.50

(7)
New

Values ☼ $50
☽ $50

Cherish Every Step
#795224
Issued: 2001 • Open
Retail Price: $50

8

Values ✿ $64
❦ $58
& $56

Christmas Fireplace
Family Christmas Series
#524883
Issued: 1990 • Susp.: 1992
Retail Price: $37.50

KEY			
NM Pre'81	♫ 1986	& 1992	✝ 1997
▲ 1981	✿ 1987	♀♀ 1993	◷◷ 1998
I 1982	⬥ 1988	▭ 1994	★ 1999
◀ 1983	⊕ 1989	△ 1995	☼ 2000
✝ 1984	♠ 1990	♡ 1996	☽ 2001
& 1985	& 1991	UM Unmarked	

General Figurines

	Price Paid	Value
1.		
2.		
3.		
4.		
5.		
6.		
7.		
8.		
9.		

Totals

9

Values I $86
◀ $78
✝ $73
❦ $70
♫ $68

**Christmas Joy From
Head To Toe**
#E2361
Issued: 1982 • Susp.: 1986
Retail Price: $25 – $27.50

1

Values ⏰ $25
📷 $25

Photo Unavailable

Christmas Tree Accessories
Precious Scapes Series
#750123
Issued: 2000 • Open
Retail Price: $25

2

Values ⏰ $30
📷 $30

Photo Unavailable

Christmas Tree Accessories
#788171
Issued: 2000 • Open
Retail Price: $30

3

Values 🐚 $116
✝ $104
🍃 $97
🎷 $92
▲ $88
🔷 $85
🕊 $80
★ $75

Christmastime Is For Sharing
#E0504
Issued: 1983 • Retired: 1989
Retail Price: $37 – $50

4

Values 🍃 $190
🎷 $167
▲ $146
🔷 $140
🕊 $140
★ $140
🔴 $128
🔶 $128
🎡 $128
🏺 $114
⚱ $114
♡ $114

Variation

| Crowns |

Clown Figurines (set/4)
#12238
Issued: 1985 • Susp.: 1996
Retail Price: $54 – $80
Variation: "Crowns" – $240

5

Values 🍃 $42
🎷 $37
▲ $37
🔷 $37
🕊 $35
★ $33
🔴 $33
🔶 $30
🎡 $30
🏺 $30
⚱ $30
♡ $30

Clown Figurines – Mini Boy Clown
#12238A
Issued: 1985 • Susp.: 1996
Retail Price: $13.50 – $20

General Figurines

	Price Paid	Value
1.		
2.		
3.		
4.		
5.		
6.		
7.		
8.		

Totals

6

Values 🍃 $43
🎷 $39
▲ $36
🔷 $36
🕊 $35
★ $33
🔴 $32
🔶 $32
🎡 $30
🏺 $30
⚱ $30
♡ $30

Clown Figurines – Mini Boy Clown
#12238C
Issued: 1985 • Susp.: 1996
Retail Price: $13.50 – $20

7

Values 🍃 $43
🎷 $39
▲ $36
🔷 $36
🕊 $36
★ $34
🔴 $34
🔶 $33
🎡 $33
🏺 $33
⚱ $33
♡ $33

Clown Figurines – Mini Girl Clown
#12238B
Issued: 1985 • Susp.: 1996
Retail Price: $13.50 – $20

8

Values 🍃 $44
🎷 $41
▲ $39
🔷 $37
🕊 $35
★ $35
🔴 $33
🔶 $33
🎡 $33
🏺 $32
⚱ $32
♡ $32

Clown Figurines – Mini Girl Clown
#12238D
Issued: 1985 • Susp.: 1996
Retail Price: $13.50 – $20

1 Values ✖ $118
🐟 $62
✝ $57
🕊 $54
♫ $52
🔔 $47

Collection Plaque
#E6901
Issued: 1982 • Susp.: 1986
Retail Price: $19 – $20

2 Values ♡ $77
✝ $70
👓 $55

**Color Your World
With Thanksgiving**
#183857
Issued: 1996 • Retired: 1998
Retail Price: $50

3 Values NM $300

Come Let Us Adore Him
#E2011
Issued: 1979 • Retired: 1981
Retail Price: $10 – $14

4 Values 👓 $30
★ $30
🕐 $30
📷 $30

Confirmed In The Lord
#488178
Issued: 1999 • Open
Retail Price: $30

5 Values ♫ $65
✤ $45
✤ $42
🕊 $40
★ $38
🔔 $38
🐚 $37
🔄 $37
🏺 $37
🏛 $35
♡ $35
✝ $35
👓 $35
★ $35
🕐 $35
📷 $35

Congratulations, Princess
#106208
Issued: 1987 • Open
Retail Price: $20 – $35

6 Values ♠ $85
✤ $57
🕊 $47
★ $44
🔔 $40
🐚 $40
🔄 $37
🏺 $37
🏛 $35
♡ $35
✝ $35
👓 $35
★ $35
🕐 $35
📷 $35

December
Calendar Girl Series
#110116
Issued: 1988 • Open
Retail Price: $27.50 – $35

7 Values ★ $35
🕐 $35
📷 $35

Dedicated To God
#488232
Issued: 2000 • Open
Retail Price: $35

8 Values 🕊 $110
★ $102
🔔 $95
🐚 $92
🔄 $86

**Don't Let The Holidays
Get You Down**
#522112
Issued: 1989 • Retired: 1993
Retail Price: $42.50 – $45

KEY					
NM Pre'81	♫ 1986	🐚 1992	✝ 1997
♠ 1981	♠ 1987	🔄 1993	👓 1998
✖ 1982	✤ 1988	🏺 1994	★ 1999
🐚 1983	🕊 1989	🏛 1995	🕐 2000
✝ 1984	★ 1990	♡ 1996	📷 2001
🔄 1985	🔔 1991	UM Unmarked	

General Figurines

	Price Paid	Value
1.		
2.		
3.		
4.		
5.		
6.		
7.		
8.		
9.		
10.		

Totals

9 Values 🔄 $48
🏛 $40
♡ $40
✝ $40
👓 $40
★ $40
🕐 $40
📷 $40

**Dreams Really Do
Come True**
#128309
Issued: 1995 • Open
Retail Price: $37.50 – $40

10 Values ✖ $89
🐟 $83
✝ $79

Dropping In For Christmas
#E2350
Issued: 1982 • Susp.: 1984
Retail Price: $18

1

Values	
🍂	$53
△	$48
♡	$48
†	$48
😊	$48

Dropping In For The Holidays
#531952
Issued: 1994 • Retired: 1998
Retail Price: $40 – $45

2

Values	
✕	$135
◀	$108
†	$101
🍂	$96
♫	$93
▲	$93
✚	$88
⊅	$84
⚓	$78
●	$78

Dropping Over For Christmas
#E2375
Issued: 1982 • Retired: 1991
Retail Price: $30 – $45

3

Values	
△	$82
♡	$74
†	$70
😊	$70
★	$70
⊙	$70
≈	$70

Each Hour Is Precious With You
#163791
Issued: 1996 • Open
Retail Price: $70

4

Values	
⊅	$84
⚓	$75
●	$72
⚗	$70
♀	$68
◀	$68
△	$68
♡	$65
†	$65
😊	$65
★	$65

Easter's On Its Way
#521892
Issued: 1990 • Retired: 1999
Retail Price: $60 – $65

5

Values	
NM	$135
▲	$115
✕	$100
◀	$90

Eggs Over Easy
#E3118
Issued: 1980 • Retired: 1983
Retail Price: $12 – $15

6

Values	
✧	$75
⊅	$70
⚓	$63
●	$58
⚗	$56
♀	$54
◀	$52
△	$52
♡	$50
†	$50
😊	$50
★	$50

Eggspecially For You
#520667
Issued: 1989 • Retired: 1999
Retail Price: $45 – $50

General Figurines

	Price Paid	Value
1.	70⁰⁰	82⁰⁰
2.		
3.	–	–
4.		
5.		
6.		
7.		
8.		
9.		

Totals

7

Values	
✕	$90
◀	$79
†	$74
◀	$68
UM	$140

The End Is In Sight
#E9253
Issued: 1983 • Susp.: 1985
Retail Price: $25

8
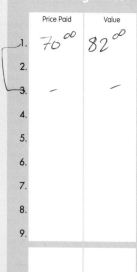

Values	
△	$42
♡	$37
†	$35
😊	$35
★	$35
⊙	$35
≈	$35

Enter His Court With Thanksgiving
#521221
Issued: 1996 • Open
Retail Price: $35

9

Values	
◀	$44
†	$40
✚	$38
♫	$36
▲	$34
✧	$32
⊅	$32
⚓	$32
UM	$50

Especially For Ewe
#E9282C
Issued: 1983 • Susp.: 1990
Retail Price: $8 – $13.50

1   Values 🔊 $145

Even The Heavens Shall Praise Him (LE-15,000)
Century Circle Figurine
#150312
Issued: 1998 • Closed: 1998
Retail Price: $125

2   Values ⊙ $50
                        ☖ $50

Everybody Has A Part (set/3)
Japanese Exclusive
#731625
Issued: 2000 • Open
Retail Price: $50

3   Values ☖ $25
New

Photo Unavailable

Everything Is Beautiful In Its Own Way
#730149
Issued: 2001 • Open
Retail Price: $25

4   Values 🍃 $67
                        ∞ $48

An Event For All Seasons (LE-1993)
Special Event Figurine
#530158
Issued: 1993 • Closed: 1993
Retail Price: $30

5   Values 🌰 $68
                        🍃 $60

An Event Worth Wading For (LE-1992)
Special Event Figurine
#527319
Issued: 1992 • Closed: 1992
Retail Price: $32.50

6   Values ↦ $170
                        ⚓ $150
                        🌰 $143
                        🍃 $123
                        ∞ $118

Faith Is A Victory
#521396
Issued: 1990 • Retired: 1993
Retail Price: $25 – $27.50

7   Values ▲ $62
                        ⚘ $50
                        ⊕ $44
                        ⚓ $42
                        ▮ $40
                        🍃 $40
                        ∞ $38
                        ⊸ $37
                        ♁ $37
                        † $37
                        🔊 $37

    Variation

Faith Takes The Plunge
#111155
Issued: 1988 • Susp.: 1998
Retail Price: $27.50 – $35
Variation: Girl with smile – $60

8   Values ⊙ $150
                        ☖ $150

Fall Festival (set/7)
#732494
Issued: 2000 • Open
Retail Price: $150

9   Values ▲ $60
                        ⚘ $49
                        ⊕ $45
                        ⚓ $42
                        🌰 $42
                        🍃 $42
                        ∞ $40
                        ⊸ $40
                        ⚠ $37.50
                        ♡ $37.50
                        † $37.50
                        🔊 $37.50
                        ★ $37.50
                        ⊙ $37.50
                        ☖ $37.50

February
Calendar Girl Series
#109991
Issued: 1988 • Open
Retail Price: $27.50 – $37.50

KEY					
NM Pre'81	⍼ 1986	🍃 1992	† 1997
▲ 1981	▲ 1987	∞ 1993	🔊 1998
▮ 1982	⚘ 1988	⊸ 1994	★ 1999
◀ 1983	⊕ 1989	⚠ 1995	⊙ 2000
† 1984	⚓ 1990	♡ 1996	☖ 2001
⚘ 1985	🌰 1991	ⅡM Unmarked	

	Price Paid	Value
1.		
2.		
3.		
4.		
5.		
6.		
7.		
8.		
9.		
Totals		

1 Values † $73

A Festival Of Precious Moments (LE-1997)
Regional Conference Figurine
#270741
Issued: 1997 • Closed: 1997
Retail Price: $30

2 Values ♪ $165
♀ $133

Fifteen Happy Years Together, What A Tweet (LE-1993)
15th Anniversary Commemorative Figurine
#530786
Issued: 1993 • Closed: 1993
Retail Price: $100

3 Values ∞ $80

Flight Into Egypt (LE-1998)
#455970
Issued: 1998 • Closed: 1998
Retail Price: $75

4 Values ✿ $37
✿ $32
▲ $30
✣ $25
Ð $25
☀ $22
🔔 $22
⚘ $20
⚭ $20
🎀 $18.50
△ $18.50
♡ $18.50
† $18.50
∞ $18.50
★ $18.50
⏱ $18.50
≈ $18.50

Flower Girl
Bridal Party Series
#E2835
Issued: 1985 • Open
Retail Price: $11 – $18.50

5 Values 🎀 $58
△ $48

Follow Your Heart (LE-1995)
Special Event Figurine
#528080
Issued: 1995 • Closed: 1995
Retail Price: $30

6 Values † $34
∞ $34
★ $34
⏱ $32.50
≈ $32.50

For The Sweetest Tu-Lips In Town
#306959
Issued: 1998 • Open
Retail Price: $30 – $32.50

General Figurines

	Price Paid	Value
1.		
2.		
3.		
4.		
5.		
6.		
7.		
8.		
9.		
10.		

Totals

7 Values 🐟 $96
† $88
✣ $86
🔥 $84
▲ $79
✣ $74
Ð $70

Forgiving Is Forgetting
#E9252
Issued: 1983 • Susp.: 1989
Retail Price: $37.50 – $47.50

8 Values ✣ $95
Ð $80
🔔 $75
🔔 $70
♪ $68
⚭ $65
🎀 $65
△ $65

A Friend Is Someone Who Cares
#520632
Issued: 1989 • Retired: 1995
Retail Price: $30 – $35

9 Values ∞ $60
★ $60
⏱ $60
≈ $60

Friends Are Forever, Sew Bee It
#455903
Issued: 1998 • Open
Retail Price: $60

10 Values ♡ $59
† $59
∞ $57
★ $57
⏱ $57

Friends From The Very Beginning
#261068
Issued: 1997 • Retired: 2000
Retail Price: $50 – $55

1

Values	
🦋	$97
🌿	$78
🔺	$76
✣	$73
⋔	$70
🎀	$69
🔔	$69
🐚	$69
🐚	$69
🖐	$67
✠	$67
✝	$67
🌸	$67
⭐	$67
🕐	$67

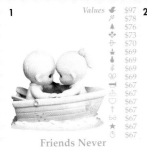

Friends Never
Drift Apart
#100250
Issued: 1986 • Retired: 2000
Retail Price: $35 – $65

2

Values	
🐚	$74
⋔	$70
🔺	$68
♡	$64

Friends To The Very End
#526150
Issued: 1994 • Retired: 1997
Retail Price: $40 – $45

3

Values	
🔔	$117
🔔	$92
🐚	$84
🖐	$80

Friendship Grows When
You Plant A Seed
#524271
Issued: 1992 • Retired: 1994
Retail Price: $40

4

Variation

Variation

Values	
✣	$95
⋔	$83
🔺	$80
🎀	$77
🔔	$77
🐚	$74
🖐	$72
🔺	$72
♡	$72
✝	$72
🌸	$72
⭐	$72
🕐	$72

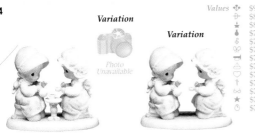

Friendship Hits The Spot
#520748
Issued: 1989 • Retired: 2000
Retail Price: $55 – $70
Variations: "Freindship Hits The Spot" – $85, Missing Table – $280

5

Values	
⭐	$35
🔵	$35
🔶	$35

Friendship's A Slice
Of Life
#634964
Issued: 2000 • Open
Retail Price: $35

6

Values	
🐚	$40
🖐	$35
🔺	$33
♡	$33
✝	$32.50
🔶	$32.50
⭐	$32.50

The Fruit Of The Spirit
Is Love
#521213
Issued: 1993 • Retired: 1999
Retail Price: $30 – $32.50

7

Values	
🕐	$200
🔶	$200

The Fun Is Being Together
Century Circle Exclusive
#730262
Issued: 2000 • Open
Retail Price: $200

KEY						
NM	Pre'81	🎀	1986	🔔	1992	✝	1997
▲	1981	🔺	1987	🐚	1993	🔶	1998
✕	1982	✣	1988	🖐	1994	⭐	1999
🔵	1983	🔔	1989	🔺	1995	🕐	2000
✝	1984	🌿	1990	♡	1996	🔵	2001
🦋	1985	🔔	1991	UM	Unmarked		

	Price Paid	Value
1.		
2.		
3.		
4.		
5.		
6.		
7.		
8.		
9.		

Totals

8

Values	
✝	$54
🦋	$42
🌿	$40

Get Into The Habit
Of Prayer
#12203
Issued: 1985 • Susp.: 1986
Retail Price: $19

9

Values	
🕐	$60
🔶	$60

Girl Festival Additions
(set/5)
#791113
Issued: 2000 • Open
Retail Price: $60

1
New

Values 🕐 $40
📖 $40

Giving My Heart Freely
#650013
Issued: 2001 • Open
Retail Price: $40

2

Values ♪ $78

God Bless America
(LE 1986)
#102938
Issued: 1986 • Closed: 1986
Retail Price: $30

3

Values ▲ $68
✤ $63
🕂 $60
✦ $57
🕯 $57
🔔 $55
🌱 $53
📖 $52
△ $51
♡ $51
✝ $51
🕳 $51
★ $51

God Bless Our Family
#100498
Issued: 1987 • Retired: 1999
Retail Price: $35 – $50

4

Values ▲ $68
✤ $63
🕂 $60
✦ $58
🕯 $58
🔔 $56
🌱 $54
📖 $54
△ $52
♡ $50
✝ $50
🕳 $50
★ $50

God Bless Our Family
#100501
Issued: 1987 • Retired: 1999
Retail Price: $35 – $50

5

Values 🦋 $88
♪ $82
▲ $78
✤ $77
🕂 $76
★ $73
🕯 $73
🔔 $70
🌱 $70
📖 $70
△ $67
♡ $67
✝ $67
🕳 $67

God Bless Our Home
#12319
Issued: 1985 • Retired: 1998
Retail Price: $40 – $65

6

Values 🕯 $65
🔔 $62
♪ $60
▲ $60
✤ $58
🕂 $57
★ $57
🕯 $55
🔔 $55
📖 $52
🌱 $52
△ $50
♡ $50
✝ $50
🕳 $50
🕯 $50
★ $50
🦋 $50
📖 $50

God Bless The Bride
#E2832
Issued: 1984 • Open
Retail Price: $35 – $50

General Figurines

	Price Paid	Value
1.		
2.		
3.		
4.		
5.		
6.		
7.		
8.		
9.		
Totals		

7

Values 🦋 $126
▲ $120
✤ $115
🕂 $110
★ $105

God Bless The Day We
Found You
#100145
Issued: 1986 • Susp.: 1990
Retail Price: $40 – $55

8

Values 🎗 $68
♡ $63
♡ $60
✝ $60
🕳 $60
★ $60
🦋 $60
📖 $60

God Bless The Day We
Found You
#100145R
Issued: 1995 • Open
Retail Price: $60

9

Values ♪ $120
▲ $112
✤ $105
🕂 $97
★ $94

God Bless The Day We
Found You
#100153
Issued: 1986 • Susp.: 1990
Retail Price: $40 – $55

1

Values $67 / $62 / $60 / $60 / $60 / $60 / $60 / $60

God Bless The Day We
Found You
#100153R
Issued: 1995 • Open
Retail Price: $60

2

Values $47 / $40

3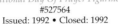

Values $55 / $43 / $40 / $40 / $40 / $38 / $38 / $36 / $36 / $36 / $36 / $36 / $36 / $36 / $35 / $35

God Bless The U.S.A.
(LE-1992)
National Day Of Prayer Figurine
#527564
Issued: 1992 • Closed: 1992
Retail Price: $32.50

God Bless You Graduate
#106194
Issued: 1987 • Open
Retail Price: $20 – $35

4 *Variation*

Values $70 / $61 / $61 / $58 / $58 / $56 / $54 / $54 / $52 / $52 / $52 / $52 / $52 / $52 / $52 / $52

God Blessed Our Year Together With
So Much Love And Happiness
#E2854
Issued: 1984 • Retired: 2000
Retail Price: $35 – $50
Variation: "God Blessed Our Years Together . . . " – $77

5

Values $70 / $63 / $62 / $62 / $58 / $56 / $54 / $54 / $52 / $50 / $50 / $50 / $50 / $50 / $50 / $50

God Blessed Our
Years Together With
So Much Love And
Happiness
#E2853
Issued: 1984 • Open
Retail Price: $35 – $50

6

Values $7? / $7? / $69 / $69 / $69 / $69 / $66 / $66 / $65 / $65 / $63 / $63 / $63

7

Values $80 / $77 / $75 / $75 / $75 / $72 / $72 / $72 / $70 / $70 / $68 / $68 / $68

God Blessed Our Years
Together With So Much
Love And Happiness
#E2855
Issued: 1984 • Susp.: 1996
Retail Price: $35 – $50

God Blessed Our Years
Together With So Much
Love And Happiness
#E2856
Issued: 1984 • Susp.: 1996
Retail Price: $35 – $50

KEY			
NM Pre'81	1986	1992	1997
1981	1987	1993	1998
1982	1988	1994	1999
1983	1989	1995	2000
1984	1990	1996	2001
1985	1991	Unmarked	

General Figurines

	Price Paid	Value
1.		
2.		
3.		
4.		
5.		
6.		
7.		
8.		
9.		
Totals		

8

Values $67 / $62 / $59 / $59 / $56 / $54 / $54 / $52 / $52 / $52 / $50 / $50 / $50 / $50 / $50 / $50

God Blessed Our
Years Together With
So Much Love And
Happiness
#E2857
Issued: 1984 • Open
Retail Price: $35 – $50

9

Values $82 / $77 / $74 / $74 / $74 / $74 / $72 / $72 / $72 / $70 / $70 / $70

God Blessed Our Years
Together With So Much
Love And Happiness
#E2859
Issued: 1984 • Susp.: 1996
Retail Price: $35 – $50

1

Values
† $80
✱ $75
♫ $72
▲ $72
✣ $72
⊕ $72
⚱ $70
✦ $70
♨ $70
⊐ $68
⎐ $65
♡ $60
✤ $55
⊶ $55
★ $50
☉ $50
⚓ $50

God Blessed Our Years Together With So Much Love And Happiness
#E2860
Issued: 1984 • Open
Retail Price: $35 – $50

2

Values
⊟ $92
⚱ $80
♡ $77

God Cared Enough To Send His Best
#524476
Issued: 1994 • Retired: 1996
Retail Price: $50 – $55

3

Values
✦ $54
♫ $50
✣ $46
✤ $42
⊕ $40
✦ $40
⚱ $36
♨ $33

God Gave His Best
Family Christmas Series
#15806
Issued: 1985 • Susp.: 1992
Retail Price: $13 – $19

4

Values
☉ $45
⚓ $45

God Gives Us Memories So We Might Have Roses In December
Compassionate Friends Benefit
#680990
Issued: 2000 • Open
Retail Price: $45

5

Values
NM $120
✱ $92
Ⅰ $83
⊷ $77
† $70
✦ $68
♫ $66
✣ $62
✤ $62
⊕ $62

God Is Love
#E5213
Issued: 1981 • Susp.: 1989
Retail Price: $17 – $30

6

Values ★ N/E

Photo Unavailable

God Is Love
Special Event Figurine
#E5213R
Issued: 1999 • Closed: 1999
Retail Price: $17

General Figurines

	Price Paid	Value
1.		
2.		
3.		
4.		
5.		
6.		
7.		
8.		
9.		
10.		
Totals		

7

Values
▲ $60
Ⅰ $45
⊷ $40
† $35
✦ $35
♫ $32

God Is Love, Dear Valentine
#E7153
Issued: 1982 • Susp.: 1986
Retail Price: $16 – $17

8

Values
▲ $60
Ⅰ $50
✦ $40
† $40
✦ $35
♫ $35

God Is Love, Dear Valentine
#E7154
Issued: 1982 • Susp.: 1986
Retail Price: $16 – $17

9

Values
⊕ $44
★ $38
♨ $37
♨ $37
♊ $34
⊟ $32
⚱ $30
† $30
⊶ $30
★ $30

God Is Love, Dear Valentine
#523518
Issued: 1990 • Retired: 1999
Retail Price: $27.50 – $30

10

Values
Ⅰ $115
⊷ $104
† $93

God Is Watching Over You
#E7163
Issued: 1982 • Susp.: 1984
Retail Price: $27.50 – $30

1

Values ★ $30
    ◷ $30
    ⌂ $30

God Knows Our Ups
And Downs
#490318
Issued: 2000 • Open
Retail Price: $30

2

Values ★ $37.50
    ◷ $37.50
    ⌂ $37.50

God Loves A
Happy Camper
#587893
Issued: 2000 • Open
Retail Price: $37.50

3

Values NM $1000

God Loveth
A Cheerful Giver
#E1378
Issued: 1979 • Retired: 1981
Retail Price: $9.50 – $15

4

Values ⊖ N/E

God Loveth A
Cheerful Giver (LE-20)
#456225
Issued: 1998 • Closed: 1998
Retail Price: N/A

5

Values ⬤ $91
    † $75
    ⬥ $69
    ⌐ $66
    ▲ $64

God Sends The Gift
Of His Love
#E6613
Issued: 1984 • Susp.: 1987
Retail Price: $22.50 – $25

6

Values ⬤ $105
    ⬥ $96
    ⬥ $92
    ⌐ $88
    ▲ $80

God Sent His Son
#E0507
Issued: 1983 • Susp.: 1987
Retail Price: $32.50 – $37

7

Values NM $144
    ▲ $110
    Ⅰ $105
    ⬤ $95
    † $92

God Understands
#E1379B
Issued: 1979 • Susp.: 1984
Retail Price: $8 – $19

8

Values ◷ $35
    ⌂ $35

A Godchild Close To My
Heart (personalized)
#804096
Issued: 2000 • Open
Retail Price: $35

9
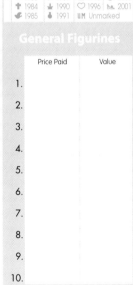

Values ◷ $35
    ⌂ $35

A Godchild Close
To My Heart
#811807
Issued: 2000 • Open
Retail Price: $35

10

Values ◷ $35
    ⌂ $35

A Godchild Close
To My Heart
#811815
Issued: 2000 • Open
Retail Price: $35

KEY			
NM Pre'81	⌁ 1986	⬥ 1992	† 1997
⬥ 1981	▲ 1987	⬥ 1993	⊖ 1998
Ⅰ 1982	⬦ 1988	⬚ 1994	★ 1999
⬥ 1983	⬧ 1989	⬚ 1995	◷ 2000
† 1984	⬥ 1990	♡ 1996	⌂ 2001
⬥ 1985	⬥ 1991	UM Unmarked	

	Price Paid	Value
1.		
2.		
3.		
4.		
5.		
6.		
7.		
8.		
9.		
10.		

Totals

1

Values ♡ $240

God's Love Is Reflected In
You (LE-15,000)
Century Circle Figurine
#175277
Issued: 1996 • Closed: 1996
Retail Price: $150

2

Values 𝕀 $95
🐟 $85
✝ $78
✞ $71
♫ $69
♪ $66

God's Promises Are Sure
#E9260
Issued: 1983 • Susp.: 1987
Retail Price: $30 – $33.50

3

Values NM $125
▲ $95
𝕀 $82
◀ $65

God's Speed
#E3112
Issued: 1980 • Retired: 1983
Retail Price: $14 – $18

4

Values 🌢 $80
🍎 $72
🐚 $69
🛏 $66
🔺 $64
♡ $62
✝ $60
👓 $60
★ $60
🕐 $60
🔖 $60

Going Home
#525979
Issued: 1992 • Open
Retail Price: $60

5

Values ★ $30
🕐 $30
🔖 $30

Good Advice Has No Price
#679828
Issued: 2000 • Open
Retail Price: $30

6

Values 🕐 $17.50
🔖 $17.50

Good Fortune
Japanese Exclusive
#731633
Issued: 2000 • Open
Retail Price: $17.50

KEY					
NM Pre '81		♪ 1986	♬ 1992	✝ 1997	
▲ 1981		▲ 1987	ꙮ 1993	1998	
𝕀 1982		⚓ 1988	🛏 1994	★ 1999	
◀ 1983		ᕵ 1989	🔺 1995	🕐 2000	
✝ 1984		★ 1990	♡ 1996	🔖 2001	
🍎 1985		🌢 1991		UM Unmarked	

General Figurines

	Price Paid	Value
1.		
2.		
3.		
4.		
5.		
6.		
7.		
8.		
9.		
10.		

Totals

7

Values 🌢 $45
🍎 $38
🍎 $37
🛏 $35
♡ $35
✝ $35
👓 $35
★ $35

Good Friends Are
For Always
#524123
Issued: 1991 • Retired: 1999
Retail Price: $27.50 – $35

8

Values ᕵ $74
★ $65
🌢 $62
🍎 $60
🛏 $57
🛏 $57
♡ $55
✝ $55
👓 $55
★ $55
🕐 $55
🔖 $55

Good Friends Are Forever
#521817
Issued: 1990 • Open
Retail Price: $50 – $55

9

Values ꙮ $730

Good Friends Are Forever
Special Event Figurine
#525049
Issued: 1990 • Closed: 1990
Retail Price: N/A

10

Values ᕵ $43
★ $38
🌢 $35
🍎 $34
ꙮ $32
🛏 $32
🔺 $30
♡ $30
✝ $30
👓 $30
★ $30
🕐 $30
🔖 $30

The Good Lord
Always Delivers
#523453
Issued: 1990 • Open
Retail Price: $27.50 – $30

1

Values ♠ $260
⬧⬧ $235

**The Good Lord Has Blessed
Us Tenfold (LE-1988)**
*10th Anniversary
Commemorative Figurine*
#114022
Issued: 1988 • Closed: 1988
Retail Price: $90

2

Values † $50
6⊃ $50
★ $50
⏰ $50
⚓ $50

**The Good Lord Will
Always Uphold Us**
#325325
Issued: 1998 • Open
Retail Price: $50

3

Values ⬧ $84
⚓ $78
⌿ $76
⟂ $74
♡ $72
† $72
⊃ $72
★ $72

Good News Is So Uplifting
#523615
Issued: 1991 • Retired: 1999
Retail Price: $60 – $70

4

Values ⏰ $25
⚓ $25

**Grandma I'll Never
Outgrow You!**
#798223
Issued: 2000 • Open
Retail Price: $25

5

Values ⏰ $25
⚓ $25

**Grandma I'll Never
Outgrow You!**
#798231
Issued: 2000 • Open
Retail Price: $25

6

New

Values ⏰ $32.50
⚓ $32.50

Gratitude With Attitude
#730041
Issued: 2001 • Open
Retail Price: $32.50

7

Values ♠ $62
⬧⬧ $49
⊃ $49
⚓ $45
⬧ $43
⚓ $43
⟂ $43
⚓ $43
♡ $43
† $43
6⊃ $43
★ $43

**The Greatest Gift
Is A Friend**
#109231
Issued: 1987 • Retired: 1999
Retail Price: $30 – $40

8

Values ⊃ $62
⚓ $55
⬧ $52

**The Greatest Of
These Is Love**
#521868
Issued: 1989 • Susp.: 1991
Retail Price: $27.50 – $30

KEY							
NM Pre'81	⌿	1986	⚓	1992	†	1997
▲ 1981	▲	1987	♉	1993	6⊃	1998
⟂ 1982	⬧⬧	1988	⟂	1994	★	1999
◄ 1983	⊃	1989	⚓	1995	⏰	2000
† 1984	⚓	1990	♡	1996	⚓	2001
⬧ 1985	⬧	1991	IIM	Unmarked		

9

Variation

*Photo
Unavailable*

Values ⌿ $42
▲ $37
⬧⬧ $32
⊃ $32
⚓ $28
⬧ $28
⚓ $28
♉ $27.50
⟂ $27.50
⚓ $27.50
♡ $27.50
† $27.50
6⊃ $27.50
★ $27.50
⏰ $27.50
⚓ $27.50

Groom
Bridal Party Series
#E2837
Issued: 1986 • Open
Retail Price: $15 – $27.50
Variation: Boy with no hands – $46

	Price Paid	Value
1.		
2.		
3.		
4.	25.00	—
5.	25.00	—
6.		
7.		
8.		
9.		

Totals

1

Values 👥 $22.50
★ $22.50
🕐 $22.50
🔺 $22.50

Growing In Wisdom
#481645
Issued: 1999 • Open
Retail Price: $22.50

2

Values 👥 $22.50
★ $22.50
🕐 $22.50
🔺 $22.50

Growing In Wisdom
#481653
Issued: 1999 • Open
Retail Price: $22.50

3

Values ✿ $72
✣ $65
⚓ $58
🔺 $55
⚜ $52
⚖ $50
🏺 $47
♡ $47
✝ $47
☙ $47
★ $47
🕐 $47

Hallelujah Country
#105821
Issued: 1988 • Retired: 2000
Retail Price: $35 – $45

4

Values 🏺 $40
🔺 $38
♡ $38
✝ $38
👥 $38
★ $38

Hallelujah For The Cross
#532002
Issued: 1995 • Retired: 1999
Retail Price: $35

5

Values 🔺 $98
♡ $64

Hallelujah Hoedown
(LE-1996)
Special Event Figurine
#163864
Issued: 1996 • Closed: 1996
Retail Price: $32.50

6

Values ✿ $223
♪ $198
🔺 $188
⚜ $182

Halo, And Merry Christmas
#12351
Issued: 1985 • Susp.: 1988
Retail Price: $40 – $47.50

General Figurines

	Price Paid	Value
1.		
2.		
3.		
4.		
5.		
6.		
7.		
8.		
9.		
10.		

Totals

7

Values NM $106
🔺 $90
𝕀 $83
☙ $76
✝ $73

The Hand That Rocks
The Future
#E3108
Issued: 1980 • Susp.: 1984
Retail Price: $13 – $19

8

Values ✿ $88
✣ $80
✦ $73
✣ $67
⚖ $65

Happiness Divine
#109584
Issued: 1988 • Retired: 1992
Retail Price: $25 – $30

9

Values ⚖ $97
🦅 $72

Happiness Is At Our
Fingertips (LE-1993)
Catalog Figurine
#529931
Issued: 1993 • Closed: 1993
Retail Price: $35

10

Values ✿ $54
♪ $52
🔺 $47
⚜ $47
✣ $45
✦ $43

Happiness Is The Lord
*Rejoice In The Lord
Band Series*
#12378
Issued: 1985 • Susp.: 1990
Retail Price: $15 – $22.50

1 Values ♡ $55

Happiness To The Core
(LE-1997)
Catalog Figurine
#261378
Issued: 1997 • Closed: 1997
Retail Price: $37.50

2 Values † $38
⊗ $38
★ $38
⊙ $35
⅄ $35

Happy Birthday Jesus
#272523
Issued: 1997 • Open
Retail Price: $35

3 Values ▲ $73
❖ $68
⊕ $67
⅄ $66
♠ $66
⚘ $60
⚘ $58

Happy Birthday Poppy
#106836
Issued: 1988 • Susp.: 1993
Retail Price: $27.50 – $35

4 Values ★ $35
⊙ $35
⅄ $35

Happy Birthday To Ewe
#531561
Issued: 2000 • Open
Retail Price: $35

5 Values ▲ $76
⊕ $73
⊕ $73
⅄ $70

Happy Days Are
Here Again
#104396
Issued: 1987 • Susp.: 1990
Retail Price: $25 – $32.50

6 Values ⊜ $40
♠ $36
† $34
⊗ $32.50
★ $32.50
⊙ $32.50
⅄ $32.50

Happy Hula Days
#128694
Issued: 1995 • Open
Retail Price: $30 – $32.50

7 Values ⊕ $92
♠ $62
⅄ $60
⚘ $57
⚘ $53
⅄ $50

Happy Trip
#521280
Issued: 1990 • Susp.: 1994
Retail Price: $35

8 Values ⊕ $46
♠ $42
⅄ $39
⚘ $35

Have A Beary
Merry Christmas
Family Christmas Series
#522856
Issued: 1989 • Susp.: 1992
Retail Price: $15 – $16.50

KEY			
NM Pre'81	✏ 1986	♠ 1992	† 1997
▲ 1981	♣ 1987	⚓ 1993	⊗ 1998
⊠ 1982	❖ 1988	⊟ 1994	★ 1999
⊟ 1983	⊕ 1989	⚘ 1995	⊙ 2000
† 1984	♠ 1990	♡ 1996	⅄ 2001
⚘ 1985	♦ 1991	UM Unmarked	

General Figurines

	Price Paid	Value
1.		
2.		
3.		
4.		
5.		
6.		
7.		
8.		
9.		
10.		

Totals

9 Values ⊗ $50
★ $50
⊙ $50
⅄ $50

Have A Cozy
Country Christmas
#455873
Issued: 1998 • Open
Retail Price: $50

10 Values ⊗ $30
★ $26
⊙ $25
⅄ $25

Have A Heavenly Journey
Care-A-Van Exclusive
#12416R
Issued: 1998 • Open
Retail Price: $25

1

Values ⏰ $50
🔥 $50

Have Faith In God
Victorian Girls Series
#505153
Issued: 2000 • Open
Retail Price: $50

2

Values ♡ $50

**Have I Toad You Lately
That I Love You? (LE-1996)**
Catalog Figurine
#521329
Issued: 1996 • Closed: 1996
Retail Price: $30

3

Values ♡ $44
† $38
6ð $35
★ $35
⏰ $35
🔥 $35

**Have You Any Room
For Jesus**
#261130
Issued: 1997 • Open
Retail Price: $35

4

Values ★ $30
⏰ $30
🔥 $30

**He Came As The Gift Of
God's Love (set/4)**
Mini-Mini Nativity
#528128
Issued: 1999 • Open
Retail Price: $30

5

Values ✿ $67
♫ $53
▲ $50
⚓ $48
🔔 $46
🔥 $46
♒ $43
⚜ $43
❀ $40
⚱ $40
♡ $40
† $40
6ð $40
★ $40
⏰ $40
🔥 $40

**He Cleansed
My Soul**
#100277
Issued: 1986 • Open
Retail Price: $24 – $40

6

Values ★ $50
⏰ $50
🔥 $50

**He Covers The Earth With
His Glory**
Four Seasons Series
#129135
Issued: 1999 • Open
Retail Price: $50

KEY					
NM Pre'81	✹ 1986	♪ 1992	† 1997		
▲ 1981	▲ 1987	♋ 1993	6ð 1998		
▮ 1982	✧ 1988	⚒ 1994	★ 1999		
➡ 1983	🔶 1989	⚏ 1995	⏰ 2000		
✝ 1984	⚓ 1990	♡ 1996	🔥 2001		
✿ 1985	🔥 1991	�llM Unmarked			

General Figurines

	Price Paid	Value
1.		
2.		
3.		
4.		
5.		
6.		
7.		
8.		
9.		
10.		

Totals

7

Values ★ $50
⏰ $50
🔥 $50

**He Graces The Earth
With Abundance**
Four Seasons Series
#129119
Issued: 1999 • Open
Retail Price: $50

8

Values ⏰ $45
🔥 $45

He Is My Salvation
Salvation Army Figurine
#135984
Issued: 2000 • Open
Retail Price: $45

9

Values ✿ $52
♫ $48
▲ $48
⚜ $43
🔶 $43
⚓ $41

He Is My Song (set/2)
Rejoice In The Lord Band Series
#12394
Issued: 1985 • Susp.: 1990
Retail Price: $17.50 – $27.50

10

Values † $80
6ð $80

**He Is Our Shelter From
The Storm**
*Boys & Girls Clubs Of America
Commemorative Figurine*
#523550
Issued: 1997 • Closed: 1997
Retail Price: $75

1

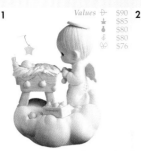

Values ⊕ $90
★ $85
☀ $80
⚱ $80
♧ $76

He Is The Star Of Morning
#522252
Issued: 1989 • Susp.: 1993
Retail Price: $55 – $60

2

Values ★ $55
⚱ $45

He Loves Me (LE-1991)
#524263
Issued: 1990 • Closed: 1991
Retail Price: $35

3

Values ◐ $160
▲ $160

He Shall Lead The
Children Into The 21st
Century (set/5)
Special Event Figurine
#127930
Issued: 2000 • Open
Retail Price: $160

4

Values ◐ $160
▲ $160

He Shall Lead The
Children Into The
21st Century (set/5)
Artist's Proof
#127930A
Issued: 2000 • Open
Retail Price: $160

5

Values ◆ $96
† $88
⚓ $84

He Upholdeth Those
Who Fall
(all pieces inscribed with "He
Upholdeth Those Who Call")
#E0526
Issued: 1983 • Susp.: 1985
Retail Price: $28.50 – $35

6

Values NM $98
▲ $90
I $82
◆ $75
† $67

He Watches Over Us All
#E3105
Issued: 1980 • Susp.: 1984
Retail Price: $11 – $17

7

Values ◐ $45
▲ $45

He'll Carry Me Through
#488089
Issued: 2000 • Open
Retail Price: $45

8

Values ⅃ $68
✢ $64
✜ $62
⊕ $60
★ $56
☀ $56
⚱ $52
♧ $52
⊸ $52
⚠ $52
† $52
⚋ $52
★ $52

He's The Healer Of
Broken Hearts
#100080
Issued: 1987 • Retired: 1999
Retail Price: $33 – $50

9

Values ⊕ $128
★ $58
☀ $50
⚱ $45
♧ $42
⊸ $37
⚠ $37
♡ $35
† $35
⚋ $35
★ $35
◐ $35
▲ $35

Heaven Bless You
#520934
Issued: 1990 • Open
Retail Price: $35

10

Values ▲ $110
✜ $96
⊕ $92
★ $92
☀ $92
⚱ $92
♧ $92
⊸ $92
⚠ $92
♡ $92
† $92
⚋ $92
★ $92

Heaven Bless
Your Togetherness
#106755
Issued: 1988 • Retired: 1999
Retail Price: $65 – $90

KEY					
NM Pre'81	✗ 1986	☿ 1992	† 1997
▲ 1981	▲ 1987	☿ 1993	⚱ 1998
I 1982	✜ 1988	⊸ 1994	★ 1999
⊸ 1983	⊕ 1989	⚠ 1995	◐ 2000
† 1984	★ 1990	♡ 1996	▲ 2001
◆ 1985	☀ 1991	UM Unmarked	

General Figurines

	Price Paid	Value
1.		
2.		
3.		
4.		
5.		
6.		
7.		
8.		
9.		
10.		

Totals

1

Values † $65
⚝ $65
★ $65
🕐 $65
🔥 $65

Heaven Must Have Sent You
#521388
Issued: 1998 • Open
Retail Price: $60 – $65

2

Values ♯ $80
♠ $73
♦ $70
Ð $66

Help, Lord I'm In A Spot
#100269
Issued: 1986 • Retired: 1989
Retail Price: $18.50 – $25

3

Values Ð $56
⚱ $52
🔥 $49
🐚 $47
♀ $40

High Hopes
#521957
Issued: 1990 • Susp.: 1993
Retail Price: $30

4

Values NM $162
▲ $140
I $120
← $103
✝ $93

His Burden Is Light
#E1380G
Issued: 1979 • Retired: 1984
Retail Price: $8 – $19

5

Values ← $134
✿ $120
🔥 $110
♯ $102
♠ $94

His Eye Is On The Sparrow
#E0530
Issued: 1983 • Retired: 1987
Retail Price: $28.50 – $32.50

6

Values ⚝ $150
★ $150
🕐 $150
🔥 $150

His Love Will Uphold The World
Millennium Figurine
#539309
Issued: 1999 • Open
Retail Price: $150

	NM Pre'81	♯ 1986	🔥 1992	† 1997
K E Y	▲ 1981	♠ 1987	🐚 1993	⚝ 1998
	I 1982	✤ 1988	🐚 1994	★ 1999
	← 1983	Ð 1989	⚠ 1995	🕐 2000
	† 1984	♦ 1990	♡ 1996	🔥 2001
	✦ 1985	🔥 1991	UM Unmarked	

General Figurines

	Price Paid	Value
1.		
2.		
3.		
4.		
5.		
6.		
7.		
8.		
9.		

Totals

7

Values 🕐 $16
🔥 $16

Hissterically Sweet
Japanese Exclusive
#821969
Issued: 2000 • Open
Retail Price: $16

8

Values I $144
← $130
† $123
✦ $118
♯ $112
♠ $107

Holy Smokes
#E2351
Issued: 1982 • Retired: 1987
Retail Price: $27 – $33.50

9

Values † $40
⚝ $40

Home Is Where The Heart Is
Catalog Figurine
#325481
Issued: 1998 • Closed: 1998
Retail Price: $37.50

1

Values 2000 $45 · 2001 $45

Home-Made Of Love
#730211
Issued: 2000 • Open
Retail Price: $45

2

Values 1998 $77

Hope Is Revealed Through God's Word
Victorian Girls Series
#488259
Issued: 1998 • Retired: 1998
Retail Price: $70

3

Values 1989 $68 · 1990 $63 · 1991 $60 · 1992 $55 · 1993 $52

Hope You're Up And On The Trail Again
#521205
Issued: 1990 • Susp.: 1993
Retail Price: $35

4

Values 1990 $57 · 1991 $50 · 1992 $48 · 1993 $44 · 1994 $44 · 1995 $42 · 1996 $42 · 1997 $42 · 1998 $42 · 1999 $42

Hoppy Easter, Friend
#521906
Issued: 1991 • Retired: 1999
Retail Price: $40

5

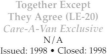

Values 1998 N/E

How Can Three Work Together Except They Agree (LE-20)
Care-A-Van Exclusive
N/A
Issued: 1998 • Closed: 1998
Retail Price: N/A

6

Values 1982 $187 · 1983 $160 · 1984 $145 · 1985 $137

How Can Two Walk Together Except They Agree
#E9263
Issued: 1983 • Susp.: 1985
Retail Price: $35

7

Values 1990 $90 · 1991 $82 · 1992 $78 · 1993 $78 · 1994 $75 · 1995 $75

Hug One Another
#521299
Issued: 1991 • Retired: 1995
Retail Price: $45 – $50

8

Values 1982 $110 · 1983 $100 · 1984 $92 · 1985 $86

I Believe In Miracles
#E7156
Issued: 1982 • Susp.: 1985
Retail Price: $17 – $19

9

Values 1987 $80 · 1988 $70 · 1989 $62 · 1990 $60 · 1991 $56

Variation

Photo Unavailable

I Believe In Miracles
#E7156R
Issued: 1987 • Retired: 1992
Retail Price: $22.50 – $27.50

***Variation:** Boy with small head/blue bird/no "Sam B." signature –* $215

KEY

NM Pre'81	1986	1992	1997
1981	1987	1993	1998
1982	1988	1994	1999
1983	1989	1995	2000
1984	1990	1996	2001
1985	1991	UM Unmarked	

General Figurines

	Price Paid	Value
1.		
2.		
3.		
4.		
5.		
6.		
7.		
8.		
9.		
Totals		

1

Values ❦ $60
 ♫ $50
 ▲ $44
 ✤ $41
 ⌥ $41
 ✦ $38
 ◗ $38
 ♣ $35
 ♋ $35
 △ $35
 ♡ $35
 ✝ $35
 ✸ $35
 ★ $35
 ⏱ $35
 ☙ $35

I Believe In The Old Rugged Cross
#103632
Issued: 1986 • Open
Retail Price: $25 – $35

2

Values ✤ $53
 ⌥ $42
 ♣ $35
 ◗ $32

I Belong To The Lord
#520853
Issued: 1989 • Susp.: 1991
Retail Price: $25 – $27.50

3

Values ☙ $62
 △ $54
 ♡ $52
 ✝ $52
 ⚭ $52
 ★ $52
 ⏱ $52

I Can't Bear To Let You Go
#532037
Issued: 1995 • Retired: 1999
Retail Price: $50

4

Values ✦ $135
 ◗ $87
 ♣ $75
 ♋ $75
 ⚶ $72

I Can't Spell Success Without You
#523763
Issued: 1991 • Susp.: 1994
Retail Price: $40 – $45

5

Values ★ $60
 ⏱ $60
 ☙ $60

I Couldn't Make It Without You
Boys & Girls Clubs Of America Commemorative Figurine
#635030
Issued: 1999 • Open
Retail Price: $60

6

Values ❦ $88
 ♫ $82
 ▲ $75
 ✤ $75
 ⌥ $70
 ✦ $67
 ◗ $67
 ♣ $64
 ♋ $64
 ⚶ $62
 △ $62
 ♡ $62

I Get A Bang Out Of You
The Clown Series
#12262
Issued: 1985 • Retired: 1997
Retail Price: $30 – $45

7

Values ⚭ $23?
 ✝ $21?
 ◗ $200
 ♫ $195

I Get A Kick Out Of You
#E2827
Issued: 1984 • Susp.: 1986
Retail Price: $50

8

Values ⚭ $86
 △ $76
 ♡ $73
 ✝ $70
 ⚭ $70
 ★ $70
 ⏱ $70
 ☙ $70

I Give You My Love Forever True
#129100
Issued: 1995 • Open
Retail Price: $70

9

Values ☙ $30
New

Photo Unavailable

I Give You My Heart
Century Circle Figurine
#801313
Issued: 2001 • Open
Retail Price: $30

10

Values ⏱ $30
 ☙ $30

I Give You My Heart
Carlton Cards Exclusive
#801313C
Issued: 2000 • Open
Retail Price: $30

KEY			
NM Pre'81	1986	✦ 1992	✝ 1997
▲ 1981	▲ 1987	♋ 1993	⚭ 1998
✖ 1982	✤ 1988	⚶ 1994	★ 1999
⚭ 1983	⌥ 1989	△ 1995	⏱ 2000
✝ 1984	✸ 1990	♡ 1996	☙ 2001
❦ 1985	◗ 1991	UM Unmarked	

General Figurines

	Price Paid	Value
1.		
2.		
3.		
4.		
5.	60⁰⁰	
6.		
7.		
8.	70⁰⁰	
9.		
10.		

Totals

1

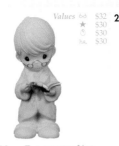

Values 6d $32
★ $30
① $30
ᴴᴬ $30

I Now Pronounce You
Man And Wife
#455938
Issued: 1998 • Open
Retail Price: $30

2

Values △ $60
♡ $57
† $57
6d $57
★ $57

I Only Have Ice For You
#530956
Issued: 1995 • Retired: 1999
Retail Price: $55

3

Values ♪ $90
▲ $82

I Picked A Very Special
Mom (LE-1987)
#100536
Issued: 1987 • Closed: 1987
Retail Price: $40

4

Values 6d $65
★ $65
① $65
ᴴᴬ $65

I Saw Mommy Kissing
Santa Claus
#455822
Issued: 1998 • Open
Retail Price: $65

5

Values ♀ $50
⊥ $35
♡ $32
† $32
6d $30
★ $30
① $30
ᴴᴬ $30

I Still Do
#530999
Issued: 1994 • Open
Retail Price: $30

6

Values ♀ $50
⊥ $35
♡ $32
† $32
6d $30
★ $30
① $30
ᴴᴬ $30

I Still Do
#531006
Issued: 1994 • Open
Retail Price: $30

7

Values † $42
6d $40
★ $40
① $40
ᴴᴬ $40

I Think You're Just Divine
#272558
Issued: 1997 • Open
Retail Price: $40

8

Values ♀ $83
⊥ $76
⊥ $69
♡ $64

I Will Always Be
Thinking Of You
#523631
Issued: 1994 • Retired: 1996
Retail Price: $45

KEY							
NM Pre'81	♪ 1986	⅃ 1992	† 1997
▲ 1981	▲ 1987	♀♀ 1993	6d 1998
ⅠⅠ 1982	◆ 1988	⊟ 1994	★ 1999
◄ 1983	⊕ 1989	△ 1995	① 2000
† 1984	★ 1990	♡ 1996	ᴴᴬ 2001
◢ 1985	♦ 1991	UM Unmarked	

General Figurines

	Price Paid	Value
1.		
2.		
3.		
4.		
5.		
6.		
7.		
8.		
9.		
10.		

Totals

97

9

Values ① $25
ᴴᴬ $25

I Will Love You All Ways
#708518
Issued: 2000 • Open
Retail Price: $25

10

Values ① $37.50
ᴴᴬ $37.50
(Can.)

*Photo
Unavailable*

I Will Make My
Country Proud
Canadian Exclusive
#820423
Issued: 2000 • Open
Retail Price: $37.50 (Canadian)

1

Values
🔔 $40
⚜ $36
⚲ $32
▬ $32
♡ $32
✝ $32
∞ $32
★ $32

**I Would Be Lost
Without You**
#526142
Issued: 1992 • Retired: 1999
Retail Price: $27.50 – $30

2

Values
▲ $30
✿ $27
Ð $25
🔔 $25
⚜ $22
⚲ $22
▬ $20
△ $20
♡ $20
✝ $20
∞ $20
★ $20
🕐 $20
ᴺᴹ $20

**I Would Be Sunk
Without You**
#102970
Issued: 1987 • Open
Retail Price: $15 – $20

3

Values
△ $48
♡ $46
✝ $46
∞ $46

I'll Give Him My Heart
#150088
Issued: 1995 • Retired: 1998
Retail Price: $40 – $45

4
New

Values
🕐 $45
ᴺᴹ $45

I'll Never Let You Down
#730165
Issued: 2001 • Open
Retail Price: $45

5

Values
Ð $92
🔔 $80
⚜ $78
⚲ $78
⚲ $77
▬ $77
△ $74
♡ $72

I'll Never Stop Loving You
#521418
Issued: 1990 • Retired: 1996
Retail Price: $37.50 – $40

6

Values
🕐 $30
ᴺᴹ $30

I'll Weight For You
#521469
Issued: 2000 • Open
Retail Price: $30

KEY							
NM Pre'81		ⅉ 1986		⚜ 1992		✝ 1997	
▲ 1981		▲ 1987		⚲ 1993		∞ 1998	
Ⅱ 1982		✥ 1988		▬ 1994		★ 1999	
◄ 1983		Ð 1989		△ 1995		🕐 2000	
✝ 1984		▲ 1990		♡ 1996		ᴺᴹ 2001	
✦ 1985		🔔 1991		UM Unmarked			

General Figurines

	Price Paid	Value
1.		
2.		
3.		
4.		
5.		
6.		
7.		
8.		
9.		
10.		

Totals

7

Values
ⅉ $90
▲ $82
✿ $77
Ð $75
🔔 $72
⚜ $72
⚜ $68
⚲ $68

I'm A Possibility
#100188
Issued: 1986 • Retired: 1993
Retail Price: $22 – $35

8

Values
Ð $53
🔔 $50

**I'm A Precious Moments
Fan (LE-1990)**
Special Event Figurine
#523526
Issued: 1990 • Closed: 1990
Retail Price: $25

9
New

Values
🕐 $28.50
ᴺᴹ $28.50

**I'm Completely Suspended
With Love**
#526096S
Issued: 2001 • To Be Retired: 2001
Retail Price: $28.50

10

Values
✝ $28
∞ $25
★ $25
🕐 $25
ᴺᴹ $25

**I'm Dreaming Of A
White Christmas**
#272590
Issued: 1997 • Open
Retail Price: $25

1

Values		
✝	$87
	$75
	$68
	$68
	$68
	$68
	$68
	$68
	$68
	$68
	$68
	$68
	$68
★	$68
	$68

I'm Sending You A White Christmas
#E2829
Issued: 1984 • Retired: 2000
Retail Price: $37.50 – $65

2

Values	
	$120
	$92
	$85
	$82

I'm So Glad That God Has Blessed Me With A Friend Like You
#523623
Issued: 1993 • Retired: 1995
Retail Price: $50 – $55

3

Values	
	$355
	$305
	$285
	$265

I'm So Glad You Fluttered Into My Life
#520640
Issued: 1989 • Retired: 1991
Retail Price: $40 – $45

4

Photo Unavailable

Values	
★	$40
	$40
	$40 (Can.)

Ice See In You A Champion
Canadian Exclusive
#649937
Issued: 2000 • Open
Retail Price: $40 (Canadian)

5

Values	
	$20
	$20

Ice Skating Pond Accessories
Precious Scapes Series
#750131
Issued: 2000 • Open
Retail Price: $20

6

Values	
	$104
✝	$88
	$82

If God Be For Us, Who Can Be Against Us
#E9285
Issued: 1983 • Susp.: 1985
Retail Price: $27.50

7

Values	
♡	$188
✝	$172

In God's Beautiful Garden Of Love (LE-15,000)
Century Circle Figurine
#261629
Issued: 1997 • Closed: 1997
Retail Price: $150

8

Values	
	$69
	$65
	$60
	$56
	$56
	$52
♡	$48

In The Spotlight Of His Grace
#520543
Issued: 1991 • Susp.: 1996
Retail Price: $35 – $37.50

KEY					
NM	Pre'81		1986		1992	✝	1997
	1981	▲	1987		1993		1998
	1982		1988		1994	★	1999
	1983		1989		1995		2000
✝	1984		1990	♡	1996		2001
	1985		1991	UM	Unmarked		

General Figurines

	Price Paid	Value
1.		
2.		
3.		
4.		
5.		
6.		
7.		
8.	35⁰⁰	
9.		
10.		

Totals

9

Values	
	$180
	$170
▲	$163

It Is Better To Give Than To Receive
#12297
Issued: 1985 • Susp.: 1987
Retail Price: $19 – $21

10

Values	
	$47
♡	$37.50
✝	$37.50
	$37.50
★	$37.50
	$37.50
	$37.50

It May Be Greener, But It's Just As Hard To Cut
#163899
Issued: 1996 • Open
Retail Price: $37.50

1
New

Values ☼ $25
 ▱ $25

It's A Banner Day,
Congratulations
#795259
Issued: 2001 • Open
Retail Price: $25

2

Values ♦ $107
 ♦ $100
 ♔ $92
 ▭ $88

It's No Yolk When I Say
I Love You
#522104
Issued: 1992 • Susp.: 1994
Retail Price: $60 – $65

3

Values ♪ $57
 ♔ $48
 ▭ $47
 ♡ $47
 † $47
 ♋ $47
 ★ $47

It's So Uplifting To Have
A Friend Like You
#522905
Issued: 1992 • Retired: 1999
Retail Price: $40 – $45

4

Values NM $140
 ▲ $130
 ▮ $122
 ➡ $110
 † $100

It's What's Inside
That Counts
#E3119
Issued: 1980 • Susp.: 1984
Retail Price: $13 – $19

5

Values ▲ $60
 ♣ $55
 ♉ $51
 ♣ $49
 ♦ $49
 ♪ $46
 ♔ $46
 ▭ $45
 ♡ $45
 † $45
 ♋ $45
 ★ $45
 ♦ $45
 ▱ $45

January
Calendar Girl Series
#109983
Issued: 1988 • Open
Retail Price: $37.50 – $45

6

Values ♣ $60
 ♪ $50

Jesus Is Coming Soon
#12343
Issued: 1985 • Susp.: 1986
Retail Price: $19 – $22.50

KEY					
NM Pre'81	♪ 1986	♦ 1992	† 1997		
▲ 1981	▲ 1987	♋ 1993	♋ 1998		
▮ 1982	♣ 1988	▭ 1994	★ 1999		
➡ 1983	♦ 1989	♧ 1995	☼ 2000		
† 1984	♣ 1990	♡ 1996	▱ 2001		
♣ 1985	♦ 1991	UM Unmarked			

General Figurines

	Price Paid	Value
1.		
2.		
3.		
4.		
5.		
6.		
7.		
8.		
9.		
10.		

Totals

7

Values ★ $75
 ☼ $75
 ▱ $75

Jesus Is My Lighthouse
(lighted)
#487945
Issued: 1999 • Open
Retail Price: $75

8

Values NM $192
 ▲ $174
 ▮ $152
 ➡ $142
 † $132

Jesus Is The Answer
#E1381
Issued: 1979 • Susp.: 1984
Retail Price: $11.50 – $22.50

9

Values ♪ $86
 ♔ $78
 ▭ $72
 ♧ $69
 ♡ $65

Jesus Is The Answer
*St. Jude Children's Research
Hospital Figurine*
#E1381R
Issued: 1992 • Retired: 1996
Retail Price: $55

10

Values NM $133
 ▲ $82
 ▮ $74
 ➡ $69
 † $66
 ♣ $58
 ♪ $55
 ▲ $50
 ♣ $45

Jesus Is The Light
#E1373G
Issued: 1979 • Retired: 1988
Retail Price: $7 – $21

1

Values $78 / $72 / $65 / $56

Jesus Is The Light That Shines
#E0502
Issued: 1983 • Susp.: 1986
Retail Price: $22.50 – $23

2

Values $82 / $73 / $70 / $70 / $65 / $65

Jesus Is The Only Way
#520756
Issued: 1989 • Susp.: 1993
Retail Price: $40 – $45

3

Values NM $127 / $75 / $55 / $45 / $42 / $42 / $37 / $37 / $33 / $33 / $33 / $33 / $33 / $32 / $32 / $32 / $32 / $32 / $32

Jesus Loves Me
#E1372B
Issued: 1979 • Retired: 1998
Retail Price: $7 – $27.50

4

Values NM $132 / $85 / $60 / $48 / $44 / $42 / $40 / $37 / $35 / $33 / $33 / $33 / $32 / $30 / $30 / $27.50 / $27.50 / $27.50 / $27.50 / $27.50 / $27.50

Jesus Loves Me
#E1372G
Issued: 1979 • Open
Retail Price: $7 – $27.50

5

Values $45 / $35 / $28 / $25 / $23 / $23 / $23 / $23 / $23 / $23 / $20 / $20 / $20 / $20 / $20 / $20

Jesus Loves Me
#E9278
Issued: 1983 • Retired: 1998
Retail Price: $9 – $17.50

6

Values $43 / $33 / $32 / $32 / $30 / $30 / $26 / $24 / $22 / $22 / $20 / $20 / $20 / $20 / $20 / $20 / $20 / $20 / $20

Jesus Loves Me
#E9279
Issued: 1983 • Retired: 2000
Retail Price: $9 – $18.50

7

Values $120 / $84 / $67 / $62 / $58 / $57 / $57 / $55 / $55 / $55 / $55 / $55 / $55 / $55 / $55 / $55 / $55

The Joy Of The Lord Is My Strength
#100137
Issued: 1986 • Open
Retail Price: $35 – $55

8

Values $71 / $66 / $58 / $54 / $55 / $55 / $55 / $55 / $55 / $55 / $55 / $55

Joy On Arrival
#523178
Issued: 1991 • Open
Retail Price: $50 – $55

9

Values $59 / $50 / $48 / $46 / $46 / $45 / $45 / $45 / $45 / $45 / $45 / $45 / $45

July
Calendar Girl Series
#110051
Issued: 1988 • Open
Retail Price: $35 – $45

KEY:

NM Pre'81	1986	1992	1997
1981	1987	1993	1998
1982	1988	1994	1999
1983	1989	1995	2000
1984	1990	1996	2001
1985	1991	UM Unmarked	

General Figurines

	Price Paid	Value
1.		
2.		
3.		
4.		
5.		
6.		
7.		
8.	50.00	
9.		

Totals

1

Values
🦋 $145
♣ $68
⊕ $65
⚓ $60
🔔 $58
🍓 $57
🎀 $55
〰 $55
△ $55
♡ $55
✝ $55
♦ $55
★ $55
🕐 $55
🔺 $55

June
Calendar Girl Series
#110043
Issued: 1988 • Open
Retail Price: $40 – $55

2

Values
🦋 $35
▲ $32
♣ $29
⊕ $27
⚓ $27
🔔 $25
🍓 $25
〰 $24
〰 $24
△ $22.50
♡ $22.50
✝ $22.50
⊖ $22.50
★ $22.50
🔺 $22.50

Junior Bridesmaid
Bridal Party Series
#E2845
Issued: 1986 • Open
Retail Price: $12.50 – $22.50

3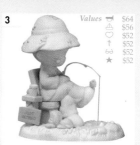

Values
〰 $64
△ $56
♡ $52
♦ $52
⊖ $52
★ $52

**Just A Line To Say
You're Special**
#522864
Issued: 1995 • Retired: 1999
Retail Price: $45 – $50

4

Values
♣ $118
⊕ $110
⚓ $104
🔔 $98
🍓 $96
🎀 $92
$92
△ $92
♡ $92

**Just A Line To Wish
You A Happy Day**
#520721
Issued: 1989 • Susp.: 1996
Retail Price: $65 – $75

5

Values
〰 $55
△ $48
♡ $46
✝ $46
⊖ $46
★ $46

Just Poppin' In To Say Halo!
#523755
Issued: 1994 • Retired: 1999
Retail Price: $45

6

Values
♡ $44
✝ $39

**Lead Me To Calvary
(Dated 1997)**
The Dated Cross Series
#260916
Issued: 1997 • Closed: 1997
Retail Price: $37.50

KEY			
NM Pre'81	🦋 1986	🍓 1992	✝ 1997
▲ 1981	▲ 1987	🎀 1993	★ 1998
🔺 1982	♣ 1988	〰 1994	♦ 1999
⊕ 1983	⊕ 1989	△ 1995	🕐 2000
✝ 1984	♦ 1990	♡ 1996	⊖ 2001
🔔 1985	⚓ 1991	UM Unmarked	

General Figurines

	Price Paid	Value
1.		
2.		
3.		
4.		
5.		
6.		
7.		
8.		
9.		
10.		

Totals

7

Values
★ $45
🕐 $45
⊖ $45

Let Freedom Ring
(special year mark available)
#681059
Issued: 1999 • Open
Retail Price: $45

8

Values
🔺 $120
▲ $85
✝ $85
♦ $82
🦋 $76
▲ $71

Let Love Reign
#E9273
Issued: 1983 • Retired: 1987
Retail Price: $22.50 – $30

9

Values
NM $215
▲ $178
🔺 $165
♦ $150
✝ $145

**Let Not The Sun Go Down
Upon Your Wrath**
#E5203
Issued: 1981 • Susp.: 1984
Retail Price: $22.50 – $30

10

Values
🔺 $146
▲ $137
✝ $126
♦ $120
🦋 $115
▲ $110

Let The Whole World Know
#E7165
Issued: 1982 • Susp.: 1987
Retail Price: $45 – $55

1

Values ★ $37.50
🜨 $37.50
🐚 $37.50
(Can.)

Let's Keep Our Eyes On The Goal
Canadian Exclusive
#549975
Issued: 1999 • Open
Retail Price: $37.50 (Canadian)

2

Values † $63
🐚 $60
★ $60
🜨 $60
🐚 $60

Let's Put The Pieces Together
#525928
Issued: 1998 • Open
Retail Price: $60

3

Values ♡ $25
† $21
🐚 $21
★ $21

Lettuce Pray
#261122
Issued: 1997 • Retired: 1999
Retail Price: $17.50

4

Values 🐚 $42

Life Can Be A Jungle
Special Event Figurine
#325457
Issued: 1998 • Closed: 1998
Retail Price: $37.50

5

New

Values 🐚 $35

Life Is So Uplifting
#878995
Issued: 2001 • Open
Retail Price: $35

6

Values 🜨 $30
🐚 $30

Life Is Worth Fighting For
NABCO Commemorative Figurine
#680982
Issued: 2000 • Open
Retail Price: $30

7

Values ★ $25
🜨 $25

Life's A Collection of Precious Moments (LE-2000)
#745510
Issued: 2000 • Closed: 2000
Retail Price: $25

8

New

Values 🐚 $25
🐚 $25

Life's Bear-y Precious With You
#642673
Issued: 2001 • Open
Retail Price: $25

General Figurines

	Price Paid	Value
1.		
2.		
3.		
4.		
5.		
6.		
7.		
8.		

Totals

1

Values	
NM	$95
▲	$83
I	$71
⚓	$62
♣	$58
♥	$55
♫	$53
♦	$50
⬦	$50
♪	$50
♦	$50
⬥	$50
♣	$50
♡	$50
◇	$50
†	$50
◡◠	$50
★	$50
◔	$50
⌂	$50

The Lord Bless You
And Keep You
#E3114
Issued: 1980 • Open
Retail Price: $16 – $50

2

Values	
NM	$53
▲	$45
I	$42
⚓	$42
†	$40
♣	$38
♫	$38
▲	$36

The Lord Bless You
And Keep You
#E4720
Issued: 1981 • Susp.: 1987
Retail Price: $14 – $22.50

3

Values	
NM	$80
▲	$57
I	$50
⚓	$46
†	$44
♣	$42
♫	$42
♦	$40
⬦	$40
♦	$38
★	$38
♡	$37
♣	$35
♥	$35
◇	$35
†	$35
◡◠	$35
★	$35
◔	$35
⌂	$35

The Lord Bless You
And Keep You
#E4721
Issued: 1981 • Open
Retail Price: $14 – $35

4

Values	
♫	$56
⬦	$54
♡	$52
♡	$50
†	$50
◡◠	$50
★	$50
◔	$50
⌂	$50

The Lord Bless You
And Keep You
#532118
Issued: 1994 • Open
Retail Price: $40 – $50

⑤

Values	
♫	$42
⬦	$37
◇	$35
♡	$35
†	$35
◡◠	$35
★	$35
◔	$35
⌂	$35

The Lord Bless You
And Keep You
#532126
Issued: 1994 • Open
Retail Price: $30 – $35

⑥

Values	
♫	$40
⬦	$37
◇	$35
♡	$35
†	$35
◡◠	$35
★	$35
◔	$35
⌂	$35

The Lord Bless You
And Keep You
#532134
Issued: 1994 • Open
Retail Price: $30 – $35

KEY					
NM	Pre '81	♫	1986	♦	1992	†	1997
▲	1981	▲	1987	♀	1993	◡◠	1998
I	1982	♦	1988	⬦	1994	★	1999
♦	1983	♦	1989	△	1995	◔	2000
†	1984	★	1990	♡	1996	⌂	2001
♥	1985	♦	1991	UM	Unmarked		

General Figurines

	Price Paid	Value
1.		
2.		
3.		
4.		
5.		
6.		
7.		
8.		

Totals

7

Values	
◔	$27.50
⌂	$27.50

The Lord Bless You
And Keep You
#795364
Issued: 2000 • Open
Retail Price: $27.50

8

Values	
◔	$27.50
⌂	$27.50

The Lord Bless You
And Keep You
#795372
Issued: 2000 • Open
Retail Price: $27.50

1 *Values* ⏱ $27.50 / ᵇᵃ $27.50

The Lord Bless You And Keep You
#795380
Issued: 2000 • Open
Retail Price: $27.50

2 *Values* ⏱ $27.50 / ᵇᵃ $27.50

The Lord Bless You And Keep You
#795399
Issued: 2000 • Open
Retail Price: $27.50

3 *Values* ⏱ $27.50 / ᵇᵃ $27.50

The Lord Bless You And Keep You
#795402
Issued: 2000 • Open
Retail Price: $27.50

4 *Values* ⏱ $27.50 / ᵇᵃ $27.50

The Lord Bless You And Keep You
#795410
Issued: 2000 • Open
Retail Price: $27.50

5 *Values* ⏱ $27.50 / ᵇᵃ $27.50

The Lord Bless You And Keep You
#874485
Issued: 2000 • Open
Retail Price: $27.50

6 *Values* ⏱ $27.50 / ᵇᵃ $27.50

The Lord Bless You And Keep You
#874493
Issued: 2000 • Open
Retail Price: $27.50

7
New

Values ⏱ $35 / ᵇᵃ $35

The Lord Can Dew Anything
#795208
Issued: 2001 • Open
Retail Price: $35

8

Values
🕊 $62
✝ $55
📖 $55
🎵 $52
🔺 $50
✢ $48
⬦ $46
⚓ $44

Lord, Give Me A Song
Rejoice In The Lord Band Series
#12386
Issued: 1985 • Susp.: 1990
Retail Price: $15 – $22.50

9

Values
I $70
↤ $64
✝ $62
🎵 $56

Lord, Give Me Patience
#E7159
Issued: 1982 • Susp.: 1985
Retail Price: $25 – $27.50

10

Values
🔺 $90
✢ $85
⬦ $80
⚓ $77
🔴 $77
⚓ $75
🌸 $75
🐟 $73
△ $73

The Lord Giveth, And The Lord Taketh Away
#100226
Issued: 1987 • Retired: 1995
Retail Price: $33.50 – $40

KEY			
NM Pre '81	♫ 1986	♠ 1992	✝ 1997
▲ 1981	♀♀ 1987	♀♀ 1993	∂∂ 1998
I 1982	✣ 1988	⊨ 1994	★ 1999
1983	⊕ 1989	△ 1995	⏱ 2000
✝ 1984	⚓ 1990	♡ 1996	ᵇᵃ 2001
✦ 1985	● 1991	UM Unmarked	

General Figurines

	Price Paid	Value
1.		
2.		
3.		
4.		
5.		
6.		
7.		
8.		
9.		
10.		

Totals

1

Values ♠ $60
⬥ $56
Ð $53
⬦ $52

Lord, Help Me Make The Grade
#106216
Issued: 1987 • Susp.: 1990
Retail Price: $25 – $32.50

2

Values Ð $74
★ $69
♦ $64
& $62
♀ $62
⬦ $60
♡ $57
♡ $57

Lord, Help Me Stick To My Job
#521450
Issued: 1990 • Retired: 1997
Retail Price: $30 – $35

3

Values ♙ $42
♡ $40
† $35
★ $35
★ $35
☉ $35
⬅ $35

Lord Help Me To Stay On Course
#532096
Issued: 1995 • Open
Retail Price: $35

4

Values ♫ $140
▲ $125
⬥ $118
Ð $118
⬦ $110
♦ $110

Lord, Help Us Keep Our Act Together
#101850
Issued: 1987 • Retired: 1992
Retail Price: $35 – $50

5

Values ◗ $96
♫ $60
▲ $53
⬥ $46
Ð $46
⬦ $43
♦ $43
& $43
♀ $40
⬦ $38
⬚ $37
♡ $35
† $35
⬅ $35
★ $35
☉ $35
⬅ $35

Lord, I'm Coming Home
#100110
Issued: 1986 • Open
Retail Price: $22.50 – $35

6

Values ★ $50
☉ $50
⬅ $50

Lord, I'm In It Again
#525944
Issued: 2000 • Open
Retail Price: $50

KEY				
NM Pre'81	♫ 1986	& 1992	† 1997	
▲ 1981	▲ 1987	♀♀ 1993	6⊃ 1998	
Ⅱ 1982	⬥ 1988	⬚ 1994	★ 1999	
⬅ 1983	Ð 1989	⬦ 1995	☉ 2000	
† 1984	♦ 1990	♡ 1996	⬅ 2001	
⬅ 1985	♦ 1991	UM Unmarked		

General Figurines

	Price Paid	Value
1.		
2.		
3.		
4.		
5.		
6.		
7.		
8.		

Totals

7

Values ⬎ $45
⬚ $40
♡ $37
† $35
6⊃ $35
★ $35
☉ $35
⬅ $35

The Lord Is Counting On You
#531707
Issued: 1994 • Open
Retail Price: $32.50 – $35

8

Values ♡ $46
† $40
6⊃ $40
★ $40
☉ $40
⬅ $40

The Lord Is The Hope Of Our Future
#261564
Issued: 1997 • Open
Retail Price: $40

1 *Values* ○ $40
     ≈ $40

The Lord Is The Hope
Of Our Future
#261564L
Issued: 2000 • Open
Retail Price: $40

2 *Values* △ $35
     ♡ $30
     ○ $29
     6∂ $29
     ★ $29

The Lord Is With You
#526835
Issued: 1996 • Retired: 1999
Retail Price: $27.50

3 *Values* ❖ $77
     ⚓ $73
     ♠ $70
     🕯 $70
     ⚘ $67
     ⚙ $67
     — $67
     △ $67
     ♡ $65
     † $65
     6∂ $65
     ★ $65
     ○ $65
     ≈ $65

The Lord Is Your Light
To Happiness
#520837
Issued: 1989 • Open
Retail Price: $50 – $65

4 *Values* 🍂 $115
     ♪ $97
     ♠ $88
     ❖ $85

Lord, Keep Me On My Toes
#100129
Issued: 1986 • Retired: 1988
Retail Price: $22.50 – $27

5 *Values* ♪ $72
     ♠ $62
     ❖ $59
     ✛ $59
     ⚓ $56
     🕯 $56
     ⚘ $54
     ⚙ $50
     — $48
     ♡ $48
     † $48
     6∂ $48

Lord, Keep Me On The Ball
The Clown Series
#12270
Issued: 1986 • Susp.: 1998
Retail Price: $30 – $45

6 *Values* ≈ $37.50
New

*Photo
Unavailable*

Lord Let Our
Friendship Bloom
#879126
Issued: 2001 • Open
Retail Price: $37.50

7 *Values* ★ $45
     ○ $45
     ≈ $45

Lord, Police Protect Us
#539953
Issued: 1999 • Open
Retail Price: $45

8 *Values* ♡ $40
     † $40
     6∂ $40
     ★ $40
     ○ $40
     ≈ $40

Lord, Spare Me
#521191
Issued: 1997 • Open
Retail Price: $37.50 – $40

KEY						
NM Pre'81	♪ 1986	⚙ 1992	† 1997			
▲ 1981	⚓ 1987	❀ 1993	6∂ 1998			
✠ 1982	❖ 1988	⊐ 1994	★ 1999			
◄ 1983	✛ 1989	⚐ 1995	○ 2000			
† 1984	♠ 1990	♡ 1996	≈ 2001			
🍂 1985	🕯 1991	∪M Unmarked				

9 *Values* 6∂ $50
     ★ $45
     ○ $45
     ≈ $45

Lord Speak To Me
#531987
Issued: 1999 • Open
Retail Price: $45

10 — $50

Lord Teach Us To Pray
(LE-1994)
*National Day Of Prayer
Figurine*
#524158
Issued: 1994 • Closed: 1994
Retail Price: $35

General Figurines

	Price Paid	Value
1.		
2.		
3.		
4.	22.50	
5.		
6.		
7.		
8.		
9.		
10.		

Totals

1

Values 🕊 $72
   🔔 $66
   🍀 $62
   💲 $62
   🛏 $58
   🏺 $58
   ♡ $54
     $52

Lord, Turn My Life Around
#520551
Issued: 1990 • Susp.: 1996
Retail Price: $35 – $37.50

2

Values 🍀 $62
   🐦 $58
   🪑 $58
   △ $55
   ♡ $54

**The Lord Turned My
Life Around**
#520535
Issued: 1992 • Susp.: 1996
Retail Price: $35.50 – $37.50

3

Values ✤ $95
   🎵 $92
   🔔 $86
   ✣ $82

**The Lord Will Carry
You Through**
The Clown Series
#12467
Issued: 1986 • Retired: 1988
Retail Price: $30 – $35

4

Values 🍀 $70
   🪑 $60

**The Lord Will Provide
(LE-1993)**
#523593
Issued: 1993 • Closed: 1993
Retail Price: $40

5

Values I $76
   † $56
   ✦ $56
   🎵 $55
   🎵 $52
   ▲ $50
   ✣ $50
   🕊 $48
   🔔 $48
   † $47
   🍀 $47
   🪑 $45
   🍴 $45
   △ $45
   ♡ $45
   ↑ $45
   6d $45
   ★ $45
     $45

**Love Beareth
All Things**
#E7158
Issued: 1982 • Open
Retail Price: $25 – $45

6

Values 🍴 $46
   △ $40

**Love Blooms Eternal
(Dated 1995)**
The Dated Cross Series
#127019
Issued: 1995 • Closed: 1995
Retail Price: $35

KEY					
NM Pre'81	🎵 1986	🍀 1992	↑ 1997		
▲ 1981	▲ 1987	🪑 1993	6d 1998		
I 1982	✦ 1988	🍴 1994	★ 1999		
◄ 1983	🕊 1989	△ 1995	◷ 2000		
† 1984	🔔 1990	♡ 1996	▰ 2001		
✤ 1985	🍀 1991	UM Unmarked			

General Figurines

	Price Paid	Value
1.		
2.		
3.		
4.		
5.		
6.		
7.		
8.		
9.		
10.		
Totals		

7

Values NM $155
   ▲ $142
   I $122
   ◄ $114
   † $110
   ✤ $100

**Love Cannot Break A
True Friendship**
#E4722
Issued: 1981 • Susp.: 1985
Retail Price: $22.50 – $27.50

8

Values † $85
   ✤ $80
   🎵 $78
   ✣ $73
   ✦ $73
   🕊 $70
   🔔 $68
   🍀 $63

Love Covers All
#12009
Issued: 1985 • Susp.: 1991
Retail Price: $27.50 – $37.50

9

Values 6d $65
   ★ $65

Love Is Color Blind
*Boys & Girls Clubs Of America
Commemorative Figurine*
#524204
Issued: 1998 • Closed: 1998
Retail Price: $60

10

Values 🕊 $80
   🔔 $75
   🍀 $70
   🍀 $70
   🪑 $68
   🍴 $68
   △ $66
   ♡ $60

Love Is From Above
#521841
Issued: 1990 • Susp.: 1996
Retail Price: $45 – $50

1

Values NM $142
▲ $116
Ⅱ $100
← $95
† $92

Love Is Kind
#E1379A
Issued: 1979 • Susp.: 1984
Retail Price: $8 – $19

2

Values ∞ $40

Love Is Kind
Special Event Figurine
#E1379R
Issued: 1998 • Closed: 1998
Retail Price: $8

3

Values † $102
🦐 $93
🎷 $86
▲ $81

Love Is Kind
#E5377
Issued: 1984 • Retired: 1987
Retail Price: $27.50 – $30

4

Values ← $98
† $88
🦐 $80

Love Is Patient
#E9251
Issued: 1983 • Susp.: 1985
Retail Price: $35

5

Values Ⅱ $185
← $170
† $163

Love Is Sharing
#E7162
Issued: 1982 • Susp.: 1984
Retail Price: $25 – $27.50

6

Values ▲ $80
🔱 $72
D $65
↓ $65

**Love Is The Glue
That Mends**
#104027
Issued: 1987 • Susp.: 1990
Retail Price: $33.50 – $40

7

Values ∞ $35
† $36
∞ $35
★ $35
🕘 $35
🐚 $35

Love Is The Key
Century Circle/Avon Figurine
#482242/#033-949
Issued: 1998 • Closed: 1998
Retail Price: $29.99

8

Values ♡ $42
† $36
∞ $35
★ $35
🕘 $35
🐚 $35

Love Letters In The Sand
#129488
Issued: 1997 • Open
Retail Price: $35

9

Values NM $178
▲ $115
Ⅱ $100
← $94
† $86
🦐 $83
🎷 $80
▲ $78
🔱 $75
D $75
↓ $73
🔥 $73
🦐 $68
👑 $68

Love Lifted Me
#E1375A
Issued: 1979 • Retired: 1993
Retail Price: $11 – $37.50

10

Values NM $125
▲ $106
Ⅱ $92
← $87
† $82

Love Lifted Me
#E5201
Issued: 1981 • Susp.: 1984
Retail Price: $25 – $33

KEY			
NM Pre'81	🦐 1986	🔥 1992	† 1997
▲ 1981	▲ 1987	🎷 1993	∞ 1998
Ⅱ 1982	🔱 1988	🌙 1994	★ 1999
← 1983	D 1989	⚱ 1995	🕘 2000
† 1984	↓ 1990	♡ 1996	🐚 2001
🦐 1985	🔥 1991	UM Unmarked	

General Figurines

	Price Paid	Value
1.		
2.		
3.		
4.		
5.		
6.		
7.		
8.		
9.		
10.		

Totals

1

Values: ★ $45 | ⏱ $45 | ⚓ $45

A Love Like No Other
#681075
Issued: 2000 • Open
Retail Price: $45

2

Values: △ $420

Love Makes The World Go 'Round (LE-15,000)
Century Circle Figurine
#139475
Issued: 1996 • Closed: 1996
Retail Price: $200

3

Values: ✦ $68 | ⅏ $55 | ▲ $52 | ✧ $48 | ⊕ $48 | ✦ $45 | ⚬ $45 | ✿ $45 | ⚬ $42 | ⊟ $42 | △ $42 | ♡ $42 | ✦ $42 | ⚓ $42 | ★ $42 | ⏱ $42 | ⚓ $42

Love Never Fails
#12300
Issued: 1985 • Retired: 2000
Retail Price: $25 – $40

4

Values: △ $49 | † $43 | ⚬ $40 | ★ $40 | ⚬ $40 | ⏱ $40 | ⚓ $40

Love Never Leaves A Mother's Arms
#523941
Issued: 1996 • Open
Retail Price: $40

5

Values: NM $138 | ▲ $92 | ⅈ $72 | ⚬ $60 | † $57 | ✦ $52 | ⅏ $50 | ✿ $50 | ✧ $48 | ✦ $46 | ✦ $45 | ⚬ $43 | ⚬ $43 | ⊟ $42 | △ $40 | † $40 | ⚬ $40 | ★ $40 | ⏱ $40 | ⚓ $40

Love One Another
#E1376
Issued: 1979 • Open
Retail Price: $10 – $40

6

Values: ⅏ $59 | ▲ $52 | ✦ $47 | ⊕ $44 | ★ $40 | ✿ $40 | ⚬ $40 | ✦ $40 | ⊟ $40 | ♡ $40 | † $40 | ⚬ $40 | ★ $40

Love Rescued Me
#102393
Issued: 1986 • Retired: 1999
Retail Price: $22.50 – $37.50

7

Values: △ $77 | ⚬ $72 | † $70 | ⚬ $70 | ★ $70 | ⏱ $70 | ⚓ $70

Love Vows To Always Bloom
#129097
Issued: 1996 • Open
Retail Price: $70

8

Values: NM $146 | ▲ $118 | ⅈ $105 | ⚬ $88 | † $85 | ✦ $85 | ✦ $83 | ▲ $80 | ✧ $80 | ✦ $80 | ✦ $75 | ⚬ $75 | ⚬ $72 | ⚬ $72

Loving Is Sharing
#E3110B
Issued: 1980 • Retired: 1993
Retail Price: $13 – $30

General Figurines

	Price Paid	Value
1.	45⁰⁰	
2.		
3.		
4.	40⁰⁰	
5.		
6.		
7.		
8.		
9.		
10.		

9

Values: NM $112 | ▲ $80 | ⅈ $68 | ✦ $50 | † $45 | ✦ $42 | ⅏ $40 | ▲ $40 | ✧ $40 | ⊕ $38 | ✦ $38 | ✿ $35 | ⚬ $35 | ⚬ $35 | ⊟ $35 | △ $35 | ♡ $35 | ✦ $35 | ⚬ $35 | ★ $35 | ⏱ $35 | ⚓ $35

Loving Is Sharing
#E3110G
Issued: 1980 • Open
Retail Price: $13 – $35

10

★ $35 | ⏱ $35 | ⚓ $35

lovingcaringsharing.com
#679860
Issued: 2000 • Open
Retail Price: $35

Totals

1

Values $39
$39
$39
$37.50
$37.50
$37.50

Luke 2:10-11
#532916
Issued: 1994 • Retired: 1999
Retail Price: $35 – $37.50

2

Values NM $135
$89
$58
$46
$44
$42
$42
$39
$39
$39
$36
$36
$36
$33
$33
$33
$33
$33
$33
$33

Make A Joyful Noise
#E1374G
Issued: 1979 • Retired: 2000
Retail Price: $8 – $32.50

3

Values $140
$98
$92
$85
$79

Make Me A Blessing
#100102
Issued: 1987 • Retired: 1990
Retail Price: $35 – $50

4

Values $60
$60
$60
$60

Make Me Strong (set/4)
#481688
Issued: 1999 • Open
Retail Price: $60

5

Values $46
$44
$42
$42

Making Spirits Bright
#150118
Issued: 1995 • Retired: 1998
Retail Price: $37.50

6

Values $360
$330
$320

Many Moons In Same
Canoe, Blessum You
#520772
Issued: 1989 • Retired: 1990
Retail Price: $50 – $55

7

Values $65

Many Years Of Blessing You
(LE-1998)
#384887
Issued: 1998 • Closed: 1998
Retail Price: $60

8

Values $62
$46
$44
$41
$40
$40
$40
$40
$40
$40
$40
$40
$40
$40

March
Calendar Girl Series
#110019
Issued: 1988 • Open
Retail Price: $27.50 – $40

KEY					
NM Pre'81		1986		1992	1997
1981		1987		1993	1998
1982		1988		1994	1999
1983		1989		1995	2000
1984		1990		1996	2001
1985		1991		UM Unmarked	

General Figurines

	Price Paid	Value
1.		
2.		
3.		
4.		
5.		
6.		
7.		
8.		
9.		
10.		

Totals

9

Values $44
$38
$35
$35
$35
$35
$35

Marching To The Beat Of
Freedom's Drum
#521981
Issued: 1996 • Open
Retail Price: $35

10

Values $58

Marvelous Grace (LE-1998)
Century Circle Figurine
#325503
Issued: 1998 • Closed: 1998
Retail Price: $50

1

Values
▲ $125
♣ $48
⊕ $42
♣ $40
♦ $40
♠ $38
♀ $36
♠ $36
♥ $35
† $35
6ð $35
★ $35
♂ $35
⅃ᴗ $35

May
Calendar Girl Series
#110035
Issued: 1988 • Open
Retail Price: $25 – $35

2

Values ♂ $30
⅃ᴗ $30

Photo Unavailable

May All Your Days Be Rosy
#781770
Issued: 2000 • Open
Retail Price: $30

3

Values ♂ $30
⅃ᴗ $30

Photo Unavailable

May All Your Days Be Rosy
Carlton Cards Exclusive
#781770C
Issued: 2000 • Open
Retail Price: $30

4

Values ♦ $70
♠ $53
♠ $47
♀ $44
♠ $40
♥ $40
† $40
6ð $40

**May Only Good Things
Come Your Way**
#524425
Issued: 1991 • Retired: 1998
Retail Price: $30 – $37.50

5

Values ♥ $70

**May The Sun Always
Shine On You (LE-1996)**
Century Circle Figurine
#184217
Issued: 1996 • Closed: 1996
Retail Price: $37.50

6

Values ♣ $57
♪ $52
▲ $49
♣ $49
⊕ $46
♦ $43
♦ $43
♠ $40

**May You Have The
Sweetest Christmas**
Family Christmas Series
#15776
Issued: 1985 • Susp.: 1992
Retail Price: $17 – $25

KEY					
NM Pre'81	♪ 1986	♠ 1992	† 1997
▲ 1981	▲ 1987	♀ 1993	6ð 1998
Ⅰ 1982	♣ 1988	⅃ 1994	★ 1999
Ⅰ 1983	⊕ 1989	▲ 1995	♂ 2000
† 1984	♦ 1990	♥ 1996	⅃ᴗ 2001
♣ 1985	♦ 1991	�UM Unmarked	

General Figurines

	Price Paid	Value
1.		
2.		
3.		
4.		
5.		
6.		
7.		
8.		
9.		
10.		

Totals

7

Values ♥ $125
† $102
♀ $97
♪ $92

**May Your Birthday
Be A Blessing**
#E2826
Issued: 1984 • Susp.: 1986
Retail Price: $37.50

8

Values ♂ N/E

Photo Unavailable

**May Your Birthday
Be A Blessing (LE-25,000)**
#E2826R
Issued: 2000 • Closed: 2000
Retail Price: N/A

9

Values ♦ $58
♦ $48
♠ $43
♀ $40
⅃ $38
▲ $37
♥ $35
† $35
6ð $35
★ $35
♂ $35
⅃ᴗ $35

**May Your Birthday
Be A Blessing**
#524301
Issued: 1991 • Open
Retail Price: $30 – $35

10

Values ♦ $83
♣ $74
♪ $70

**May Your Christmas
Be Blessed**
#E5376
Issued: 1984 • Susp.: 1986
Retail Price: $37.50

1

Values		
⚓	$94
	$83
†	$78

May Your Christmas Be Cozy
#E2345
Issued: 1982 • Susp.: 1984
Retail Price: $23 – $25

2

Values		
✿	$69
♪	$64
	$62
❖	$60
	$60
✚	$58
	$58
♨	$56
♈	$54
	$52

May Your Christmas
Be Delightful
#15482
Issued: 1985 • Susp.: 1994
Retail Price: $25 – $35

3

Values		
†	$48
⚭	$40
★	$40
⏱	$40
⚮	$40

May Your Christmas
Be Delightful
#604135
Issued: 1997 • Open
Retail Price: $40

4

Values		
⚓	$150
❖	$135
†	$127
✦	$127
♪	$122
▲	$117
❖	$114

May Your Christmas
Be Warm
#E2348
Issued: 1982 • Susp.: 1988
Retail Price: $30 – $38.50

5
New

Photo Unavailable

Values		
⚮	$55

May Your Days Be Merry
And Bright
#878901
Issued: 2001 • Open
Retail Price: $45

6

Values		
♨	$68
	$63
⚊	$58
△	$55
♡	$53
	$50
†	$50
⚭	$50
★	$50
⏱	$50
	$50

May Your Every Wish
Come True
#524298
Issued: 1993 • Open
Retail Price: $50

7

Values		
♨	$49
♈	$47
⚊	$44
△	$44
♡	$42
†	$40
⚭	$40
★	$40
⏱	$40
⚮	$40

May Your Future
Be Blessed
#525316
Issued: 1993 • Open
Retail Price: $35 – $40

8

Values		
⊕	$68
♨	$62
⚊	$58
♨	$56
	$52
⚊	$52
♡	$52
†	$52
	$52
	$52

May Your Life Be Blessed
With Touchdowns
#522023
Issued: 1989 • Retired: 1998
Retail Price: $45 – $50

9

Values		
★	$37.50
⏱	$37.50
⚮	$37.50

May Your Seasons Be Jelly
And Bright
#587885
Issued: 1999 • Open
Retail Price: $37.50

10

Values		
♨	$90
♨	$84
♈	$80
⚊	$76
△	$72
♡	$70

May Your World Be
Trimmed With Joy
#522082
Issued: 1991 • Susp.: 1996
Retail Price: $55

KEY					
NM Pre'81	♪ 1986	♨ 1992	† 1997
▲ 1981	▲ 1987	♈ 1993	⚭ 1998
⚓ 1982	❖ 1988	1994	★ 1999
✦ 1983	⊕ 1989	△ 1995	⏱ 2000
† 1984	▲ 1990	♡ 1996	⚮ 2001
✿ 1985	♨ 1991	UM Unmarked	

General Figurines

	Price Paid	Value
1.	23 00	
2.		
3.		
4.		
5.		
6.	50 00	
7.		
8.		
9.		
10.		

Totals

113

1

Values 🦋 $52
🍴 $46

Memories Are Made Of This (LE-1994)
Special Event Figurine
#529982
Issued: 1994 • Closed: 1994
Retail Price: $30

2

Values ♣ $58
🦋 $48
⚓ $45
🕯 $42
🎐 $40
🐚 $40
🎀 $39
△ $39
♡ $37
† $37
👓 $37
★ $37
🕐 $37

Meowie Christmas
#109800
Issued: 1988 • Retired: 2000
Retail Price: $30 – $35

3

Values ⚓ $105
🦋 $95
⚓ $92
🎐 $90
🐚 $90
🎀 $88
△ $88
♡ $85

Merry Christmas Deer
#522317
Issued: 1989 • Retired: 1997
Retail Price: $50 – $60

4

New

Values ➷ $37.50

Photo Unavailable

Missing You
#524107
Issued: 2001 • Open
Retail Price: $37.50

5

Values † $50
👓 $45
★ $45
🕐 $45
➷ $45

Missum You
#306991
Issued: 1998 • Open
Retail Price: $45

6

Values 👓 $43

Mom, You Always Make Our House A Home (LE-1998)
Catalog Figurine
#325465
Issued: 1998 • Closed: 1998
Retail Price: $37.50

KEY					
NM Pre'81	🦋 1986	⚙ 1992	† 1997
▲ 1981	▲ 1987	👓 1993	👓 1998
✕ 1982	♣ 1988	🎐 1994	★ 1999
➷ 1983	➷ 1989	△ 1995	🕐 2000
† 1984	♡ 1990	♡ 1996	➷ 2001
🦋 1985	⚓ 1991	UM Unmarked	

General Figurines

	Price Paid	Value
1.		
2.		
3.		
4.		
5.		
6.		
7.		
8.		
9.		
10.	22ᴰ	

Totals

7

Values ★ $35

Mom, You're A Royal Gem
Avon Figurine
#588083
Issued: 1999 • Closed: 1999
Retail Price: $30

8

Values 👓 $43
★ $40

Mom, You're My Special-tea (LE-1999)
#325473
Issued: 1999 • Closed: 1999
Retail Price: $25 – $30

9

Values 👓 $37
★ $35
🕐 $35
➷ $35

Mom, You've Given Me So Much
#488046
Issued: 1999 • Open
Retail Price: $35

(10)

Values ▲ $46
♣ $42
➷ $40
⚓ $37
⚓ $35
🎐 $32
🐚 $32
🎀 $30
△ $30
♡ $30
† $30
👓 $30
★ $30
🕐 $30
➷ $30

Mommy, I Love You
#109975
Issued: 1988 • Open
Retail Price: $22.50 – $30

1

Values ▲ $48
△ $42
⊕ $38
★ $36
⬧ $33
⬧ $31
⬱ $30
⬒ $30
♡ $30
† $30
⬅ $30
★ $30
⬧ $30
⬡ $30

Mommy, I Love You
#112143
Issued: 1988 • Open
Retail Price: $22.50 – $30

2

Values ⬅ $87
△ $80
♡ $76

Money's Not The Only Green Thing Worth Saving
#531073
Issued: 1995 • Retired: 1996
Retail Price: $50

3

Values ⬱ $48
★ $46
⬡ $46

Mornin' Pumpkin
#455687
Issued: 1998 • Retired: 1999
Retail Price: $45

4

Values ♡ $49
† $46

The Most Precious Gift Of All
Catalog Figurine
#183814
Issued: 1997 • Closed: 1997
Retail Price: $37.50 – $40

5

Values NM $90
▲ $70
I $50
⬅ $45
† $41
⬧ $41
⬱ $37
▲ $37
⬧ $37
⊕ $37
★ $37
⬧ $37
⬧ $37
⬱ $37
⬒ $37
♡ $37
† $37
⬅ $37
★ $37
⬡ $37
⬱ $37

Mother Sew Dear
#E3106
Issued: 1980 • Open
Retail Price: $13 – $35

6

Values ⬡ N/E

Mr. Fujioka
Special Event Figurine
#781851
Issued: 2000 • Closed: 2000
Retail Price: N/A

7

Values ⬧ $124
⊕ $112
⬧ $106
⬧ $100

Variation

My Days Are Blue Without You
#520802
Issued: 1989 • Susp.: 1991
Retail Price: $65 – $70
Variation: Girl smiling – $130

KEY			
NM Pre'81	⬚ 1986	⬧ 1992	† 1997
▲ 1981	▲ 1987	⬱ 1993	⬱ 1998
I 1982	⬧ 1988	⬱ 1994	★ 1999
⬅ 1983	⊕ 1989	△ 1995	⬡ 2000
† 1984	♡ 1990	♡ 1996	⬱ 2001
⬧ 1985	⬧ 1991	UM Unmarked	

8

Values ⬧ $80
⊕ $70
⬧ $68
⬧ $67
⬧ $64
⬱ $62
⬱ $62
▲ $61
♡ $61
† $61
⬱ $61
★ $61

My Heart Is Exposed With Love
#520624
Issued: 1989 • Retired: 1999
Retail Price: $45 – $60

1

Values ★ $37.50
⊙ $37.50
▲ $37.50

**My Life Is A Vacuum
Without You**
#587907
Issued: 1999 • Open
Retail Price: $37.50

2

Values △ $58
♡ $53
† $50
66 $50
★ $50
⊙ $50
▲ $50

My Love Blooms For You
#521728
Issued: 1996 • Open
Retail Price: $50

3

Values † $42
66 $40
★ $40
⊙ $40

**My Love Will Keep
You Warm**
Catalog Figurine
#272957
Issued: 1998 • Closed: 1998
Retail Price: $37.50

4

Values ♬ $63
▲ $57
✧ $50
Ð $47
⚓ $44
▲ $44
✦ $42
♋ $40
➡ $40
△ $40
♡ $40
† $40
66 $40
★ $40
⊙ $40
▲ $40

**My Love Will
Never Let You Go**
#103497
Issued: 1987 • Open
Retail Price: $25 – $40

5

Values ♡ $44
♬ $40
66 $40
★ $40
⊙ $40
▲ $40

My True Love Gave To Me
#529273
Issued: 1996 • Open
Retail Price: $40

6

Values 66 $48
★ $48

My Universe Is You
#487902
Issued: 1999 • Retired: 1999
Retail Price: $45

	KEY			
NM Pre'81	♬ 1986	✦ 1992	† 1997
▲ 1981	▲ 1987	♋ 1993	66 1998
✗ 1982	✧ 1988	➡ 1994	★ 1999
➡ 1983	Ð 1989	△ 1995	⊙ 2000
† 1984	⚓ 1990	♡ 1996	▲ 2001
✦ 1985	▲ 1991	UM Unmarked	

General Figurines

	Price Paid	Value
1.		
2.		
3.		
4.		
5.		
6.		
7.		
8.		
9.		

Totals

7

Values ✦ $112
✦ $107
♋ $102
➡ $98
△ $95
♡ $95

**My Warmest Thoughts
Are You**
#524085
Issued: 1992 • Retired: 1996
Retail Price: $55 – $60

8

Values ▲ $102
Ð $83
✧ $78
⚓ $76
⚓ $74
✦ $74
➡ $72
△ $70
♡ $70
† $70
66 $70
★ $70
⊙ $70
▲ $70

No Tears Past The Gate
#101826
Issued: 1987 • Open
Retail Price: $40 – $70

9

Variation

Values ✗ $93
⚓ $85
† $82
➡ $79
♬ $77
▲ $73
✧ $70
Ð $68
⚓ $65

Nobody's Perfect
#E9268
Issued: 1983 • Retired: 1990
Retail Price: $21 – $30
Variation: Boy smiling – $557

1

Values 🐚 $45
�"—" $38
♡ $35
✝ $35
★ $35
⏾ $35
🐚 $35

Nothing Can Dampen The Spirit Of Caring
The Good Samaritan Series
#603864
Issued: 1994 • Open
Retail Price: $35

2

Values ❖ $58
✿ $48
♠ $45
♣ $43
☘ $42
🐚 $40
�"—" $37.50
△ $37.50
♡ $37.50
✝ $37.50
❀ $37.50
★ $37.50
⏾ $37.50
🐚 $37.50

November
Calendar Girl Series
#110108
Issued: 1988 • Open
Retail Price: $32.50 – $37.50

3

Values ◀ $58
♣ $49
♡ $46

Now I Lay Me Down To Sleep
#522058
Issued: 1994 • Retired: 1997
Retail Price: $30 – $35

4

Values ✗ $108
▲ $92
✝ $86
❧ $82
♫ $78

O Come All Ye Faithful
#E2353
Issued: 1982 • Retired: 1986
Retail Price: $27.50 – $30

5 New

Values ⏾ $50
🐚 $50

O-Fish-Aly Friends For A Lifetime
#795305
Issued: 2001 • Open
Retail Price: $50

6

Values NM $157
▲ $137
✗ $114
�" $102
✝ $95

O, How I Love Jesus
#E1380B
Issued: 1979 • Retired: 1984
Retail Price: $8 – $19

7

Values ❧ $58
♫ $52
▲ $48
❖ $45
✿ $44
✦ $42
♦ $42
☘ $40
🐚 $40
�"—" $40
△ $40
♡ $40
✝ $40
❀ $40
★ $40
⏾ $40
🐚 $40

O Worship The Lord
#100064
Issued: 1986 • Open
Retail Price: $24 – $40

8

Values ❧ $55
♫ $48
▲ $48
❖ $44
✿ $44
✦ $42
♦ $42
☘ $40
🐚 $40
�"—" $40
△ $40
♡ $40
✝ $40
❀ $40
★ $40
⏾ $40
🐚 $40

O Worship The Lord
#102229
Issued: 1986 • Open
Retail Price: $24 – $40

General Figurines

	Price Paid	Value
1.		
2.		
3.		
4.		
5.		
6.		
7.		
8.		
9.		
10.		

Totals

9

Values ❖ $60
✿ $55
✦ $48
♦ $46
☘ $45
🐚 $45
�"—" $45
△ $45
♡ $45
✝ $45
❀ $45
★ $45
⏾ $45
🐚 $45

October
Calendar Girl Series
#110094
Issued: 1988 • Open
Retail Price: $35 – $45

10

Values ▲ $135
❖ $124
✦ $120
✦ $118
♦ $114
☘ $112
🐚 $112
�"—" $112
△ $112
♡ $112
✝ $112
❀ $112

Oh What Fun It Is To Ride
#109819
Issued: 1987 • Retired: 1998
Retail Price: $85 – $110

1
New

Values 📷 $30

Photo
Unavailable

On A Scale From 1 To 10
You Are The Deerest
#878944
Issued: 2001 • Open
Retail Price: $30

2

Values ♡ $52
† $47
6ð $45
★ $45
🕙 $45
🔮 $45

On My Way To A
Perfect Day
#522872
Issued: 1997 • Open
Retail Price: $45

3

Values 6ð $17.50
★ $17.50
🕙 $17.50
🔮 $17.50

On Our Way To A
Special Day
#481602
Issued: 1999 • Open
Retail Price: $17.50

4

Values 6ð $17.50
★ $17.50
🕙 $17.50
🔮 $17.50

On Our Way To A
Special Day
#481610
Issued: 1999 • Open
Retail Price: $17.50

5

Values † $37
6ð $35
★ $35
🕙 $35
🔮 $35

Only One Life To Offer
#325309
Issued: 1998 • Open
Retail Price: $35

6

Values ⬸ $68
† $52
♪ $50
ℱ $47
▲ $45
❖ $43
ᛞ $43
↓ $43
♦ $40
♪ $40
♋ $40
⊐ $40
△ $40
♦ $40
† $40
6ð $40
★ $40
🕙 $40
🔮 $40
UM $150

Onward Christian
Soldiers
#E0523
Issued: 1983 • Open
Retail Price: $24 – $40

General Figurines

	Price Paid	Value
1.		
2.		
3.		
4.		
5.		
6.		
7.		
8.		

Totals

7

Values ℤ $105
♦ $95
† $90
⬸ $82

Our First
Christmas Together
#E2377
Issued: 1982 • Susp.: 1985
Retail Price: $35 – $37.50

8

Values ❖ $88
ᛞ $76
↓ $75
♦ $75

Our First
Christmas Together
#115290
Issued: 1988 • Susp.: 1991
Retail Price: $50 – $60

1

Values 🐚 $82
          ⚘ $75
          ⇥ $73
          ♡ $70
          ✦ $70
          ✦ $70
          ✦ $70
          ★ $70

Our Friendship Is
Soda-licious
#524336
Issued: 1993 • Retired: 1999
Retail Price: $65 – $70

2

New

Photo
Unavailable

Our Friendship Was
Made To Order
#879134
Issued: 2001 • Open
Retail Price: $35

Values 🐚 $35

3

Values 6∂ N/E

Our Future Is Looking
Much Brighter
PRECIOUS MOMENTS
Collection 20th Anniversary
Cruise Figurine
#325511
Issued: 1998 • Closed: 1998
Retail Price: N/A

4

Values ○ $50
          🐚 $50

Our Love Will Never
Be Endangered (LE-5,000)
Reef Hallmark Exclusive
#824119S
Issued: 2000 • Open
Retail Price: $50

5

Values ✝ $95
          ▲ $89
          ⅍ $85
          ▲ $83
          ✤ $78
          ⊕ $73

Part Of Me Wants
To Be Good
#12149
Issued: 1985 • Susp.: 1989
Retail Price: $19 – $25

6

Values NM $112
          ▲ $93
          I $87
          ↞ $85
          ✝ $80

Peace Amid The Storm
#E4723
Issued: 1981 • Susp.: 1984
Retail Price: $22.50 – $27.50

7

Values ○ $125
          🐚 $125

Peace In The Valley
(LE-12,500)
#649929
Issued: 2000 • Open
Retail Price: $125

8

Values NM $160
          ▲ $150
          I $140
          ↞ $136
          ✝ $130

Peace On Earth
#E2804
Issued: 1980 • Susp.: 1984
Retail Price: $20 – $27.50

KEY						
NM Pre'81	⅍ 1986	♪ 1992	✝ 1997
▲ 1981	▲ 1987	♋ 1993	6∂ 1998
I 1982	✤ 1988	⟼ 1994	★ 1999
↞ 1983	⊕ 1989	⚘ 1995	○ 2000
✝ 1984	↓ 1990	♡ 1996	🐚 2001
✦ 1985	♦ 1991	UM Unmarked	

General Figurines

	Price Paid	Value
1.		
2.		
3.		
4.		
5.		
6.		
7.		
8.		
9.		
10.		

Totals

9

Values ○ $57

Peace On Earth (LE-1999)
#E2804R
Issued: 1999 • Closed: 1999
Retail Price: $50

10

Values NM $112
          ▲ $88
          I $80
          ↞ $75
          ✝ $73

Peace On Earth
#E4725
Issued: 1981 • Susp.: 1984
Retail Price: $25 – $30

1

Values 🦋 $200
🕊 $190
🦚 $182
🎵 $175

Peace On Earth
#E9287
Issued: 1983 • Susp.: 1986
Retail Price: $37.50

2

Values † $72

The Pearl Of Great Price
(LE-1997)
Century Circle Figurine
#526061
Issued: 1997 • Closed: 1997
Retail Price: $50

3

Values 🦚 $37
★ $35
🕐 $35
🔔 $35

Peas On Earth
#455768
Issued: 1998 • Open
Retail Price: $35

4

Values ⚓ $85
† $80
🕊 $72
🦋 $66
🎵 $60

The Perfect Grandpa
#E7160
Issued: 1982 • Susp.: 1986
Retail Price: $25 – $27.50

5

Values 🦋 $63
🔺 $59
♡ $57
🔔 $57
🦚 $57
★ $57

Perfect Harmony
#521914
Issued: 1994 • Retired: 1999
Retail Price: $55

6

Values † $56
🦚 $56
★ $56
🕐 $55
🔔 $55

Pizza On Earth
#521884
Issued: 1997 • Open
Retail Price: $55

7

Values 🦋 $46
🔺 $40
♡ $37
† $37
🦚 $37

A Poppy For You
#604208
Issued: 1995 • Susp.: 1998
Retail Price: $35

8

Values ♡ $32
† $25
★ $25
🕐 $25
🔔 $25

Potty Time
#531022
Issued: 1997 • Open
Retail Price: $25

General Figurines

	Price Paid	Value
1.		
2.		
3.		
4.		
5.		
6.		
7.		
8.		
9.		
10.		

Totals

9

Values 🦚 $40
★ $40
🕐 $40
🔔 $40

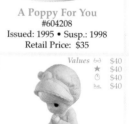

Praise God From Whom
All Blessings Flow
#455695
Issued: 1998 • Open
Retail Price: $40

10

Values 🦚 $50
★ $50
🕐 $50
🔔 $50

Praise The Lord And
Dosie-Do
#455733
Issued: 1998 • Open
Retail Price: $50

1

Values NM $115
▲ $100
Ⅱ $78

Praise The Lord Anyhow
#E1374B
Issued: 1979 • Retired: 1982
Retail Price: $8 – $17

2

Values Ⅱ $126
✝ $98
✝ $95
✐ $90
⚓ $90
▲ $85
⚓ $85
⚓ $83
★ $82
⚪ $80
⚪ $72
♋ $70
♋ $65

Praise The Lord Anyhow
#E9254
Issued: 1983 • Retired: 1994
Retail Price: $35 – $55

3

Values NM $240
▲ $175
⚓ $163
⚓ $155
✝ $150

Prayer Changes Things
#E1375B
Issued: 1979 • Susp.: 1984
Retail Price: $11 – $22.50

4

Values NM $180
✝ $160
Ⅱ $125
⚓ $110
✝ $105
⚓ $102

Variation

Photo Unavailable

Prayer Changes Things
#E5214
Issued: 1981 • Susp.: 1984
Retail Price: $35 – $37.50
Variation: "Holy Bible" on back cover – NM – $184 ▲ – $160

5

Values ⚓ $137
✐ $85
⚓ $80
⚓ $80
▲ $77
⚓ $75
⚓ $75
★ $73
⚪ $70
⚪ $70
♋ $68
♋ $68
⚓ $66
⚓ $66
✝ $66
⚓ $66
★ $66

Precious Memories
#E2828
Issued: 1984 • Retired: 1999
Retail Price: $45 – $65

6

Values ⚓ $79
⚓ $64
⚓ $60
★ $57
⚪ $55
⚪ $55
♋ $55
⚓ $55
⚓ $55
♡ $55
✝ $55
⚓ $55
★ $55
⚪ $55
⚓ $55
⚓ $55

Precious Memories
#106763
Issued: 1988 • Open
Retail Price: $37.50 – $55

7

Values ⚓ $78
♡ $73
✝ $70
⚓ $70
★ $70
⚪ $70
⚓ $70

**Precious Moments
To Remember**
#163848
Issued: 1996 • Open
Retail Price: $70

General Figurines

	Price Paid	Value
1.		
2.		
3.		
4.		
5.		
6.		
7.		
8.		
9.		

Totals

8

Values ★ $40

**Precious Moments Will
Last Forever**
Special Event Figurine
#681008
Issued: 1999 • Closed: 1999
Retail Price: $35

9

Values Ⅱ $107
⚓ $85
✝ $80
⚓ $76
⚓ $73
⚓ $71
⚓ $71
✝ $67
⚓ $67
★ $67
⚪ $65
♋ $65
⚓ $65
⚓ $65
♡ $65
✝ $65
⚓ $65
★ $65

Press On
#E9265
Issued: 1983 • Retired: 1999
Retail Price: $40 – $65

1

Values ⟨symbol⟩ $44
♡ $38
† $35
∞ $35
★ $35
◐ $35
≈ $35

Pretty As A Princess
#526053
Issued: 1996 • Open
Retail Price: $35

2

Values ⟨symbol⟩ $44
♡ $38
† $38
∞ $38
★ $38
◐ $38

A Prince Of A Guy
#526037
Issued: 1996 • Retired: 2000
Retail Price: $35

3

Values ⟨symbol⟩ $32
⟨symbol⟩ $27
⟨symbol⟩ $25
⟨symbol⟩ $25
⟨symbol⟩ $22
⟨symbol⟩ $22
⟨symbol⟩ $22
⟨symbol⟩ $22
♡ $20
† $20
∞ $20
★ $20

Puppy Love
#520764
Issued: 1989 • Retired: 1999
Retail Price: $12.50 – $17.50

4

Values ▲ $100
⟨symbol⟩ $94
⟨symbol⟩ $90
⟨symbol⟩ $88
⟨symbol⟩ $86
⟨symbol⟩ $86
⟨symbol⟩ $83
⟨symbol⟩ $80
⟨symbol⟩ $80

Puppy Love Is From Above
#106798
Issued: 1988 • Retired: 1995
Retail Price: $45 – $55

5

Values ★ $29

Purr-fect Friends
Catalog Figurine
#488364
Issued: 1999 • Closed: 1999
Retail Price: $25

6

Values NM $83
▲ $73
Ⅱ $48
⟨symbol⟩ $45
† $42
⟨symbol⟩ $40
⟨symbol⟩ $38
▲ $38
⟨symbol⟩ $38
⟨symbol⟩ $38
⟨symbol⟩ $38
⟨symbol⟩ $38
⟨symbol⟩ $38
⟨symbol⟩ $35
⟨symbol⟩ $35
♡ $35
† $35
∞ $35
★ $35
◐ $35
≈ $35

The Purr-fect Grandma
#E3109
Issued: 1980 • Open
Retail Price: $13 – $35

General Figurines

	Price Paid	Value
1.		
2.		
3.		
4.		
5.		
6.		
7.		
8.		
9.		
10.		

Totals

7

Values ◐ $35
≈ $35

Raisin' Cane On The Holidays
#730130
Issued: 2000 • Open
Retail Price: $35

8

Values ◐ N/E

Ready In The Nick Of Time (LE-1,500)
Special Event Figurine
#804088
Issued: 2000 • Closed: 2000
Retail Price: N/A

9

Values ⟨symbol⟩ $70
⟨symbol⟩ $65
⟨symbol⟩ $60
⟨symbol⟩ $56
⟨symbol⟩ $54
⟨symbol⟩ $52
♡ $52
† $51
∞ $51
★ $51

A Reflection Of His Love
#522279
Issued: 1991 • Retired: 1999
Retail Price: $50

10

Values NM $110
▲ $82
Ⅱ $75
⟨symbol⟩ $72
† $68
⟨symbol⟩ $65
⟨symbol⟩ $65
▲ $62
⟨symbol⟩ $60
⟨symbol⟩ $57
⟨symbol⟩ $57
⟨symbol⟩ $57
⟨symbol⟩ $55
⟨symbol⟩ $55
⟨symbol⟩ $55
♡ $55
† $55
∞ $55
★ $55
◐ $55
⟨symbol⟩ $55

Rejoicing With You
#E4724
Issued: 1981 • Open
Retail Price: $25 – $55

1

Values ○ $30
⌂ $30

Repunt Or Else
#729620
Issued: 2000 • Open
Retail Price: $30

2

Values ✝ $35
🕊 $30
♫ $27
▲ $25
✤ $23
⊕ $21
☆ $21
● $20
♨ $20
♀♀ $18.50
━ $18.50
△ $18.50
♡ $18.50
✝ $18.50
6∂ $18.50
★ $18.50
○ $18.50
⌂ $18.50

Ring Bearer
Bridal Party Series
#E2833
Issued: 1985 • Open
Retail Price: $11 – $18.50

3

Values 💰 $175
♀♀ $160
━ $155
△ $140
♡ $135

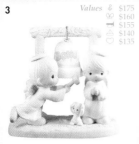

Ring Those Christmas Bells
#525898
Issued: 1992 • Retired: 1996
Retail Price: $95 – $100

4

Values △ $35

New

Photo Unavailable

Roll Away, Roll Away,
Roll Away
#879002
Issued: 2001 • Open
Retail Price: $35

5

Values ★ $45
○ $45
⌂ $45

RV Haven' Fun Or What
#587915
Issued: 1999 • Open
Retail Price: $45

6

Values 💰 $40
♀♀ $36
━ $34
△ $32.50
♡ $32.50
✝ $32.50
6∂ $32.50
★ $32.50
○ $32.50
⌂ $32.50

Safe In The Arms Of Jesus
Child Evangelism
Fellowship Figurine
#521922
Issued: 1993 • Open
Retail Price: $30 – $32.50

7

Values ━ $550
6∂ $550
★ $550
○ $550
⌂ $550

Sailabration Cruise (LE-1995)
PRECIOUS MOMENTS
Collectors' Club 15th
Anniversary Cruise Figurine
#150061
Issued: 1995 • Closed: 1995
Retail Price: N/A

8

Values ♡ $60
6∂ $60
★ $60
○ $60
⌂ $60

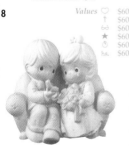

Say I Do
#261149
Issued: 1997 • Open
Retail Price: $55 – $60

9

Values ♫ $85
▲ $80
✤ $75
⊕ $66
☆ $60
● $58

Scent From Above
#100528
Issued: 1987 • Retired: 1991
Retail Price: $19 – $27.50

KEY			
NM Pre '81	♫ 1986	💰 1992	✝ 1997
▲ 1981	▲ 1987	♀♀ 1993	6∂ 1998
✖ 1982	✤ 1988	━ 1994	★ 1999
━ 1983	⊕ 1989	△ 1995	○ 2000
✝ 1984	☆ 1990	♡ 1996	⌂ 2001
● 1985	● 1991	UM Unmarked	

General Figurines

	Price Paid	Value
1.		
2.		
3.		
4.		
5.		
6.		
7.		
8.		
9.		

Totals

1

Variation

Photo Unavailable

Values ○ $40

Scoopin' Up Some Love
Century Circle Figurine
#635049
Issued: 2000 • Closed: 2000
Retail Price: $35
Variation: With rainbow sherbert – N/E

2

Values ★ $25
○ $25
🔈 $25

Scootin' Your Way To A Perfect Day
Care-A-Van Exclusive
#634999
Issued: 1999 • Open
Retail Price: $25

3

Values 🐚 $95
🎵 $90
🔈 $86
🔺 $82
♡ $77

Sealed With A Kiss
#524441
Issued: 1993 • Retired: 1996
Retail Price: $50 – $60

4

Values 🐚 $52
✝ $48
🌿 $46
🎵 $42

Seek Ye The Lord
#E9261
Issued: 1983 • Susp.: 1986
Retail Price: $21

5

Values 🐚 $77
✝ $68
🌿 $65
🎵 $58

Seek Ye The Lord
#E9262
Issued: 1983 • Susp.: 1986
Retail Price: $21

General Figurines

	Price Paid	Value
1.		
2.		
3.		
4.		
5.		
6.		
7.		
8.		
9.		
Totals		

6

Values 🐚 $77
🎵 $70
▲ $68
✤ $65
⅁ $65
↓ $63
◑ $62

Sending My Love
#100056
Issued: 1986 • Susp.: 1991
Retail Price: $22.50 – $32.50

7

Values 🐚 $64
🔺 $58

Sending My Love Your Way (LE-1995)
Catalog Figurine
#528609
Issued: 1995 • Closed: 1995
Retail Price: $40

8

Values 🐚 $112
✝ $98
🦋 $95
🎵 $90

Sending You A Rainbow
#E9288
Issued: 1983 • Susp.: 1986
Retail Price: $22.50

9

Values ▲ $72
✤ $58
⅁ $55
↓ $52
◑ $50
🐚 $48
♈ $46
🔈 $46
🔺 $46
♡ $46
✝ $46
🔈 $46
★ $46
○ $46

Sending You My Love
#109967
Issued: 1988 • Retired: 2000
Retail Price: $35 – $45

1

Values $67
$50
$46

Sending You Oceans Of Love
#532010
Issued: 1995 • Retired: 1996
Retail Price: $35 – $37.50

2

Values $92
$82
$75
$72
$68

Sending You Showers Of Blessings
#520683
Issued: 1989 • Retired: 1992
Retail Price: $32.50 – $35

3

Values $55
$48
$42
$40
$40
$37.50
$37.50
$37.50
$37.50
$37.50
$37.50
$37.50
$37.50

September
Calendar Girl Series
#110086
Issued: 1988 • Open
Retail Price: $27.50 – $37.50

4

Values $43
$40
$39
$37.50
$37.50
$37.50
$37.50
$37.50
$37.50

Serenity Prayer Boy
#530700
Issued: 1994 • Open
Retail Price: $35 – $37.50

5

Values $45
$40
$40
$37.50
$37.50
$37.50
$37.50
$37.50
$37.50

Serenity Prayer Girl
#530697
Issued: 1994 • Open
Retail Price: $35 – $37.50

6

Values $84
$77
$72
$67
$67
$62

Serving The Lord
#100161
Issued: 1986 • Susp.: 1990
Retail Price: $19 – $27.50

7

Values $67
$60
$54
$50
$47
$44

Serving The Lord
#100293
Issued: 1986 • Susp.: 1990
Retail Price: $19 – $27.50

8

Values $99
$94
$91
$88
$88
$86
$84
$82
$80
$76

Sew In Love
#106844
Issued: 1988 • Retired: 1997
Retail Price: $45 – $55

KEY					
NM Pre'81		1986		1992	† 1997
▲ 1981	▲	1987	♈	1993	6∂ 1998
✕ 1982	✢	1988	➡	1994	★ 1999
➡ 1983	ⅅ	1989	⚖	1995	☾ 2000
† 1984	▲	1990	♡	1996	☇ 2001
✦ 1985	●	1991	**UM** Unmarked		

	Price Paid	Value
1.		
2.		
3.		
4.		
5.		
6.		
7.		
8.		
9.		
10.		

9

Values $82
$50

Sharing Begins In The Heart (LE-1989)
Special Event Figurine
#520861
Issued: 1989 • Closed: 1989
Retail Price: $25

10

Values $95
$88
$82

Sharing Our Christmas Together
#102490
Issued: 1986 • Susp.: 1988
Retail Price: $37 – $45

Totals

1

Values † $35
⚮ $35
★ $35
◷ $35
⚱ $35

Sharing Our
Christmas Together
#531944
Issued: 1997 • Open
Retail Price: $35

2

Values ♫ $70
♠ $65
⬧ $63
⊕ $57
⚱ $55
⚱ $52

Sharing Our Joy Together
#E2834
Issued: 1986 • Susp.: 1991
Retail Price: $31 – $40

3

Values ➴ $170
† $155
⬧ $148
♫ $140

Sharing Our
Season Together
#E0501
Issued: 1983 • Susp.: 1986
Retail Price: $50

4

Values ★ $123

Sharing Our Time Is So
Precious (LE-15,000)
Century Circle Figurine
#456349
Issued: 1999 • Closed: 1999
Retail Price: $110

5

Values ★ $80

Sharing Our Winter
Wonderland (LE-1999)
#539988
Issued: 1999 • Closed: 1999
Retail Price: $75

6

Values ♋ $55
⬧ $48
⬧ $47
♡ $47
† $47
⚮ $47
★ $47

Sharing Sweet
Moments Together
#526487
Issued: 1994 • Retired: 1999
Retail Price: $45

KEY			
NM Pre'81	♫ 1986	⚘ 1992	† 1997
▲ 1981	♠ 1987	♋ 1993	⚮ 1998
✠ 1982	⬧ 1988	➴ 1994	★ 1999
➴ 1983	⊕ 1989	⬧ 1995	◷ 2000
† 1984	⚱ 1990	♡ 1996	⚱ 2001
⬧ 1985	⚱ 1991	�] UM Unmarked	

General Figurines

	Price Paid	Value
1.		
2.		
3.		
4.		
5.		
6.		
7.		
8.		
9.		
10.		

Totals

7

Values ◷ $20
⚮ $20

Sharing Sweet
Moments Together
#731579
Issued: 2000 • Open
Retail Price: $20

8

Values ⬧ $80
♡ $74
† $70
⚮ $70
★ $70
◷ $70
⚱ $70

Sharing The Gift Of 40
Precious Years
#163821
Issued: 1996 • Open
Retail Price: $70

9

Values † $35
⚮ $35
★ $35
◷ $35
⚱ $35

Sharing The Light Of Love
#272531
Issued: 1997 • Open
Retail Price: $35

10

Values ⚮ $20
★ $20
◷ $20
⚱ $20

Shiny New And Ready
For School
#481637
Issued: 1999 • Open
Retail Price: $20

1

Values ⚭ $20
★ $20
⊙ $20
🐚 $20

**Shiny New And Ready
For School**
#481629
Issued: 1999 • Open
Retail Price: $20

2

Values ♡ $69
† $67

**Shoot For The Stars You'll
Never Strike Out**
*Boys & Girls Clubs Of America
Commemorative Figurine*
#521701
Issued: 1996 • Closed: 1996
Retail Price: $60

3

Values △ $78
♡ $74
† $70
⚭ $70
★ $70
⊙ $70
🐚 $70

**A Silver Celebration
To Share**
#163813
Issued: 1996 • Open
Retail Price: $70

4

Values ▲ $70
❖ $62
⊕ $58
⚓ $55
● $50

Sitting Pretty
#104825
Issued: 1987 • Susp.: 1990
Retail Price: $22.50 – $30

5

Values ♪ $205
▲ $190
❖ $170
⊕ $158
⚓ $145
● $140

Smile Along The Way
#101842
Issued: 1987 • Retired: 1991
Retail Price: $30 – $45

6

Values NM $114
▲ $86
Ⅱ $73
⇔ $70
† $55

Smile, God Loves You
#E1373B
Issued: 1979 • Retired: 1984
Retail Price: $7 – $17

7

Values ★ $55
⊙ $55
🐚 $55

Snow Man Like My Man
#587877
Issued: 1999 • Open
Retail Price: $55

8

Values ♡ $22
† $18.50
⚭ $18.50
★ $18.50
⊙ $18.50
🐚 $18.50

**Snowbunny Loves
You Like I Do**
#183792
Issued: 1996 • Open
Retail Price: $18.50

KEY							
NM Pre'81	♪ 1986		✦ 1992		† 1997		
▲ 1981	▲ 1987		℘ 1993		⚭ 1998		
Ⅱ 1982	❖ 1988		⊟ 1994		★ 1999		
⇔ 1983	⊕ 1989		△ 1995		⊙ 2000		
† 1984	⚓ 1990		♡ 1996		🐚 2001		
✦ 1985	● 1991		UM Unmarked				

General Figurines

	Price Paid	Value
1.		
2.		
3.		
4.		
5.		
6.		
7.		
8.		
9.		
10.		

Totals

9

Values ℘ $58
⇔ $50

**So Glad I Picked You As A
Friend (LE-1994)**
Catalog Figurine
#524379
Issued: 1994 • Closed: 1994
Retail Price: $40

10

Values ♡ $40
† $40
⚭ $40
★ $40
⊙ $40
🐚 $40

**Some Plant, Some Water, But
God Giveth The Increase**
*Growing In God's
Garden Of Love Series*
#176958
♦ Issued: 1996 • Open
Retail Price: $37.50 – $40

1

Values �*/* $88
🕇 $82
⚓ $82
⚑ $79
⚓ $73

Someday My Love
#520799
Issued: 1989 • Retired: 1992
Retail Price: $40 – $45

2

Values ♡ $57
🕇 $55
🔆 $55
★ $55
🌕 $55
🔔 $55

Something Precious
From Above
#524360
Issued: 1997 • Open
Retail Price: $50 – $55

3

Values 🌿 $87
🕇 $82
⚓ $77
⚑ $72

Something's Missing When
You're Not Around
#105643
Issued: 1988 • Susp.: 1991
Retail Price: $32.50 – $37.50

4

Values ♡ $55
🕇 $50
🕇 $50
★ $50
🌕 $50
🔔 $50

Sometimes You're Next
To Impossible
#530964
Issued: 1997 • Open
Retail Price: $50

5

Values 🔺 $42
♡ $38
🕇 $37
🔆 $37
★ $37

Soot Yourself To A
Merry Christmas
#150096
Issued: 1995 • Retired: 1999
Retail Price: $35

6

Values 🔺 $45
♡ $40
🕇 $37.50
🔆 $37.50
★ $37.50
🌕 $37.50
🔔 $37.50

Sowing Seeds Of Kindness
*Growing In God's
Garden Of Love Series*
#163856
Issued: 1996 • Open
Retail Price: $37.50

KEY					
NM Pre'81	♪ 1986	⚓ 1992	🕇 1997		
▲ 1981	▲ 1987	⚯ 1993	🔆 1998		
✕ 1982	⚜ 1988	🌱 1994	★ 1999		
✦ 1983	Ð 1989	🔺 1995	🌕 2000		
✝ 1984	⚑ 1990	♡ 1996	🔔 2001		
✦ 1985	⚓ 1991	UM Unmarked			

General Figurines

	Price Paid	Value
1.		
2.		
3.		
4.		
5.		
6.		
7.		
8.		
9.		
10.		
Totals		

7

Values ⚯ $54
🌱 $50
🔺 $46
♡ $46

A Special Chime For Jesus
#524468
Issued: 1993 • Retired: 1997
Retail Price: $32.50 – $35

8

Values ⚓ $42
⚑ $40
⚯ $35
🌱 $33
🔺 $33
♡ $32.50
🕇 $32.50
🔆 $32.50
★ $32.50
🌕 $32.50
🔔 $32.50

A Special Delivery
#521493
Issued: 1991 • Open
Retail Price: $30 – $32.50

9

Values ▲ $90
⚜ $85
Ð $80
⚓ $75
⚓ $70

The Spirit Is Willing, But
The Flesh Is Weak
#100196
Issued: 1987 • Retired: 1991
Retail Price: $19 – $30

10

Values 🌕 $45
🔔 $45

Squeaky Clean
Century Circle Exclusive
#731048
Issued: 2000 • Open
Retail Price: $45

1

Values ⛪ $47
♡ $40

Standing In The Presence
Of The Lord (Dated 1996)
The Dated Cross Series
#163732
Issued: 1996 • Closed: 1996
Retail Price: $37.50

2

New

Values 🔖 $100

Photo Unavailable

Starsmith (set/3)
Heavenly Daze Series
#879586
Issued: 2001 • Open
Retail Price: $100

3

Values 🐟 $67
🌿 $60
▲ $58
✤ $58
⊹ $56
⊥ $56
● $51
⚓ $51

The Story Of God's Love
Family Christmas Series
#15784
Issued: 1985 • Susp.: 1992
Retail Price: $22.50 – $35

4

Values ✝ $112
🔖 $100

Summer's Joy (LE-1985)
The Four Seasons Figurine Series
#12076
Issued: 1985 • Closed: 1985
Retail Price: $30

5

Values ⛪ $44
♡ $42
✝ $40
👓 $40
★ $40

The Sun Is Always
Shining Somewhere
#163775
Issued: 1996 • Retired: 1999
Retail Price: $37.50

6

Values ◐ $37.50
🔖 $37.50

Sure Could Use Less
Hustle And Bustle
#737550
Issued: 2000 • Open
Retail Price: $37.50

7

Values 🐟 $89
✝ $85
🌿 $82
🔖 $80
♣ $75
✤ $75
⊹ $72

Surrounded With Joy
#E0506
Issued: 1983 • Retired: 1989
Retail Price: $21 – $27.50

8

Values ⊕ $135
⊥ $88
● $78
⚓ $65
♀ $60
⬛ $60
△ $55
♡ $55

Sweep All Your
Worries Away
#521779
Issued: 1990 • Retired: 1996
Retail Price: $40

KEY			
NM Pre'81	🌿 1986	♣ 1992	✝ 1997
▲ 1981	▲ 1987	♀ 1993	👓 1998
▮ 1982	✤ 1988	⬛ 1994	★ 1999
◀ 1983	⊕ 1989	△ 1995	◐ 2000
✝ 1984	● 1991	♡ 1996	🔖 2001
🔖 1985	⚓ 1991	⸀M Unmarked	

General Figurines

	Price Paid	Value
1.		
2.		
3.		
4.		
5.		
6.		
7.		
8.		
9.		
10.		

Totals

9

Values ♡ $72
✝ $65
👓 $63

Sweeter As The Years
Go By
#522333
Issued: 1996 • Retired: 1998
Retail Price: $60

10

Values ● $82
⚓ $77
♀ $73
$67

Take Heed When You Stand
#521272
Issued: 1991 • Susp.: 1994
Retail Price: $55

1 Values ⌂ $38 / ♡ $33 / † $30 / 👁 $30 / ★ $30 / ☉ $30 / ≈ $30

Take It To The Lord
In Prayer
#163767
Issued: 1996 • Open
Retail Price: $30

2 New Values ☉ $32.50 / ≈ $32.50

Take Thyme For Yourself
#731064
Issued: 2001 • Open
Retail Price: $32.50

3 Values ★ $43

Take Time To Smell The
Roses (LE-1999)
Carlton Cards Exclusive
#634980C
Issued: 1999 • Closed: 1999
Retail Price: $35

4 Values ⌐ $83 / † $77 / ⚓ $73 / ⚘ $70

Taste And See That The
Lord Is Good
#E9274
Issued: 1983 • Retired: 1986
Retail Price: $22.50

5 Values ⚘ $63 / ⚓ $50 / ▲ $47 / ⚖ $43 / ⚲ $42 / ⌂ $40 / ♡ $40 / † $40 / 👁 $40 / ★ $40 / ☉ $40 / ≈ $40

Tell It To Jesus
#521477
Issued: 1989 • Open
Retail Price: $35 – $40

6 Values ⚘ $42 / ⚘ $36 / ▲ $36 / ⚓ $33 / ⚲ $32 / ⚖ $32 / ⚓ $28 / ⚖ $26

Tell Me A Story
Family Christmas Series
#15792
Issued: 1985 • Susp.: 1992
Retail Price: $10 – $15

KEY					
NM Pre'81	⚘ 1986	⚖ 1992	† 1997		
▲ 1981	▲ 1987	⚲ 1993	👁 1998		
⚊ 1982	⚓ 1988	⚊ 1994	★ 1999		
⚊ 1983	⚲ 1989	⌂ 1995	☉ 2000		
† 1984	⚓ 1990	♡ 1996	≈ 2001		
⚘ 1985	⚓ 1991	∪M Unmarked			

General Figurines

	Price Paid	Value
1.		
2.	32 50	
3.		
4.		
5.		
6.		
7.		
8.		
9.		
10.		

Totals

7 Values ⚊ $126 / ⚊ $110 / † $104 / ⚘ $97

Tell Me The Story Of Jesus
#E2349
Issued: 1983 • Susp.: 1985
Retail Price: $30 – $33

8 Values ⌂ $79 / ♡ $73 / † $70 / 👁 $70 / ★ $70 / ☉ $70 / ≈ $70

Ten Years Heart To Heart
#163805
Issued: 1996 • Open
Retail Price: $70

9 Values NM $165 / ▲ $142 / ⚊ $127 / ⚊ $120 / † $113

Thank You For Coming
To My Ade
#E5202
Issued: 1981 • Susp.: 1984
Retail Price: $22.50 – $30

10 Values ⚲ $100 / ⚓ $90 / ⚓ $87 / ⚖ $84 / ⚲ $84

Thank You, Lord,
For Everything
#522031
Issued: 1989 • Susp.: 1993
Retail Price: $60

1

Values ★ $25
🕐 $25
🐚 $25

Thank You Sew Much
#587923
Issued: 1999 • Open
Retail Price: $25

2

Values ▮ $65
🐚 $52
✝ $48

Thanking Him For You
#E7155
Issued: 1982 • Susp.: 1984
Retail Price: $16 – $17

3

Values ★ $65
🔥 $58
🐚 $58
🎯 $54
🗝 $52
⚖ $52
♡ $52
✝ $51
👓 $51
★ $51
🕐 $51

That's What Friends Are For
#521183
Issued: 1990 • Retired: 2000
Retail Price: $45 – $50

4

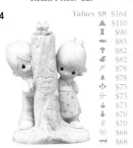

Values NM $164
▲ $110
▮ $90
🐚 $85
✝ $82
🎯 $82
🎵 $78
🔥 $78
✤ $75
🕊 $73
🕐 $73
🔥 $70
$ $70
🎯 $68
🗝 $68

Thee I Love
#E3116
Issued: 1980 • Retired: 1994
Retail Price: $16.50 – $40

5

Values ✝ $18
👓 $15
★ $15
🕐 $15
🐚 $15

There Are Two Sides
To Every Story
#325368
Issued: 1998 • Open
Retail Price: $15

6

Values ▮ $74
🐚 $63
✝ $60
🔥 $56
🎵 $54

There Is Joy In Serving Jesus
#E7157
Issued: 1982 • Retired: 1986
Retail Price: $17 – $19

7

Values $ $44
🎯 $37
🗝 $33
△ $32
♡ $32
✝ $32
👓 $32

There Is No Greater
Treasure Than To Have
A Friend Like You
#521000
Issued: 1993 • Retired: 1998
Retail Price: $30

8

Values 🕊 $86
🔥 $80
🔥 $76
$ $76
🎯 $73
🗝 $72
△ $72
♡ $72
✝ $72
🕐 $72
★ $72

There Shall Be Showers
Of Blessings
#522090
Issued: 1990 • Retired: 1999
Retail Price: $60 – $70

KEY							
NM Pre'81	🎵 1986	$ 1992	✝ 1997
▲ 1981	▲ 1987	🎯 1993	👓 1998
🐚 1982	✤ 1988	🗝 1994	★ 1999
🐚 1983	🕊 1989	△ 1995	🕐 2000
✝ 1984	🔥 1990	♡ 1996	🐚 2001
🔥 1985	🔥 1991	ⅡⓂ Unmarked	

9

Values 🔥 $92
🔥 $87
$ $84
🔥 $82
🗝 $78
🐚 $76
♡ $73

There's A Light At The
End Of The Tunnel
#521485
Issued: 1991 • Susp.: 1996
Retail Price: $55 – $60

10

Values 🎵 $60
🎵 $55
▲ $53
✤ $53
🕊 $50
🔥 $50

There's A Song In My Heart
Rejoice In The Lord Band Series
#12173
Issued: 1985 • Susp.: 1990
Retail Price: $11 – $16.50

1

Values ○ $45
🔔 $45

**There's Sno-boredom
With You**
#730122
Issued: 2000 • Open
Retail Price: $45

2

Values ○ $45
🔔 $45

**Things Are Poppin' At Our
House This Christmas**
#455806
Issued: 2000 • Open
Retail Price: $45

3

Values Ɖ $65
⚓ $54
🍎 $50
ß $48
❀ $44
🔚 $44
△ $42
♡ $42

**Thinking Of You Is What
I Really Like To Do**
#522287
Issued: 1990 • Susp.: 1996
Retail Price: $30 – $32.50

4

Values Ɖ $47
⚓ $40
🍎 $38
ß $37
❀ $37
🔚 $35
△ $35
♡ $35
✝ $35
6ठ $35
★ $35
○ $35
🔔 $35

**This Day Has Been
Made In Heaven**
#523496
Issued: 1990 • Open
Retail Price: $30 – $35

5

Values ★ $30
○ $30
🔔 $30

**This Day Has Been
Made In Heaven**
#679852
Issued: 2000 • Open
Retail Price: $30

6

Values ⅌ $107
▲ $78
⚓ $76
Ɖ $72
⚓ $66

**This Is The Day Which
The Lord Has Made**
#12157
Issued: 1987 • Susp.: 1990
Retail Price: $20 – $30

KEY							
NM	Pre'81	⅌	1986	ß	1992	✝	1997
▲	1981	▲	1987	❀	1993	6ठ	1998
Ⅱ	1982	⚓	1988	🔚	1994	★	1999
⬤	1983	Ɖ	1989	△	1995	○	2000
✝	1984	⚓	1990	♡	1996	🔔	2001
⬤	1985	🍎	1991	UM	Unmarked		

General Figurines

	Price Paid	Value
1.		
2.		
3.		
4.		
5.		
6.		
7.		
8.		
9.		
10.		

Totals

7

Values ▲ $227

**This Is The Day Which The
Lord Hath Made (LE-1987)**
Bridal Party Series
#E2838
Issued: 1987 • Closed: 1987
Retail Price: $185

8

Values ✝ $113
⬤ $105
⅌ $97
▲ $95
⚓ $90

This Is Your Day To Shine
#E2822
Issued: 1984 • Retired: 1988
Retail Price: $37.50 – $40

9

Values ß $43

**This Land Is Our Land
(LE-1992)**
#527777
Issued: 1992 • Closed: 1992
Retail Price: $35

10

Values ▲ $47
⚓ $42
Ɖ $40
⚓ $37
🍎 $35
ß $33
❀ $32
🔚 $32
△ $32
♡ $32
✝ $32
6ठ $32
★ $32

This Too Shall Pass
#114014
Issued: 1988 • Retired: 1999
Retail Price: $23 – $30

1

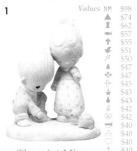

Values	
NM	$98
▲	$74
I	$62
←	$57
✝	$55
←	$51
❀	$50
←	$47
⚓	$47
⟊	$45
★	$43
♨	$43
&	$42
♈	$42
▬	$40
△	$40
✝	$40
○	$40
▨	$40

Thou Art Mine
#E3113
Issued: 1980 • Open
Retail Price: $16 – $40

2

Values	
⟊	$90
&	$80
&	$77
♈	$75
▬	$73
✝	$70
♡	$70

Thumb-body Loves You
#521698
Issued: 1991 • Susp.: 1996
Retail Price: $55 – $60

3

Values	
♈	$68
▬	$58
△	$56
♡	$54

Tied Up For The Holidays
#527580
Issued: 1993 • Susp.: 1996
Retail Price: $40 – $45

4

Values	
↢	$35
★	$35
○	$35
▨	$35

Time For A Holy Holiday
#455849
Issued: 1998 • Open
Retail Price: $35

5

Values	
⟊	$52
&	$45
&	$42
♈	$42
▬	$41
△	$41
♡	$41
✝	$41
★	$41
○	$41

Time Heals
#523739
Issued: 1990 • Retired: 2000
Retail Price: $37.50 – $40

6

Values	
⟊	$66
⟊	$62
⟊	$57
&	$54
&	$50
♈	$47
▬	$47
△	$45
♡	$45

'Tis The Season
#111163
Issued: 1988 • Susp.: 1996
Retail Price: $27.50 – $35

7

Values	
NM	$78
▲	$62
I	$52
←	$47
✝	$45
←	$43
❀	$42
▲	$42
⟊	$42
⟊	$40
⟊	$39
&	$37
&	$37
♈	$37
▬	$37
△	$37
○	$37
✝	$37
↢	$37

To A Special Dad
#E5212
Issued: 1981 • Susp.: 1998
Retail Price: $20 – $35

8

Values	
⟊	$52
&	$45
&	$40
♈	$40
▬	$36
△	$36
♡	$36
✝	$36
○	$36
★	$36

To A Special Mum
#521965
Issued: 1991 • Retired: 1999
Retail Price: $30 – $35

9

Values	
✝	$62
⟊	$57
❀	$52
▲	$50
⟊	$48
⟊	$47
⟊	$47
&	$43
&	$42
♈	$42
▬	$40
△	$40
♡	$40
✝	$40
↢	$40
★	$40
○	$40
↢	$40

To A Very
Special Mom
#E2824
Issued: 1984 • Open
Retail Price: $27.50 – $40

10

Values	
&	$57
&	$53
♈	$50

To A Very Special
Mom And Dad
#521434
Issued: 1991 • Susp.: 1993
Retail Price: $35

KEY			
NM Pre'81	❀ 1986	& 1992	✝ 1997
▲ 1981	⟊ 1987	♈ 1993	↢ 1998
I 1982	⟊ 1988	▬ 1994	★ 1999
← 1983	⟊ 1989	△ 1995	○ 2000
✝ 1984	♡ 1990	♡ 1996	↢ 2001
← 1985	& 1991	UM Unmarked	

General Figurines

	Price Paid	Value
1.		
2.		
3.		
4.		
5.		
6.		
7.		
8.		
9.		
10.		

Totals

1

Values	
†	$82
🐦	$66
🎋	$62
▲	$60
⬥	$60
⽥	$60
♨	$58
⚘	$55
⚑	$55
⌑	$52
♡	$52
♡	$50
†	$50
6⌐	$50
★	$50
○	$50
🔔	$50

**To A Very
Special Sister**
#E2825
Issued: 1984 • Open
Retail Price: $37.50 – $50

2

Values	
⬎	$70
⬧	$65
♡	$65
†	$65
6⌐	$65
★	$65
○	$65
🔔	$65

To A Very Special Sister
#528633
Issued: 1994 • Open
Retail Price: $60 – $65

3

Values	
⬤	$132
†	$98
🐦	$92
🎋	$88
▲	$83

To God Be The Glory
#E2823
Issued: 1984 • Susp.: 1987
Retail Price: $40 – $45

4

Values	
○	N/E

To God Be The Glory
Special Event Figurine
#E2823R
Issued: 2000 • Closed: 2000
Retail Price: $45

5

Values	
🎋	$105
▲	$72
⬥	$63
⽥	$60
♨	$54
⚘	$52
⚑	$50
⌑	$50
⬧	$50
♡	$50
†	$50
6⌐	$50
★	$50
○	$50
🔔	$50

To My Deer Friend
#100048
Issued: 1987 • Open
Retail Price: $33 – $50

6

Values	
🐦	$90
🎋	$75
▲	$70
⬥	$65

To My Favorite Paw
#100021
Issued: 1986 • Susp.: 1988
Retail Price: $22.50 – $27

General Figurines

	Price Paid	Value
1.		
2.		
3.		
4.		
5.		
6.		
7.		
8.		
9.		

Totals

7

Values	
🐦	$120
🎋	$75
▲	$68
⬥	$62
⽥	$60
♨	$58
⚘	$57
⚑	$55
⌑	$55
⬧	$55
♡	$55
†	$55
6⌐	$55
★	$55
○	$55
🔔	$55

To My Forever Friend
#100072
Issued: 1986 • Open
Retail Price: $33 – $55

8

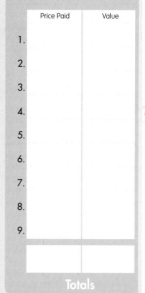

Values	
⏃	$47
🐦	$43
†	$43
▲	$40
🎋	$37
▲	$37
⬥	$33
⽥	$33
♨	$32
UM	$45

To Some Bunny Special
#E9282A
Issued: 1983 • Susp.: 1990
Retail Price: $8 – $13.50

9

Values	
▲	$240
⬥	$232
⽥	$220
♨	$214

**To Tell The Tooth,
You're Special**
#105813
Issued: 1987 • Susp.: 1990
Retail Price: $38.50 – $50

1

Values
🐝	$42
◁	$38
♡	$37
○	$37
†	$37
♣	$37
★	$37

To The Apple Of God's Eye
#522015
Issued: 1993 • Retired: 1999
Retail Price: $32.50 – $35

2 New

Values
○	$35
≥	$35

To The Sweetest Girl In The Cast
#742880
Issued: 2001 • Open
Retail Price: $35

3

Values
NM	$97
▲	$81
Ⅱ	$72
◄	$70
†	$70
♣	$60
♪	$60

To Thee With Love
#E3120
Issued: 1980 • Susp.: 1986
Retail Price: $13 – $19

4

Values
🐟	$88
†	$82
♪	$75
♪	$70
▲	$66

Trust In The Lord
#E9289
Issued: 1983 • Susp.: 1987
Retail Price: $20 – $23

5

Values
▲	$46
✤	$42
◆	$40
⚓	$38
♠	$36
♧	$35
🐝	$34
⊐	$34
♡	$34
†	$34
♣	$34

A Tub Full Of Love
#104817
Issued: 1987 • Susp.: 1998
Retail Price: $22.50 – $32.50

6

Values
▲	$46
✤	$42
◆	$40
⚓	$38
♠	$36
♧	$35
🐝	$34
⊐	$32.50
△	$32.50
♡	$32.50
†	$32.50
♣	$32.50
★	$32.50
○	$32.50
≥	$32.50

A Tub Full Of Love
#112313
Issued: 1987 • Open
Retail Price: $22.50 – $32.50

7

Values
†	$65
♣	$65

Twenty Years And The Vision's Still The Same
(LE-1998)
20th Anniversary Commemorative Figurine
#306843
Issued: 1998 • Closed: 1998
Retail Price: $55

8

Values ♣ $47

Under His Wings I Am Safely Abiding
(Dated 1998)
The Dated Cross Series
#306835
Issued: 1998 • Closed: 1998
Retail Price: $40

KEY					
NM Pre'81	♪ 1986	♠ 1992	† 1997
▲ 1981	▲ 1987	♣ 1993	⊐ 1998
Ⅱ 1982	✤ 1988	⊐ 1994	★ 1999
◄ 1983	◆ 1989	△ 1995	○ 2000
† 1984	♠ 1990	♡ 1996	≥ 2001
♣ 1985	♪ 1991	UM Unmarked	

General Figurines

	Price Paid	Value
1.		
2.		
3.		
4.		
5.		
6.		
7.		
8.		
9.		
10.		

Totals

9

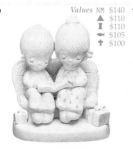

Values
NM	$140
▲	$110
Ⅱ	$110
◄	$105
†	$100

Unto Us A Child Is Born
#E2013
Issued: 1979 • Susp.: 1984
Retail Price: $12 – $25

10

Values
⊐	$42
△	$37
♡	$35
†	$35
♣	$35
★	$35
○	$35
≥	$35

Vaya Con Dios
#531146
Issued: 1995 • Open
Retail Price: $32.50 – $35

1

Values 👓 $70
★ $70
🕐 $70
👓 $70

A Very Special Bond
#488240
Issued: 1999 • Open
Retail Price: $70

2

Values ✝ $300
🍃 $280

The Voice Of Spring (LE-1985)
The Four Seasons Figurine Series
#12068
Issued: 1985 • Closed: 1985
Retail Price: $30

3

Values ✝ $113
🍃 $106
♫ $102
⚜ $99
⚓ $93
Ð $90

Waddle I Do Without You
The Clown Series
#12459
Issued: 1985 • Retired: 1989
Retail Price: $30 – $40

4
New

Values 🕐 $30
🍂 $30

Wait Patiently On The Lord
#325279
Issued: 2001 • Open
Retail Price: $30

5

Values 🕐 $70

Waiting For A Merry Christmas
#527637
Issued: 2000 • Retired: 2000
Retail Price: $65

6

Values 🔺 $42
♡ $35
✝ $35
👓 $35
★ $35
🕐 $35
🍂 $35

Walk In The Sonshine
#524212
Issued: 1995 • Open
Retail Price: $35

General Figurines

	Price Paid	Value
1.		
2.		
3.		
4.		
5.		
6.		
7.		
8.		
9.		
10.		

Totals

7

Values NM $136
🔺 $114
▮ $102
◄ $92
✝ $87
🍃 $85
♫ $85
⚜ $85
⚓ $85
Ð $85
↓ $85
⚘ $82
👓 $82
🎀 $82
△ $82
♡ $82
✝ $82
👓 $82
★ $82
🕐 $82

Walking By Faith
#E3117
Issued: 1980 • Retired: 2000
Retail Price: $35 – $80

8

Values ★ $50
🕐 $50
🍂 $50

Warmest Wishes For The Holidays
#455830
Issued: 1999 • Open
Retail Price: $50

9

Values ✝ $40
👓 $35
★ $35
🕐 $35
🍂 $35

Water-Melancholy Day Without You
#521515
Issued: 1998 • Open
Retail Price: $35

10

Values ♡ $38
✝ $35
👓 $35
★ $35
🕐 $35
🍂 $35

We All Have Our Bad Hair Days
#261157
Issued: 1997 • Open
Retail Price: $35

1 Values ▲ $80

We Are All Precious In His
Sight (LE-1987)
#102903
Issued: 1987 • Closed: 1987
Retail Price: $30

2 Values ✕ $63
❄ $46
✝ $44
✿ $42
♪ $42
▲ $40
✤ $40
Ð $37
★ $37
♣ $37
♫ $35
☷ $35
❦ $35
♡ $35
✝ $35
✿ $35
★ $35
☉ $35
❧ $35

We Are God's
Workmanship
#E9258
Issued: 1983 • Open
Retail Price: $19 – $35

3 Values ♦ $235

We Belong To The Lord
Damien-Dutton Figurine
#103004
Issued: 1986 • Closed: 1986
Retail Price: $50

4 Values ▲ $340
✤ $290
Ð $280
★ $270
♣ $265
♫ $265
♫ $260
☷ $260
❦ $255

We Gather Together To Ask
The Lord's Blessing (set/6)
#109762
Issued: 1987 • Retired: 1995
Retail Price: $130 – $150

5 Values ★ $40
☉ $40
❧ $40

We Knead You Grandma
#679844
Issued: 2000 • Open
Retail Price: $40

6 Values ✤ $65
Ð $60
★ $58
♣ $55

We Need A Good Friend
Through The Ruff Times
#520810
Issued: 1989 • Susp.: 1991
Retail Price: $35 – $37.50

7 Values ☉ $40
❧ $40

We're A Family That
Sticks Together
#730114
Issued: 2000 • Open
Retail Price: $40

8 Values ★ $72
♣ $65
♫ $60
♫ $60
☷ $60
❦ $60
✝ $60
✿ $60
★ $60
☉ $60
❧ $60

We're Going To Miss You
#524913
Issued: 1990 • Open
Retail Price: $50 – $60

KEY			
NM Pre '81	♪ 1986	♣ 1992	✝ 1997
▲ 1981	▲ 1987	♫ 1993	6∂ 1998
✕ 1982	✤ 1988	❝ 1994	★ 1999
◄ 1983	Ð 1989	☷ 1995	☉ 2000
✝ 1984	★ 1990	♡ 1996	❧ 2001
◄ 1985	♣ 1991	UM Unmarked	

	Price Paid	Value
1.		
2.		
3.		
4.		
5.		
6.		
7.		
8.		
9.		
10.		

Totals

9 Values ✕ $98
◄ $89
✝ $85
✿ $80
♪ $78
▲ $76
✤ $70
Ð $70
★ $66

We're In It Together
#E9259
Issued: 1983 • Susp.: 1990
Retail Price: $24 – $35

10 Values ▲ $85
✤ $78
Ð $74
★ $69
♣ $67

We're Pulling For You
#106151
Issued: 1987 • Susp.: 1991
Retail Price: $40 – $55

1 *Values* ♡ $47

We're So Hoppy You're Here (LE-1997)
Special Event Figurine
#261351
Issued: 1997 • Closed: 1997
Retail Price: $32.50

2 *Values* 🎵 $62
▲ $58
⬧ $53
⬦ $50
⚱ $48
⚱ $46
⚭ $40

Wedding Arch
Bridal Party Series
#102369
Issued: 1987 • Susp.: 1992
Retail Price: $22.50 – $30

3 *Values* ✝ $55
6⌐ $50
★ $50
🕐 $50
≈ $50

Well, Blow Me Down It's Yer Birthday
#325538
Issued: 1998 • Open
Retail Price: $50

4 *Values* 🕐 N/E

Whale Have Oceans Of Fun
PRECIOUS MOMENTS
Cruise Figurine
N/A
Issued: 2000 • Closed: 2000
Retail Price: N/A

5 *Values* ⬧ $58
♡ $53
✝ $50
6⌐ $50
★ $50
🕐 $50
≈ $50

What A Difference You've Made In My Life
#531138
Issued: 1996 • Open
Retail Price: $50

6 *Values* 6⌐ $30
★ $30
🕐 $30
≈ $30

What Better To Give Than Yourself
#487988
Issued: 1999 • Open
Retail Price: $30

	KEY				
NM Pre'81	🎵 1986	✦ 1992	✝ 1997
▲ 1981	▲ 1987	⅋⅋ 1993	6⌐ 1998
Ⅱ 1982	⬧ 1988	⬥ 1994	★ 1999
◄ 1983	⧓ 1989	⬧ 1995	🕐 2000
✝ 1984	▲ 1990	♡ 1996	≈ 2001
⬢ 1985	⬢ 1991	UM Unmarked	

	Price Paid	Value
1.		
2.		
3.	50 ⁰⁰	
4.		
5.		
6.		
7.		
8.		
9.		
10.		

Totals

7 *Values* ⬜ $55
⬧ $50
⬦ $48
✝ $47
⬧ $46
★ $46

What The World Needs Is Love
#531065
Issued: 1995 • Retired: 1999
Retail Price: $45

8 *Values* 🔔 $83
⅋⅋ $78
♈ $75
⬥ $72
⬧ $71
♡ $71

What The World Needs Now
#524352
Issued: 1992 • Retired: 1997
Retail Price: $50

9 *Values* ♡ $55
✝ $47
6⌐ $40
★ $40
🕐 $40
≈ $40

Who's Gonna Fill Your Shoes
Catalog Early Release
#531634
Issued: 1997 • Open
Retail Price: $37.50 – $40

10 *Values* ✝ $40
6⌐ $40
★ $40
🕐 $40
≈ $40

Who's Gonna Fill Your Shoes
Catalog Early Release
#532061
Issued: 1998 • Open
Retail Price: $37.50 – $40

1
New

Values ○ $35
    $35

A Winning Spirit Comes From Within
Special Olympics Commemorative Figurine
#813044
Issued: 2001 • Open
Retail Price: $35

2

Values $142
    $128

Winter's Song (LE-1986)
The Four Seasons Figurine Series
#12092
Issued: 1986 • Closed: 1986
Retail Price: $30

3

Values ★ $43

Wishes For The World
Special Event Figurine
#530018
Issued: 1999 • Closed: 1999
Retail Price: $35

4

Values ▲ $50
   ⬥ $44
   Ð $40
   ⚓ $40
   ● $38
   ⚘ $37
   ♋ $37
   ⚊ $37
   △ $36
   ♡ $36
   † $36
   ᨞ $36
   ★ $36

Wishing You A Basket Full Of Blessings
#109924
Issued: 1988 • Retired: 1999
Retail Price: $23 – $35

5
New

Values ○ $40
    $40

Wishing You A Birthday Full Of Surprises
#795313
Issued: 2001 • Open
Retail Price: $40

6

Values ★ $30
   ○ $30
   ᨞ $30

Wishing You A Blow Out Birthday (personalized)
#680184
Issued: 2000 • Open
Retail Price: $30

7

Values Ð $70
   ⚓ $67
   ● $63
   ⚘ $63
   ♋ $60

Wishing You A Cozy Season
#521949
Issued: 1989 • Susp.: 1993
Retail Price: $42.50 – $50

8

Values ▲ $50
   ⬥ $43
   Ð $38
   ⚓ $37
   ● $37
   ⚘ $37
   ♋ $37
   ⚊ $37
   ♡ $37
   † $37
   ᨞ $36
   ★ $36

Wishing You A Happy Easter
#109886
Issued: 1988 • Retired: 1999
Retail Price: $23 – $35

KEY						
NM Pre'81	⚘ 1986	⚘ 1992	† 1997			
▲ 1981	▲ 1987	♋ 1993	᨞ 1998			
I 1982	⬥ 1988	⚊ 1994	★ 1999			
✝ 1983	Ð 1989	△ 1995	○ 2000			
† 1984	● 1990	♡ 1996	⦿ 2001			
⚘ 1985	● 1991	UM Unmarked				

	Price Paid	Value
1.		
2.		
3.		
4.		
5.		
6.		
7.		
8.		
9.		
10.		

Totals

9

Values ⚘ $53
   ♋ $49
   ⚊ $48
   △ $45
   ♡ $45
   † $45
   ᨞ $45
   ★ $45
   ○ $45
   ᨞ $45

Wishing You A Ho, Ho, Ho
#527629
Issued: 1992 • Open
Retail Price: $40 – $45

10

Values ⬥ $85
   Ð $75
   ⚓ $70
   ● $70
   ⚘ $70
   ♋ $70
   ⚊ $70
   △ $70
   ♡ $70
   † $70
   ᨞ $70
   ★ $70
   ○ $70
   ᨞ $70

Wishing You A Perfect Choice
#520845
Issued: 1989 • Open
Retail Price: $55 – $70

1

NM $125
▲ $117
Ⅱ $102
🖝 $92
✝ $89
🐦 $84

Wishing You A Season
Filled With Joy
#E2805
Issued: 1980 • Retired: 1985
Retail Price: $20 – $27.50

2

Values ⊅ $85
🐦 $79
⬥ $77
🐟 $75
∞ $72
🍜 $71
△ $71
♡ $71
✝ $71
⭐ $71

Wishing You A Very
Successful Season
#522120
Issued: 1989 • Retired: 1999
Retail Price: $60 – $70

3

Values ▲ $72
⬥ $68
⊅ $64
🐦 $60
🐟 $58
🐟 $56
∞ $54
🍜 $54

Wishing You A
Yummy Christmas
#109754
Issued: 1987 • Susp.: 1994
Retail Price: $35 – $50

4

Values 🐦 $30
⭐ $30
🕐 $30
🔔 $30

Wishing You A
Yummy Christmas
#455814
Issued: 1998 • Open
Retail Price: $30

5

Values ⭐ $184

Wishing You An Old Fashioned Christmas
(set/6, LE-1999, with lighted tree)
#534778
Issued: 1999 • Closed: 1999
Retail Price: $175

KEY				
NM Pre'81	🖝 1986	🐟 1992	✝ 1997	
▲ 1981	▲ 1987	∞ 1993	🐦 1998	
Ⅱ 1982	⬥ 1988	🍜 1994	⭐ 1999	
✝ 1983	⊅ 1989	△ 1995	🕐 2000	
✝ 1984	🐟 1990	♡ 1996	🐦 2001	
🐦 1985	🐟 1991	UM Unmarked		

General Figurines

	Price Paid	Value
1.		
2.		
3.		
4.		
5.		
6.		
7.		
8.		

Totals

6

Values ⬥ $93
⊅ $85
🐟 $85
🐟 $79
🐟 $79
∞ $77
🍜 $75
△ $75
♡ $75
✝ $75
🐦 $75
⭐ $75
🕐 $75
🔔 $75

Wishing You
Roads Of Happiness
#520780
Issued: 1989 • Open
Retail Price: $60 – $75

7

Values ⭐ $25
🕐 $25
🔔 $25

Witch Way Do You
Spell Love?
#587869
Issued: 1999 • Open
Retail Price: $25

8

Values ▲ $83
⬥ $76
⊅ $73
🐟 $72
🐟 $70
🐟 $68
∞ $67
🍜 $65
△ $65
♡ $65
✝ $65
🐦 $65
⭐ $65
🕐 $65
🔔 $65

With This Ring I . . .
#104019
Issued: 1987 • Open
Retail Price: $40 – $65

1

Values ⚖ $79
♡ $70
† $70
6ᴣ $70
★ $70
◔ $70
⊑ $70

A Year Of Blessings
#163783
Issued: 1996 • Open
Retail Price: $70

2

Photo Unavailable

Values ★ $63
◔ $63
⊑ $63

Yes Dear, You Are
Always Right
Century Circle Exclusive
#523186
Issued: 2000 • Closed: 2000
Retail Price: $60

3

Values ⊕ $58
↓ $55
⚬ $49
⅛ $47
⚭ $47

Yield Not To Temptation
#521310
Issued: 1990 • Susp.: 1993
Retail Price: $27.50 – $30

4

Values 6ᴣ $50
★ $50
◔ $50
⊑ $50

You Always Stand Behind Me
#492140
Issued: 1999 • Open
Retail Price: $50

5

Values ◔ $40
⊑ $40

You Are Always In My Heart
Special Event Figurine
#768952
Issued: 2001 • Open
Retail Price: $40

6

Values ◔ $40
⊑ $40

You Are Always In My Heart
Special Event Figurine
#768987
Issued: 2001 • Open
Retail Price: $40

7

Values † $42
⚭ $42
★ $41
◔ $41

You Are Always On
My Mind
#306967
Issued: 1998 • Retired: 2000
Retail Price: $37.50 – $40

8

Values ♡ $55
† $50
6ᴣ $50
★ $50
◔ $50
⊑ $50

You Are Always
There For Me
#163597
Issued: 1997 • Open
Retail Price: $50

9

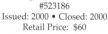

Values ⚖ $5
♡ $5
† $55
6ᴣ $55
★ $55
◔ $55
⊑ $55

You Are Always
There For Me
#163600
Issued: 1996 • Open
Retail Price: $50 – $55

10

Values ♡ $55
† $55
6ᴣ $55
★ $55
◔ $55
⊑ $55

You Are Always
There For Me
#163619
Issued: 1997 • Open
Retail Price: $50 – $55

KEY			
NM Pre'81	♨ 1986	♣ 1992	† 1997
▲ 1981	▲ 1987	⚭ 1993	6ᴣ 1998
∥ 1982	✿ 1988	⊷ 1994	★ 1999
⊷ 1983	⊕ 1989	⚖ 1995	◔ 2000
† 1984	↓ 1990	♡ 1996	⊑ 2001
⊷ 1985	⚬ 1991	UM Unmarked	

General Figurines

	Price Paid	Value
1.		
2.		
3.		
4.		
5.		
6.		
7.		
8.		
9.		
10.		

Totals

1

Values △ $57
♡ $52
† $50
6∂ $50
★ $50
🕐 $50
🔔 $50

**You Are Always
There For Me**
#163627
Issued: 1996 • Open
Retail Price: $50

2

Values ♡ $55
† $50
6∂ $50
★ $50
🕐 $50
🔔 $50

**You Are Always
There For Me**
#163635
Issued: 1996 • Open
Retail Price: $50

3

Values 🔔 $100
♋ $94
🗝 $90
△ $85
♡ $80

You Are My Favorite Star
#527378
Issued: 1992 • Retired: 1997
Retail Price: $60

4

Values 🔔 $76
🔔 $68

**You Are My Happiness
(LE-1992)**
#526185
Issued: 1992 • Closed: 1992
Retail Price: $37.50

5

Values ▲ $63
⟐ $58

Variation

You Are My Main Event (LE-1988)
Special Event Figurine
#115231
Issued: 1988 • Closed: 1988
Retail Price: $30
Variation: Pink strings – $84

KEY						
NM Pre'81	♪ 1986	🔔 1992	† 1997
▲ 1981	▲ 1987	♋ 1993	6∂ 1998
Ⅱ 1982	⟐ 1988	➡ 1994	★ 1999
➡ 1983	Ð 1989	△ 1995	🕐 2000
† 1984	♠ 1990	♡ 1996	🔔 2001
♪ 1985	♠ 1991	UM Unmarked	

General Figurines

	Price Paid	Value
1.		
2.		
3.		
4.		
5.		
6.		
7.		
8.		
9.		

Totals

6

Values ⟐ $50
♋ $43
➡ $40
🔔 $38
🔔 $36
♋ $36
△ $36
♡ $36
† $36
6∂ $36

You Are My Number One
#520829
Issued: 1989 • Susp.: 1998
Retail Price: $25 – $35

7

Values † $47
6∂ $46
★ $46
🕐 $46

**You Are My Once In
A Lifetime**
#531030
Issued: 1998 • Retired: 2000
Retail Price: $45

8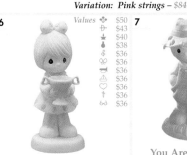

Values 🔔 $50
♋ $42
➡ $38
△ $37
♡ $35
† $35
🔔 $35
★ $35
🕐 $35
🔔 $35

**You Are Such A
Purr-fect Friend**
#524395
Issued: 1993 • Open
Retail Price: $35

9

Values 🕐 $50
🔔 $50

New

You Are The Queen Of Hearts
#795151
Issued: 2001 • Open
Retail Price: $50

1

Values   🔥 $60
   🔔 $52
   🐝 $48
   ➖ $45
   △ $45
   ♡ $45
   † $45
   😊 $45
   ★ $45
   🕐 $45
   🔖 $45

You Are The Type I Love
#523542
Issued: 1992 • Open
Retail Price: $40 – $45

2
New

Values 🕐 $32.50
  🔖 $32.50

You Are The Wind Beneath My Wings
#795267
Issued: 2001 • Open
Retail Price: $32.50

3

Values ⚖ $56
  🔥 $48

You Can Always Bring A Friend (LE-1991)
Special Event Figurine
#527122
Issued: 1991 • Closed: 1991
Retail Price: $27.50

4

Values 🐝 $35
  ★ $35
  🕐 $35
  🔖 $35

You Can Always Count On Me
#487953
Issued: 1999 • Open
Retail Price: $35

5

Values 🐝 $35
  ★ $35
  🕐 $35
  🔖 $35

You Can Always Fudge A Little During The Season
#455792
Issued: 1998 • Open
Retail Price: $35

6

Values ⚜ $75
  ▲ $68
  ⚙ $64

You Can Fly
#12335
Issued: 1986 • Susp.: 1988
Retail Price: $25 – $30

7
New

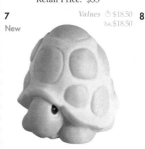

Values 🕐 $18.50
  🔖 $18.50

You Can't Hide From God
#795194
Issued: 2001 • Open
Retail Price: $18.50

8

Values Ⅱ $174
  ◀ $115
  † $102
  ✦ $93
  ♪ $92
  ▲ $90
  ⚙ $88
  ⊕ $85

You Can't Run Away From God
#E0525
Issued: 1983 • Retired: 1989
Retail Price: $28.50 – $38.50

KEY					
NM Pre'81	♪ 1986	⚖ 1992	† 1997
▲ 1981	▲ 1987	🐝 1993	🐝 1998
Ⅱ 1982	⚙ 1988	◀ 1994	★ 1999
Ⅱ 1983	⊕ 1989	△ 1995	🕐 2000
† 1984	▲ 1990	♡ 1996	🔖 2001
✦ 1985	🔥 1991	UM Unmarked	

9

Values 🐝 $25
  ★ $25
  🕐 $25
  🔖 $25

You Can't Take It With You
#488321
Issued: 1999 • Open
Retail Price: $25

10

Values ★ $33

You Color Our World With Loving Caring And Sharing
10th Anniversary Chapel Commemorative Figurine
#644463
Issued: 1999 • Closed: 1999
Retail Price: $19 – $30

1

Values ★ $37.50
○ $37.50
≈ $37.50

You Complete My Heart
#681067
Issued: 2000 • Open
Retail Price: $37.50

2

Values 6∂ $25
★ $25
○ $25
≈ $25

You Count
#488372
Issued: 1999 • Open
Retail Price: $25

3

Values △ $65
♡ $58
† $58
6∂ $58

**You Deserve A Halo –
Thank You**
#531693
Issued: 1996 • Retired: 1998
Retail Price: $55

4

Values ₰ $47
♋ $44
⚱ $42
△ $37.50
♡ $37.50
† $37.50
6∂ $37.50
★ $37.50
○ $37.50
≈ $37.50

You Deserve An Ovation
#520578
Issued: 1992 • Open
Retail Price: $35 – $37.50

5

Values ○ $55
≈ $55

**You Have a Special Place
In My Heart**
#737534
Issued: 2000 • Open
Retail Price: $55

6

Values 6∂ $43

**You Have Mastered The
Art Of Caring**
Catalog Early Release
#456276
Issued: 1998 • Closed: 1998
Retail Price: $40

General Figurines

	Price Paid	Value
1.		
2.		
3.		
4.		
5.		
6.		
7.		
8.		
9.		
10.		

Totals

7

Values ≈ $35

**You Have The Beary
Best Heart**
Special Event Figurine
#730254
Issued: 2001 • To Be Closed: 2001
Retail Price: $35

8

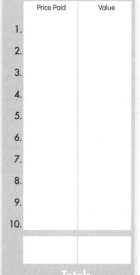

Values ★ $25
○ $25
≈ $25

**You Have The
Sweetest Heart**
#689548
Issued: 2000 • Open
Retail Price: $25

9

Values ⇌ $83
† $73
♋ $66
♫ $63
▲ $60
✦ $56
⊅ $56
✦ $56
♦ $54
₰ $54
♋ $52
◄ $50
♡ $50
♡ $47

**You Have Touched
So Many Hearts**
#E2821
Issued: 1984 • Susp.: 1996
Retail Price: $25 – $37.50

10

Values ♡ $40
† $40
6∂ $40
★ $40
○ $40
≈ $40

**You Have Touched
So Many Hearts**
#261084
Issued: 1997 • Open
Retail Price: $37.50 – $40

1

Values 🌢 $42
⚜ $40
⚘ $40
✂ $39
♡ $39
♡ $39

You Have Touched So Many
Hearts (personalized)
#527661
Issued: 1992 • Susp.: 1996
Retail Price: $35 – $37.50

2

Values 👓 $35
★ $35
🕐 $35
🔊 $35

You Just Can't Replace A
Good Friendship
#488054
Issued: 1999 • Open
Retail Price: $35

3

Values 👓 $36

You Make Such A
Lovely Pair
Catalog Figurine
#531588
Issued: 1998 • Closed: 1998
Retail Price: $32.50

4

Values ★ $40

You Oughta Be In Pictures
Special Event Figurine
#490327
Issued: 1999 • Closed: 1999
Retail Price: $32.50

5

Values 🕐 $27.50
🔊 $27.50

You Should Be As Proud
As A Peacock –
Congratulations
#733008
Issued: 2000 • Open
Retail Price: $27.50

6

Values 🔾 $40
⚜ $38
♡ $37
✝ $36
👓 $36
★ $36

You Suit Me To A Tee
#526193
Issued: 1994 • Retired: 1999
Retail Price: $35

7

New

Values 🕐 $60
🔊 $60

8

Values 🕐 $50
🔊 $50

You Tug On My
Heart Strings
*Boys & Girls Clubs Of America
Commemorative Figurine*
#795526
Issued: 2001 • Open
Retail Price: $60

You Will Always Be
Daddy's Little Girl
#488224
Issued: 2000 • Open
Retail Price: $50

KEY							
NM Pre'81	〽 1986	🎗 1992	✝ 1997
▲ 1981	♣ 1987	〽 1993	👓 1998
∑ 1982	✦ 1988	〽 1994	★ 1999
⬰ 1983	⊅ 1989	🔺 1995	🕐 2000
✝ 1984	♡ 1990	♡ 1996	🔊 2001
⚘ 1985	♣ 1991	UM Unmarked	

	Price Paid	Value
1.		
2.		
3.		
4.		
5.		
6.		
7.		
8.	50⁰⁰	
9.		
10.		

Totals

9

New

Values 🕐 $45
🔊 $45

You Will Always Be Mine
#795186
Issued: 2001 • Open
Retail Price: $45

10

Values 🔺 $50

You Will Always Be Our
Hero (LE-1995)
WWII Commemorative Figurine
#136271
Issued: 1995 • Closed: 1995
Retail Price: $40

1

Values ⓞ $27.50
🔔 $27.50

You're a Dandy Mom
And I'm Not Lion
#795232V
Issued: 2000 • Open
Retail Price: $27.50

2
New

Values ⓞ $32.50
🔔 $32.50

You're A Honey
#795283
Issued: 2001 • Open
Retail Price: $32.50

3

Values ♡ $40
† $37
👓 $37
★ $37
ⓞ $36

You're A Life Saver To Me
#204854
Issued: 1997 • Retired: 2000
Retail Price: $35

4
New

Values ⓞ $35
🔔 $35

You're As Sweet As
Apple Pie
#795275
Issued: 2001 • Open
Retail Price: $35

5

Values † $60
👓 $55
★ $55
ⓞ $55
🔔 $55

You're Just Too Sweet
To Be Scary
#183849
Issued: 1997 • Open
Retail Price: $55

6

Values 👓 $20
★ $20
ⓞ $20
🔔 $20

You're My Honey Bee
#487929
Issued: 1999 • Open
Retail Price: $20

KEY			
NM Pre'81	✗ 1986	✤ 1992	† 1997
▲ 1981	♣ 1987	∾ 1993	👓 1998
I 1982	✤ 1988	� 1994	★ 1999
⬅ 1983	⤴ 1989	△ 1995	ⓞ 2000
✝ 1984	★ 1990	♡ 1996	🔔 2001
✦ 1985	♦ 1991	UM Unmarked	

General Figurines

	Price Paid	Value
1.		
2.		
3.		
4.		
5.		
6.		
7.		
8.		
9.		
10.		

7

Values I $43
♣ $40
✝ $38
✤ $36
✗ $36
▲ $35
✤ $35
⤴ $33
★ $33
UM $50

You're Worth Your
Weight In Gold
#E9282B
Issued: 1983 • Susp.: 1990
Retail Price: $8 – $13.50

8

Value ✤ $107
⤴ $97
★ $90
✦ $82
♦ $82
∾ $80
➾ $77
♡ $77
ⓞ $77
† $77
👓 $77

Your Love Is So Uplifting
#520675
Issued: 1989 • Retired: 1998
Retail Price: $60 – $75

9

Values ⓞ $40
🔔 $40

Your Love Keeps Me
Toasty Warm
Catalog Figurine
#788031
Issued: 2000 • Closed: 2000
Retail Price: $37.50

10

Values ♡ $110

Your Precious Spirit Comes
Shining Through (LE-1996)
Regional Conference Figurine
#212563
Issued: 1996 • Closed: 1996
Retail Price: $30

Totals

LITTLE MOMENTS®

These figurines may be small in stature, but the LITTLE MOMENTS collection is a big hit with fans of the Enesco PRECIOUS MOMENTS line. LITTLE MOMENTS figurines were first introduced in 1996 and the line has since grown to include almost 100 different pieces. Many of the pieces are part of the general line, though there are several series within the collection. Also included in LITTLE MOMENTS are several pieces exclusive to the *Avon* catalog.

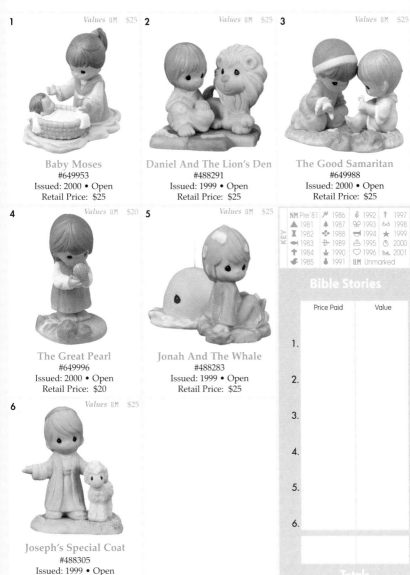

1   *Values* UM $25

Baby Moses
#649953
Issued: 2000 • Open
Retail Price: $25

2   *Values* UM $25

Daniel And The Lion's Den
#488291
Issued: 1999 • Open
Retail Price: $25

3   *Values* UM $25

The Good Samaritan
#649988
Issued: 2000 • Open
Retail Price: $25

4   *Values* UM $20

The Great Pearl
#649996
Issued: 2000 • Open
Retail Price: $20

5   *Values* UM $25

Jonah And The Whale
#488283
Issued: 1999 • Open
Retail Price: $25

6   *Values* UM $25

Joseph's Special Coat
#488305
Issued: 1999 • Open
Retail Price: $25

KEY			
NM Pre'81	✗ 1986	✦ 1992	✝ 1997
▲ 1981	▲ 1987	✿ 1993	👓 1998
✕ 1982	✤ 1988	⌐ 1994	★ 1999
◄ 1983	⌐ 1989	△ 1995	◑ 2000
✝ 1984	⌐ 1990	♡ 1996	⬌ 2001
✦ 1985	⌐ 1991	UM Unmarked	

Bible Stories

	Price Paid	Value
1.		
2.		
3.		
4.		
5.		
6.		

Totals

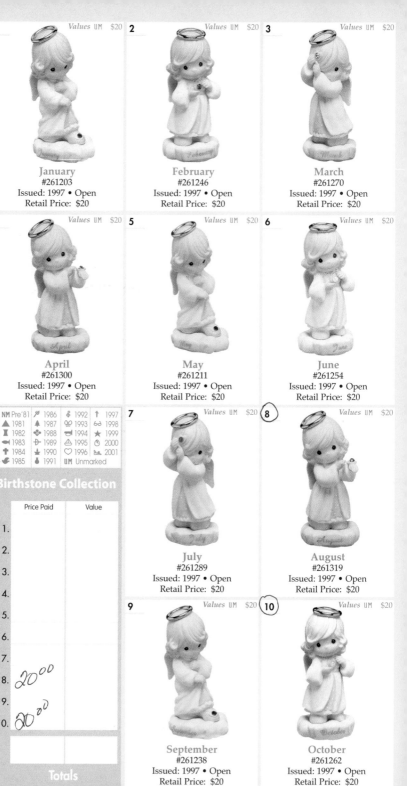

1 *Values* ⅡM $20

January
#261203
Issued: 1997 • Open
Retail Price: $20

2 *Values* ⅡM $20

February
#261246
Issued: 1997 • Open
Retail Price: $20

3 *Values* ⅡM $20

March
#261270
Issued: 1997 • Open
Retail Price: $20

4 *Values* ⅡM $20

April
#261300
Issued: 1997 • Open
Retail Price: $20

5 *Values* ⅡM $20

May
#261211
Issued: 1997 • Open
Retail Price: $20

6 *Values* ⅡM $20

June
#261254
Issued: 1997 • Open
Retail Price: $20

KEY			
NM Pre'81	✗ 1986	✦ 1992	✝ 1997
▲ 1981	✦ 1987	✿ 1993	6∂ 1998
✗ 1982	✦ 1988	✥ 1994	★ 1999
⬤ 1983	❄ 1989	✿ 1995	✪ 2000
✝ 1984	★ 1990	♡ 1996	⬛ 2001
✦ 1985	♦ 1991	ⅡM Unmarked	

Birthstone Collection

	Price Paid	Value
1.		
2.		
3.		
4.		
5.		
6.		
7.		
8.	20⁰⁰	
9.		
10.	20²⁰	

Totals

7 *Values* ⅡM $20

July
#261289
Issued: 1997 • Open
Retail Price: $20

(8) *Values* ⅡM $20

August
#261319
Issued: 1997 • Open
Retail Price: $20

9 *Values* ⅡM $20

September
#261238
Issued: 1997 • Open
Retail Price: $20

(10) *Values* ⅡM $20

October
#261262
Issued: 1997 • Open
Retail Price: $20

1 *Values* UM $20

November
#261297
Issued: 1997 • Open
Retail Price: $20

2 *Values* UM $20

December
#261327
Issued: 1997 • Open
Retail Price: $20

3 *Values* UM $20

Photo Unavailable

Dad
#848743
Issued: 2000 • Open
Retail Price: $20

4 *Values* UM $20

Dad
#880841
Issued: 2000 • Open
Retail Price: $20

5 *Values* UM $20

Family Cat
#848832
Issued: 2000 • Open
Retail Price: $20

6 *Values* UM $20

Family Dog
#848824
Issued: 2000 • Open
Retail Price: $20

7 *Values* UM $20

Infant Daughter
#848808
Issued: 2000 • Open
Retail Price: $20

8 *Values* UM $20

Photo Unavailable

Infant Daughter
#880906
Issued: 2000 • Open
Retail Price: $20

9 *Values* UM $20

Infant Son
#848816
Issued: 2000 • Open
Retail Price: $20

10 *Values* UM $20

Photo Unavailable

Infant Son
#880914
Issued: 2000 • Open
Retail Price: $20

KEY: NM Pre'81, 1981, 1982, 1983, 1984, 1985, 1986, 1987, 1988, 1989, 1990, 1991, 1992, 1993, 1994, 1995, 1996, 1997, 1998, 1999, 2000, 2001, UM Unmarked

Birthstone Collection

	Price Paid	Value
1.		
2.	20⁰⁰	

Build Your Own Family

3.		
4.		
5.		
6.		
7.	20⁰⁰	
8.		
9.	20⁰⁰	
10.		

Totals

149

1 *Values* UM $20

Mom
#848735
Issued: 2000 • Open
Retail Price: $20

2 *Values* UM $20

Photo
Unavailable

Mom
#880833
Issued: 2000 • Open
Retail Price: $20

3 *Values* UM $20

Teen Daughter
#848751
Issued: 2000 • Open
Retail Price: $20

4 *Values* UM $20

Photo
Unavailable

Teen Daughter
#880868
Issued: 2000 • Open
Retail Price: $20

5 *Values* UM $20

Photo
Unavailable

Teen Son
#848778
Issued: 2000 • Open
Retail Price: $20

6 *Values* UM $20

Teen Son
#880876
Issued: 2000 • Open
Retail Price: $20

KEY			
NM Pre'81	✐ 1986	✦ 1992	✝ 1997
▲ 1981	♠ 1987	✇ 1993	∞ 1998
Ⅱ 1982	✤ 1988	☙ 1994	★ 1999
➤ 1983	⊕ 1989	⌂ 1995	◑ 2000
✝ 1984	✚ 1990	♡ 1996	☇ 2001
✦ 1985	✿ 1991	UM Unmarked	

Build Your Own Family

	Price Paid	Value
1.		
2.		
3.		
4.		
5.		
6.		
7.	20 00	
8.		
9.		
10.	20 00	

Totals

7 *Values* UM $20

6/27

Toddler Daughter
#848786
Issued: 2000 • Open
Retail Price: $20

8 *Values* UM $20

Photo
Unavailable

Toddler Daughter
#880884
Issued: 2000 • Open
Retail Price: $20

9 *Values* UM $20

Photo
Unavailable

Toddler Son
#848794
Issued: 2000 • Open
Retail Price: $20

10 *Values* UM $20

6/27

Toddler Son
#880892
Issued: 2000 • Open
Retail Price: $20

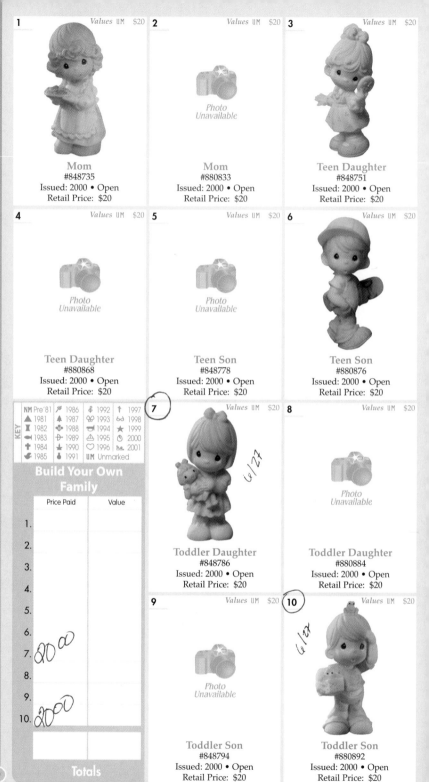

1 *Values* UM $20

The Child That's Born On
The Sabbath Day
#692077
Issued: 2000 • Open
Retail Price: $20

2 *Values* UM $20

Monday's Child
Is Fair Of Face
#692085
Issued: 2000 • Open
Retail Price: $20

3 *Values* UM $20

Tuesday's Child
Is Full Of Grace
#692093
Issued: 2000 • Open
Retail Price: $20

4 *Values* UM $20

Wednesday's Child
Is Full Of Woe
#692107
Issued: 2000 • Open
Retail Price: $20

5 *Values* UM $20

Thursday's Child
Has Far To Go
#692115
Issued: 2000 • Open
Retail Price: $20

6 *Values* UM $20

Friday's Child
Is Loving & Caring
#692123
Issued: 2000 • Open
Retail Price: $20

7 *Values* UM $20

Saturday's Child
Works Hard For A Living
#692131
Issued: 2000 • Open
Retail Price: $20

8 *Values* UM $20

*Photo
Unavailable*

Cross Walk
#649511
Issued: 1999 • Open
Retail Price: $20

9 *Values* UM $20

Go For It
#649538
Issued: 1999 • Open
Retail Price: $20

KEY			
NM Pre'81	♫ 1986	✦ 1992	† 1997
▲ 1981	▲ 1987	♉ 1993	6∂ 1998
✘ 1982	✧ 1988	⊐ 1994	★ 1999
◀ 1983	Ɗ 1989	△ 1995	☾ 2000
† 1984	⏚ 1990	♡ 1996	ఆ 2001
✔ 1985	♠ 1991	UM Unmarked	

Days Of The Week Collection

	Price Paid	Value
1.		
2.		
3.		
4.		
5.		
6.		
7.		

Highway To Happiness

8.		
9.		

Totals

151

1 *Values* UM $20

God's Children At Play
#649481
Issued: 1999 • Open
Retail Price: $20

2 *Values* UM $20

Highway To Happiness
#649457
Issued: 1999 • Open
Retail Price: $20

3 *Values* UM $20

I'll Never Stop Loving You
#649465
Issued: 1999 • Open
Retail Price: $20

4 *Values* UM $20

There's No Wrong Way
With You
#649473
Issued: 1999 • Open
Retail Price: $20

5 *Values* UM $20

Afri-can Be There For You,
I Will Be (Kenya)
#456462
Issued: 1998 • Open
Retail Price: $20

6 *Values* UM $20

Don't Rome Too Far From
Home (Italy)
#456403
Issued: 1998 • Open
Retail Price: $20

KEY			
NM Pre'81	🖋 1986	✤ 1992	† 1997
▲ 1981	▲ 1987	❀ 1993	❧ 1998
✕ 1982	❖ 1988	❀ 1994	★ 1999
◄ 1983	✧ 1989	♨ 1995	☺ 2000
† 1984	★ 1990	♡ 1996	☙ 2001
✦ 1985	● 1991	UM Unmarked	

Highway To Happiness

	Price Paid	Value
1.		
2.		
3.		
4.		

International Collection

5.		
6.		
7.		
8.		
9.		
10.		

Totals

7 *Values* UM $20

6/27

Hola, Amigo! (Mexico)
#456454
Issued: 1998 • Open
Retail Price: $20

8 *Values* UM $20

I'd Travel The Highlands To
Be With You (Scotland)
#456470
Issued: 1998 • Open
Retail Price: $20

9 *Values* UM $20

Life Is A Fiesta (Spain)
#456381
Issued: 1998 • Open
Retail Price: $20

10 *Values* UM $20

Love's Russian Into My
Heart (Russia)
#456446
Issued: 1998 • Open
Retail Price: $20

1 *Values* UM $20

My Love Will Stand Guard
Over You (England)
#456934
Issued: 1998 • Open
Retail Price: $20

2 *Values* UM $20

Our Friendship Is Always
In Bloom (Japan)
#456926
Issued: 1998 • Open
Retail Price: $20

3 *Values* UM $20

Sure Would Love To
Squeeze You (Germany)
#456896
Issued: 1998 • Open
Retail Price: $20

4 *Values* UM $20

You Are A Dutch-ess To
Me (Holland)
#456373
Issued: 1998 • Open
Retail Price: $20

5 *Values* UM $20

You Are My Amour (France)
#456918
Issued: 1998 • Open
Retail Price: $20

6 *Values* UM $20

You Can't Beat The
Red, White And Blue
(United States)
#456411
Issued: 1998 • Open
Retail Price: $20

7 *Values* UM $20

All Things Grow With Love
#139505
Issued: 1996 • Open
Retail Price: $20

8 *Values* UM $20

Birthday Wishes With
Hugs And Kisses
#139556
Issued: 1996 • Open
Retail Price: $20

9 *Values* UM $20

Bless Your Little Tutu
#261173
Issued: 1997 • Open
Retail Price: $20

10 *Values* UM $20

Holiday Wishes, Sweety Pie!
(w/scented potpourri pie)
#312444
Issued: 1998 • Open
Retail Price: $20

KEY					
NM Pre'81		1986		1992	1997
1981		1987		1993	1998
1982		1988		1994	1999
1983		1989		1995	2000
1984		1990		1996	2001
1985		1991		UM Unmarked	

International Collection

	Price Paid	Value
1.	20⁰⁰	
2.		
3.		
4.		
5.		
6.		

General Figurines

7.		
8.	20 ⁰⁰	
9.		
10.		

Totals

153

1 *Values* ⅡM $17

I'm A Reflection Of Your Love
Avon Figurine
#730238
Issued: 2000 • Closed: 2000
Retail Price: $14.99

2 *Values* ⅡM $20

It's Ruff To Always Be Cheery
#272639
Issued: 1997 • Open
Retail Price: $20

3 *Values* ⅡM $20

Just The Facts . . . You're Terrific
#320668
Issued: 1997 • Open
Retail Price: $20

4 *Values* ⅡM $22.50

Life's Filled With Little Surprises
Hallmark Exclusive
#524034
Issued: 2000 • Open
Retail Price: $22.50

5 *Values* ⅡM $20

Loving Is Caring
#320579
Issued: 1997 • Open
Retail Price: $20

6 *Values* ⅡM $20

Loving Is Caring
#320595
Issued: 1997 • Open
Retail Price: $20

KEY					
NM Pre'81	✐ 1986	✿ 1992	✝ 1997		
▲ 1981	♣ 1987	⅋ 1993	⚭ 1998		
✗ 1982	✤ 1988	⚙ 1994	★ 1999		
◀ 1983	✠ 1989	△ 1995	⊙ 2000		
✞ 1984	⚓ 1990	♡ 1996	⚮ 2001		
✦ 1985	⚒ 1991	ⅡM Unmarked			

General Figurines

	Price Paid	Value
1.		
2.		
3.		
4.		
5.		
6.		
7.		
8.		
9.		

Totals

7 *Values* ⅡM $23

Soap Bubbles, Soap Bubbles, All Is Soap Bubbles
Avon Figurine
#490342
Issued: 1999 • Closed: 1999
Retail Price: $19.99

8 *Values* ⅡM $24

Photo Unavailable

Thank You For The Time We Share
Avon Figurine
#384836
Issued: 1998 • Closed: 1998
Retail Price: $19.99

9 *Values* ⅡM $25

What Would I Do Without You?
#320714
Issued: 1997 • Open
Retail Price: $25

1 *Values* UM $20

Where Would I Be
Without You?
#139491
Issued: 1996 • Open
Retail Price: $20

2 *Values* UM $19.99

Winter Wishes Warm The Heart
Century Circle Exclusive/
Avon Figurine
#184241S
Issued: 2000 • Open
Retail Price: $19.99

3 *Values* UM $25

You Have Such A Special
Way Of Caring Each And
Every Day
#320706
Issued: 1997 • Open
Retail Price: $25

4 *Values* UM $20

You Make My Spirit Soar
#139564
Issued: 1996 • Open
Retail Price: $20

5 *Values* UM $20

You Make The World
A Sweeter Place
#139521
Issued: 1996 • Open
Retail Price: $20

6 *Values* UM $20

You Set My Heart Ablaze
#320625
Issued: 1997 • Open
Retail Price: $20

7 *Values* UM $20

You Will Always Be
A Winner To Me
#272612
Issued: 1997 • Open
Retail Price: $20

8 *Values* UM $20

You Will Always Be
A Winner To Me
#283460
Issued: 1997 • Open
Retail Price: $20

9 *Values* UM $25

You're Forever In My Heart
#139548
Issued: 1996 • Open
Retail Price: $25

KEY					
NM Pre'81		1986		1992	1997
1981		1987		1993	1998
1982		1988		1994	1999
1983		1989		1995	2000
1984		1990		1996	2001
1985		1991		UM Unmarked	

General Figurines

	Price Paid	Value
1.		
2.		
3.		
4.		
5.		
6.		
7.	2000	
8.	2000	
9.		

Totals

1 *Values* UM $25

You're Just Perfect In My Book
#320560
Issued: 1997 • Open
Retail Price: $25

2 *Values* UM $20

You're The Berry Best
#139513
Issued: 1997 • Open
Retail Price: $20

3 *Values* UM $20

World's Best Helper
#491608
Issued: 1999 • Open
Retail Price: $20

4 *Values* UM $20

World's Greatest Student
#491586
Issued: 1999 • Open
Retail Price: $20

5 *Values* UM $20

World's Greatest Student
#491616
Issued: 1999 • Open
Retail Price: $20

6 *Values* UM $20

World's Sweetest Girl
#491594
Issued: 1999 • Open
Retail Price: $20

KEY			
NM Pre'81	✻ 1986	✾ 1992	✝ 1997
▲ 1981	✦ 1987	✿ 1993	✾ 1998
▮ 1982	✤ 1988	✠ 1994	★ 1999
◄ 1983	✢ 1989	✧ 1995	☉ 2000
✝ 1984	✿ 1990	♡ 1996	✿ 2001
✿ 1985	✤ 1991	UM Unmarked	

7 *Values* UM $20

General Figurines

	Price Paid	Value
1.		
2.		

Trophies

3.		
4.		
5.		
6.		
7.		
8.		

Totals

You're No. 1
#491624
Issued: 1999 • Open
Retail Price: $20

8 *Values* UM $20

You're No. 1
#491640
Issued: 1999 • Open
Retail Price: $20

Ornament Series

Through the years, Enesco has added hundreds of ornaments to its line of PRECIOUS MOMENTS collectibles. Of these items, several have come from popular series. Included in the Ornament Series section are six series, including a collection of special annual Christmas pieces which have always been a favorite of collectors.

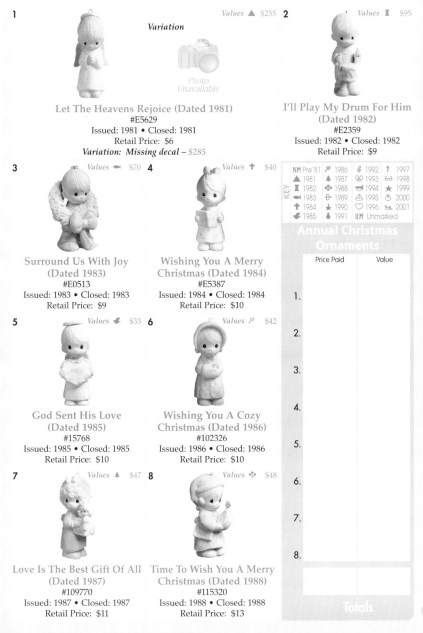

1   *Values* ▲ $255

Variation

Photo Unavailable

Let The Heavens Rejoice (Dated 1981)
#E5629
Issued: 1981 • Closed: 1981
Retail Price: $6
Variation: Missing decal – $285

2   *Values* Ⅰ $95

I'll Play My Drum For Him
(Dated 1982)
#E2359
Issued: 1982 • Closed: 1982
Retail Price: $9

3   *Values* ◄ $70

Surround Us With Joy
(Dated 1983)
#E0513
Issued: 1983 • Closed: 1983
Retail Price: $9

4   *Values* ✝ $40

Wishing You A Merry
Christmas (Dated 1984)
#E5387
Issued: 1984 • Closed: 1984
Retail Price: $10

KEY							
NM	Pre'81	⅛	1986	⅜	1992	†	1997
▲	1981	▲	1987	℗	1993	↔	1998
Ⅰ	1982	⚓	1988	⊶	1994	★	1999
◄	1983	♄	1989	△	1995	◉	2000
✝	1984	✚	1990	♡	1996	≈	2001
✦	1985	♪	1991	UM	Unmarked		

5   *Values* ✦ $33

God Sent His Love
(Dated 1985)
#15768
Issued: 1985 • Closed: 1985
Retail Price: $10

6   *Values* ♪ $42

Wishing You A Cozy
Christmas (Dated 1986)
#102326
Issued: 1986 • Closed: 1986
Retail Price: $10

7   *Values* ▲ $47

Love Is The Best Gift Of All
(Dated 1987)
#109770
Issued: 1987 • Closed: 1987
Retail Price: $11

8   *Values* ⚓ $48

Time To Wish You A Merry
Christmas (Dated 1988)
#115320
Issued: 1988 • Closed: 1988
Retail Price: $13

Annual Christmas Ornaments

	Price Paid	Value
1.		
2.		
3.		
4.		
5.		
6.		
7.		
8.		

Totals

157

1 *Values* ᚦ $35

Oh Holy Night (Dated 1989)
#522848
Issued: 1989 • Closed: 1989
Retail Price: $13.50

2 *Values* ⚓ $36

Once Upon A Holy Night (Dated 1990)
#523852
Issued: 1990 • Closed: 1990
Retail Price: $15

3 *Values* ♦ $36

May Your Christmas Be Merry (Dated 1991)
#524174
Issued: 1991 • Closed: 1991
Retail Price: $15

4 *Values* ⚘ $46

But The Greatest Of These Is Love (Dated 1992)
#527696
Issued: 1992 • Closed: 1992
Retail Price: $15

5 *Values* ∾ $40

Wishing You The Sweetest Christmas (Dated 1993)
#530212
Issued: 1993 • Closed: 1993
Retail Price: $15

6 *Values* ⟃ $36

You're As Pretty As A Christmas Tree (Dated 1994)
#530395
Issued: 1994 • Closed: 1994
Retail Price: $16

KEY			
NM Pre'81	ᛘ 1986	⨳ 1992	✝ 1997
▲ 1981	▲ 1987	∾ 1993	ᚼ 1998
✕ 1982	⬦ 1988	⊒ 1994	★ 1999
◄ 1983	ᚦ 1989	△ 1995	☉ 2000
✝ 1984	⚓ 1990	♡ 1996	≈ 2001
◄ 1985	♦ 1991	**UM** Unmarked	

Annual Christmas Ornaments

	Price Paid	Value
1.		
2.		
3.		
4.		
5.		
6.		
7.		
8.		
9.		
10.		
11.		
Totals		

7 *Values* △ $35

He Covers The Earth With His Beauty (Dated 1995)
#142662
Issued: 1995 • Closed: 1995
Retail Price: $17

8 *Values* ♡ $30

Peace On Earth . . . Anyway (Dated 1996)
#183369
Issued: 1996 • Closed: 1996
Retail Price: $18.50

9 *Values* ✝ $28

Cane You Join Us For A Merry Christmas (Dated 1997)
#272698
Issued: 1997 • Closed: 1997
Retail Price: $18.50

10 *Values* ᚼ $21

I'm Sending You A Merry Christmas (Dated 1998)
#455628
Issued: 1998 • Closed: 1998
Retail Price: $18.50

11 *Values* ★ $22

Slide Into The Next Millennium With Joy (Dated 1999)
#587788
Issued: 1999 • Closed: 1999
Retail Price: $20

1 *Values* ⏱ $21

2 *Values* ㅅ $19

New

Variation

Photo Unavailable

Photo Unavailable

The Future Is In Our Hands (Dated 2000)
#730076
Issued: 2000 • Closed: 2000
Retail Price: $19
***Variation: With cardinal** – $22*

May Your Christmas Begin With A Bang (Dated 2001)
#877441
Issued: 2001 • To Be Closed: 2001
Retail Price: $19

3 *Values* ♦ $38

4 *Values* ✏ $42

5 *Values* ९९ $42

May Your Christmas Be Merry (set/2, Dated 1991)
The Masterpiece Series
#526940
Issued: 1991 • Closed: 1991
Retail Price: $30

But The Greatest Of These Is Love (set/2, Dated 1992)
#527734
Issued: 1992 • Closed: 1992
Retail Price: $30

Wishing You The Sweetest Christmas (set/2, Dated 1993)
#530190
Issued: 1993 • Closed: 1993
Retail Price: $30

6 *Values* ➡ $44

7 *Values* △ $42

You're As Pretty As A Christmas Tree (set/2, Dated 1994)
#530387
Issued: 1994 • Closed: 1994
Retail Price: $30

He Covers The Earth With His Beauty (set/2, Dated 1995)
#142689
Issued: 1995 • Closed: 1995
Retail Price: $30

KEY						
NM Pre'81	✷ 1986	✤ 1992	† 1997
▲ 1981	♠ 1987	९९ 1993	ба 1998
✕ 1982	✤ 1988	➡ 1994	★ 1999
◄ 1983	Ð 1989	△ 1995	⏱ 2000
† 1984	✦ 1990	♡ 1996	ㅅ 2001
✔ 1985	♦ 1991	UM Unmarked	

8 *Values* ♡ $40

9 *Values* † $33

Peace On Earth . . . Anyway (set/2, Dated 1996)
#183350
Issued: 1996 • Closed: 1996
Retail Price: $30

Cane You Join Us For A Merry Christmas (set/2, Dated 1997)
#272728
Issued: 1997 • Closed: 1997
Retail Price: $30

Annual Christmas Ornaments

	Price Paid	Value
1.		
2.		

Annual Christmas Ball Ornaments

3.		
4.		
5.		
6.		
7.		
8.		
9.		

Totals

1 *Values* ⚗ $190

Reindeer (Dated 1986)
#102466
Issued: 1986 • Closed: 1986
Retail Price: $11

2 *Values* ♣ $25

Bear The Good News Of
Christmas (Dated 1987)
#104515
Issued: 1987 • Closed: 1987
Retail Price: $12.50

3 *Values* ✤ $33

Hang On For The Holly
Days (Dated 1988)
#520292
Issued: 1988 • Closed: 1988
Retail Price: $13

4 *Values* ⌀ $38

Christmas Is Ruff Without
You (Dated 1989)
#520462
Issued: 1989 • Closed: 1989
Retail Price: $13

5 *Values* ⚓ $34

Wishing You A Purr-fect
Holiday (Dated 1990)
#520497
Issued: 1990 • Closed: 1990
Retail Price: $15

6 *Values* ⚬ $32

Sno-Bunny Falls For You
Like I Do (Dated 1991)
#520438
Issued: 1991 • Closed: 1991
Retail Price: $15

KEY			
NM Pre'81	⚗ 1986	⚘ 1992	✝ 1997
▲ 1981	♣ 1987	⚙ 1993	1998
Ⅱ 1982	✤ 1988	⚛ 1994	★ 1999
1983	⌀ 1989	△ 1995	☯ 2000
✝ 1984	⚓ 1990	♡ 1996	2001
⚘ 1985	⚬ 1991	UM Unmarked	

**Birthday Series
Ornaments**

	Price Paid	Value
1.		
2.		
3.		
4.		
5.		
6.		
7.		
8.		
9.		
10.		
11.		
12.		
Totals		

7 *Values* ⚘ $25

I'm Nuts About You
(Dated 1992)
#520411
Issued: 1992 • Closed: 1992
Retail Price: $16

8 *Values* ⚙ $28

Slow Down And Enjoy The
Holidays (Dated 1993)
#520489
Issued: 1993 • Closed: 1993
Retail Price: $16

9 *Values* ⚛ $26

You Are Always In My
Heart (Dated 1994)
#530972
Issued: 1994 • Closed: 1994
Retail Price: $16

10 *Values* △ $28

Hippo Holly Days
(Dated 1995)
#520403
Issued: 1995 • Closed: 1995
Retail Price: $17

11 *Values* ♡ $27

Owl Be Home For
Christmas (Dated 1996)
#128708
Issued: 1996 • Closed: 1996
Retail Price: $18.50

12 *Values* ✝ $25

Slow Down For The
Holidays (Dated 1997)
#272760
Issued: 1997 • Closed: 1997
Retail Price: $18.50

1

Values 😊 $15
★ $15
🕐 $15
🐞 $15

May Your Christmas Be Warm (Baby)
#470279
Issued: 1998 • Open
Retail Price: $15

2

Values 😊 $15
★ $15
🕐 $15
🐞 $15

Merry Christmas, Little Lamb (Age 1)
#521078
Issued: 1998 • Open
Retail Price: $15

3

Values 😊 $15
★ $15
🕐 $15
🐞 $15

God Bless You This Christmas (Age 2)
#521094
Issued: 1998 • Open
Retail Price: $15

4

Values 😊 $15
★ $15
🕐 $15
🐞 $15

Heaven Bless Your Special Christmas (Age 3)
#521086
Issued: 1998 • Open
Retail Price: $15

5

Values 😊 $15
★ $15
🕐 $15
🐞 $15

May Your Christmas Be Gigantic (Age 4)
#521108
Issued: 1998 • Open
Retail Price: $15

6

Values 😊 $15
★ $15
🕐 $15
🐞 $15

Christmas Is Something To Roar About (Age 5)
#521116
Issued: 1998 • Open
Retail Price: $15

7

Values 😊 $15
★ $15
🕐 $15
🐞 $15

Christmas Keeps Looking Up (Age 6)
#521124
Issued: 1998 • Open
Retail Price: $15

8

Values UM $12

Always In His Care (Dated 1990)
#225290
Issued: 1990 • Closed: 1990
Retail Price: $8

9

Values UM $10

Sharing A Gift Of Love (Dated 1991)
#233196
Issued: 1991 • Closed: 1991
Retail Price: $8

10

Values UM $12

A Universal Love (Dated 1992)
#238899
Issued: 1992 • Closed: 1992
Retail Price: $8

KEY					
NM Pre'81	✗ 1986	🔥 1992	✝ 1997
▲ 1981	▲ 1987	🎵 1993	😊 1998
✕ 1982	✣ 1988	✥ 1994	★ 1999
✦ 1983	☦ 1989	△ 1995	🕐 2000
✝ 1984	✚ 1990	♡ 1996	🐞 2001
✦ 1985	♦ 1991	UM Unmarked	

Birthday Train Series Ornaments

	Price Paid	Value
1.		
2.		
3.		
4.		
5.		
6.		
7.		

Easter Seals Commemorative Ornaments

8.		
9.		
10.		

Totals

1 *Values* UM $12

You're My Number One
Friend (Dated 1993)
#250112
Issued: 1993 • Closed: 1993
Retail Price: $8

2 *Values* UM $10

It Is No Secret What God
Can Do (Dated 1994)
#244570
Issued: 1994 • Closed: 1994
Retail Price: $6.50

3 *Values* UM $12

Take Time To Smell The
Roses (Dated 1995)
#128899
Issued: 1995 • Closed: 1995
Retail Price: $7.50

4 *Values* UM $10

You Can Always Count On
Me (Dated 1996)
#152579
Issued: 1995 • Closed: 1996
Retail Price: $6.50

5 *Values* UM $9

Give Ability A Chance
(Dated 1997)
#192384
Issued: 1996 • Closed: 1997
Retail Price: $6

6 *Values* UM $9

Somebody Cares
(Dated 1998)
#272922
Issued: 1997 • Closed: 1998
Retail Price: $6.50

KEY			
NM Pre'81	ᴹ 1986	♣ 1992	✝ 1997
▲ 1981	▲ 1987	✿ 1993	6∂ 1998
⊠ 1982	⬥ 1988	➡ 1994	★ 1999
◀ 1983	Ð 1989	⌂ 1995	◑ 2000
✝ 1984	★ 1990	♡ 1996	✍ 2001
✔ 1985	♦ 1991	UM Unmarked	

**Easter Seals
Commemorative Ornaments**

	Price Paid	Value
1.		
2.		
3.		
4.		
5.		
6.		
7.		
8.		

7 *Values* UM $8

*Photo
Unavailable*

Heaven Bless You Easter
Seal (Dated 1999)
#475076
Issued: 1998 • Closed: 1999
Retail Price: $6.50

8 *Values* UM $11

Give Your Whole Heart
(Dated 2000)
#634751
Issued: 1999 • Closed: 2000
Retail Price: $9.50

**Twelve Days Of Christmas
Series Ornaments**

9.		
10.		
11.		
12.		

Totals

9 *Values* 6∂ $22
★ $20
◑ $20
✍ $20

My True Love Gave To Me
1st Day Of Christmas
#455989
Issued: 1998 • Open
Retail Price: $20

10 *Values* 6∂ $22
★ $20
◑ $20
✍ $20

We're Two Of A Kind
2nd Day Of Christmas
#455997
Issued: 1998 • Open
Retail Price: $20

11 *Values* 6∂ $22
★ $20
◑ $20
✍ $20

Saying "Oui" To Our Love
3rd Day Of Christmas
#456004
Issued: 1998 • Open
Retail Price: $20

12 *Values* 6∂ $22
★ $20
◑ $20
✍ $20

Ringing In The Season
4th Day Of Christmas
#456012
Issued: 1998 • Open
Retail Price: $20

1

Values ★ $20
⏱ $20
🔔 $20

The Golden Rings Of Friendship
5th Day Of Christmas
#456020
Issued: 1999 • Open
Retail Price: $20

2

Values ★ $20
⏱ $20
🔔 $20

Hatching The Perfect Holiday
6th Day Of Christmas
#456039
Issued: 1999 • Open
Retail Price: $20

3

Values ★ $20
⏱ $20
🔔 $20

Swimming Into Your Heart
7th Day Of Christmas
#456047
Issued: 1999 • Open
Retail Price: $20

4

Values ★ $20
⏱ $20
🔔 $20

Eight Mice A Milking
8th Day Of Christmas
#456055
Issued: 1999 • Open
Retail Price: $20

5

Values ⏱ $20
🔔 $20

Nine Ladies Dancing With Joy
9th Day Of Christmas
#456063
Issued: 2000 • Open
Retail Price: $20

6

Values ⏱ $20
🔔 $20

Leaping Into The Holidays
10th Day Of Christmas
#456071
Issued: 2000 • Open
Retail Price: $20

7

Values ⏱ $20
🔔 $20

Piping In Perfect Harmony
11th Day Of Christmas
#456098
Issued: 2000 • Open
Retail Price: $20

8

Values ⏱ $20
🔔 $20

Twelve Drummers Drumming Up Fun
12th Day Of Christmas
#456101
Issued: 2000 • Open
Retail Price: $20

KEY					
NM Pre '81	⌘ 1986	⚑ 1992	† 1997
▲ 1981	♠ 1987	♈ 1993	🕰 1998
Ⅱ 1982	♣ 1988	➥ 1994	★ 1999
➟ 1983	✈ 1989	⚖ 1995	⏱ 2000
† 1984	★ 1990	♡ 1996	🔔 2001
➥ 1985	🔔 1991	**UM** Unmarked	

Twelve Days Of Christmas Series Ornaments

	Price Paid	Value
1.		
2.		
3.		
4.		
5.		
6.		
7.		
8.		
Totals		

General Ornaments

Since their introduction in 1981, the number of PRECIOUS MOMENTS ornaments has grown to over 175 pieces. Each year, new pieces are added including many highly collectible dated editions.

1

Values | $25
| $20

15 Years Tweet Music Together (LE-1993)
#530840
Issued: 1993 • Closed: 1993
Retail Price: $15

2

Values | $24

20 Years And The Vision's Still The Same (LE-1998)
#451312
Issued: 1998 • Closed: 1998
Retail Price: $22.50

3

Values | $9

Angel Icicle (Dated 2000)
Avon Exclusive
N/A
Issued: 2000 • Closed: 2000
Retail Price: $7.99

4

Values	
	$32
▲	$30
	$22
	$20
	$20
	$20
	$20
	$18.50
	$18.50
	$18.50
	$18.50
	$18.50
	$18.50
★	$18.50
	$18.50
	$18.50

Angel Of Mercy
#102407
Issued: 1986 • Open
Retail Price: $10 – $18.50

KEY							
NM	Pre'81		1986		1992	†	1997
▲	1981	▲	1987		1993		1998
	1982		1988		1994	★	1999
	1983		1989		1995		2000
†	1984		1990	♡	1996		2001
	1985		1991	UM	Unmarked		

5

Variation

Values	
†	$46
	$43
	$42
▲	$36
	$36
UM	$62

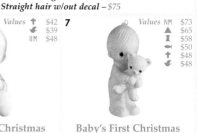

Baby's First Christmas
#E2362
Issued: 1982 • Susp.: 1988
Retail Price: $9 – $12.50
Variations: Straight hair w/decal – $70
Straight hair w/out decal – $75

6

Values	
†	$42
	$39
UM	$48

Baby's First Christmas
#E2372
Issued: 1982 • Susp.: 1985
Retail Price: $9 – $10

7

Values	
NM	$73
▲	$65
	$58
	$50
†	$48
	$48

Baby's First Christmas
#E5631
Issued: 1981 • Susp.: 1985
Retail Price: $6 – $10

8

Values	
NM	$76
▲	$67
	$60
	$54
†	$52
	$50

Baby's First Christmas
#E5632
Issued: 1981 • Susp.: 1985
Retail Price: $6 – $10

	Price Paid	Value
1.		
2.		
3.		
4.		
5.		
6.		
7.		
8.		
Totals		

1   *Values* 🍃 $50

Baby's First Christmas
(Dated 1985)
#15903
Issued: 1985 • Closed: 1985
Retail Price: $10

2   *Values* 🍃 $46

Baby's First Christmas
(Dated 1985)
#15911
Issued: 1985 • Closed: 1985
Retail Price: $10

3   *Values* ⚕ $32

Baby's First Christmas
(Dated 1986)
#102504
Issued: 1986 • Closed: 1986
Retail Price: $10

4   *Values* ⚕ $30

Baby's First Christmas
(Dated 1986)
#102512
Issued: 1986 • Closed: 1986
Retail Price: $10

5   *Values* ▲ $44

Baby's First Christmas
(Dated 1987)
#109401
Issued: 1987 • Closed: 1987
Retail Price: $12

6   *Values* ▲ $44

Baby's First Christmas
(Dated 1987)
#109428
Issued: 1987 • Closed: 1987
Retail Price: $12

7   *Values* ⚜ $25

Baby's First Christmas
(Dated 1988)
#115282
Issued: 1988 • Closed: 1988
Retail Price: $15

8   *Values* ⚜ $26

Baby's First Christmas
(Dated 1988)
#520241
Issued: 1988 • Closed: 1988
Retail Price: $15

General Ornaments

	Price Paid	Value
1.		
2.		
3.		
4.		
5.		
6.		
7.		
8.		
9.		
10.		
11.		
12.		

Totals

9   *Values* ⊕ $28

Baby's First Christmas
(Dated 1989)
#523194
Issued: 1989 • Closed: 1989
Retail Price: $15

10   *Values* ⊕ $32

Baby's First Christmas
(Dated 1989)
#523208
Issued: 1989 • Closed: 1989
Retail Price: $15

11   *Values* ↧ $30

Baby's First Christmas
(Dated 1990)
#523771
Issued: 1990 • Closed: 1990
Retail Price: $15

12   *Values* ↧ $26

Baby's First Christmas
(Dated 1990)
#523798
Issued: 1990 • Closed: 1990
Retail Price: $15

1   *Values* 🌢 $30

Baby's First Christmas
(Dated 1991)
#527084
Issued: 1991 • Closed: 1991
Retail Price: $15

2   *Values* 🌢 $30

Baby's First Christmas
(Dated 1991)
#527092
Issued: 1991 • Closed: 1991
Retail Price: $15

3   *Values* ♬ $30

Baby's First Christmas
(Dated 1992)
#527475
Issued: 1992 • Closed: 1992
Retail Price: $15

4   *Values* ♬ $28

Baby's First Christmas
(Dated 1992)
#527483
Issued: 1992 • Closed: 1992
Retail Price: $15

5   *Values* ♉ $28

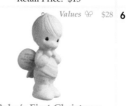

Baby's First Christmas
(Dated 1993)
#530859
Issued: 1993 • Closed: 1993
Retail Price: $15

6   *Values* ♉ $30

Baby's First Christmas
(Dated 1993)
#530867
Issued: 1993 • Closed: 1993
Retail Price: $15

KEY					
NM Pre'81	♩ 1986	♬ 1992	✝ 1997
▲ 1981	▲ 1987	♉ 1993	Ꮷ 1998
I 1982	✤ 1988	⊐ 1994	★ 1999
⊷ 1983	ߦ 1989	⚖ 1995	☉ 2000
✝ 1984	✦ 1990	♡ 1996	▲ 2001
⚘ 1985	🌢 1991	UM Unmarked	

General Ornaments

	Price Paid	Value
1.		
2.		
3.		
4.		
5.		
6.		
7.		
8.		
9.		
10.		
11.		
12.		
	Totals	

7   *Values* ⊐ $30

Baby's First Christmas
(Dated 1994)
#530255
Issued: 1994 • Closed: 1994
Retail Price: $16

8   *Values* ⊐ $30

Baby's First Christmas
(Dated 1994)
#530263
Issued: 1994 • Closed: 1994
Retail Price: $16

9   *Values* ⚖ $30

Baby's First Christmas
(Dated 1995)
#142719
Issued: 1995 • Closed: 1995
Retail Price: $17.50

10   *Values* ⚖ $30

Baby's First Christmas
(Dated 1995)
#142727
Issued: 1995 • Closed: 1995
Retail Price: $17.50

11   *Values* ♡ $26

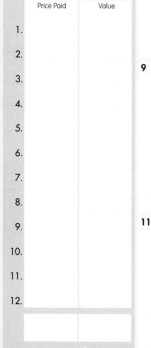

Baby's First Christmas
(Dated 1996)
#183938
Issued: 1996 • Closed: 1996
Retail Price: $17.50

12   *Values* ♡ $26

Baby's First Christmas
(Dated 1996)
#183946
Issued: 1996 • Closed: 1996
Retail Price: $17.50

1 Values † $23

Baby's First Christmas
(Dated 1997)
#272744
Issued: 1997 • Closed: 1997
Retail Price: $18.50

2 Values † $23

Baby's First Christmas
(Dated 1997)
#272752
Issued: 1997 • Closed: 1997
Retail Price: $18.50

3 Values 6∂ $22

Baby's First Christmas
(Dated 1998)
#455644
Issued: 1998 • Closed: 1998
Retail Price: $18.50

4 Values 6∂ $22

Baby's First Christmas
(Dated 1998)
#455652
Issued: 1998 • Closed: 1998
Retail Price: $18.50

5 Values ★ $21

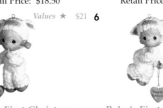

Baby's First Christmas
(Dated 1999)
#587826
Issued: 1999 • Closed: 1999
Retail Price: $18.50

6 Values ★ $21

Baby's First Christmas
(Dated 1999)
#587834
Issued: 1999 • Closed: 1999
Retail Price: $18.50

7 Values ⊘ $20

Baby's First Christmas
(Dated 2000)
#730092
Issued: 2000 • Closed: 2000
Retail Price: $19

8 Values ⊘ $20

Baby's First Christmas
(Dated 2000)
#730106
Issued: 2000 • Closed: 2000
Retail Price: $19

KEY						
NM	Pre'81	♪	1986	♧	1992	† 1997
▲	1981	♠	1987	♉	1993	6∂ 1998
☰	1982	♣	1988	⌐	1994	★ 1999
⇐	1983	♆	1989	△	1995	⊘ 2000
✝	1984	☆	1990	♡	1996	▨ 2001
✦	1985	♨	1991	UM	Unmarked	

9 Values ▨ $19
New

Photo
Unavailable

Baby's First Christmas
(Dated 2001)
#877506
Issued: 2001 • To Be Closed: 2001
Retail Price: $19

10 Values ▨ $19
New

Photo
Unavailable

Baby's First Christmas
(Dated 2001)
#877514
Issued: 2001 • To Be Closed: 2001
Retail Price: $19

11 Values ⇐ $44

Blessed Are The Pure In
Heart (Dated 1983)
#E0518
Issued: 1983 • Closed: 1983
Retail Price: $9

12 Values † $39

Blessed Are The Pure In
Heart (Dated 1984)
#E5392
Issued: 1984 • Closed: 1984
Retail Price: $10

General Ornaments

	Price Paid	Value
1.		
2.		
3.		
4.		
5.		
6.		
7.		
8.		
9.		
10.		
11.		
12.		

Totals

1

Values 🛷 $22
⛪ $18.50
♡ $18.50
† $18.50
∞ $18.50

**Bringing You A
Merry Christmas**
#528226
Issued: 1994 • Retired: 1998
Retail Price: $16 – $18.50

2

Values ★ $32

Bundles Of Joy (LE-1990)
#525057
Issued: 1990 • Closed: 1990
Retail Price: $15

3

Values NM $113
▲ $105
Ⅰ $97
↩ $93
† $87
✦ $81

But Love Goes On Forever
#E5627
Issued: 1981 • Susp.: 1985
Retail Price: $6 – $10

4

Values NM $130
▲ $125
Ⅰ $115
↩ $105
† $100
✦ $100

But Love Goes On Forever
#E5628
Issued: 1981 • Susp.: 1985
Retail Price: $6 – $10

5

Values Ⅰ $90
↩ $83
† $75
UM $102

**Camel, Cow And Donkey
(set/3)**
#E2386
Issued: 1982 • Susp.: 1984
Retail Price: $25 – $27.50

6

Values ✿ $35
Ð $33
★ $32
✦ $30

Cheers To The Leader
#113999
Issued: 1988 • Susp.: 1991
Retail Price: $13.50 – $15

	KEY				
NM Pre'81		1986	✔ 1992	† 1997
▲ 1981		1987	✾ 1993	∞ 1998
Ⅰ 1982		1988	🛷 1994	★ 1999
↩ 1983	Ð	1989	⚘ 1995	☉ 2000
† 1984	★	1990	♡ 1996	☙ 2001
✦ 1985		1991	UM Unmarked	

	Price Paid	Value
1.		
2.		
3.		
4.		
5.		
6.		
7.		
8.		
9.		
10.		
11.		
12.		

Totals

7

Values NM $155
▲ $147
Ⅰ $140
↩ $130
† $124

**Come Let Us Adore
Him (set/4)**
#E5633
Issued: 1981 • Susp.: 1984
Retail Price: $20 – $31.50

8

Values ★ $39
♦ $34
₤ $30
✾ $28
↩ $27

**Dashing Through
The Snow**
#521574
Issued: 1990 • Susp.: 1994
Retail Price: $15 – $16

9

Values ★ $46
♦ $42
₤ $38
⚘ $36
↩ $32

**Don't Let The Holidays
Get You Down**
#521590
Issued: 1990 • Retired: 1994
Retail Price: $15 – $16

10

Values Ⅰ $58
↩ $54
† $50
✦ $48
℘ $45
UM $63

Dropping In For Christmas
#E2369
Issued: 1982 • Retired: 1986
Retail Price: $9 – $10

11

Values Ⅰ $58
↩ $49
† $44
✦ $41

**Dropping Over
For Christmas**
#E2376
Issued: 1982 • Retired: 1985
Retail Price: $9 – $10

12

Values ☙ $36

**Even The Heavens Shall
Praise Him (LE-1998)**
Century Circle Ornament
#475084
Issued: 1998 • Closed: 1998
Retail Price: $30

1 *Values* △ $72

An Event Filled With Sunshine And Smiles (set/2, LE-1995)
Regional Conference Ornament
#160334 (A-G)
Issued: 1995 • Closed: 1995
Retail Price: $35

2 *Values* ♀♀ $25

An Event For All Seasons (LE-1993)
Special Event Ornament
#529974
Issued: 1993 • Closed: 1993
Retail Price: $15

3 *Values* ◄ $100

An Event Showered With Love (set/2, LE-1994)
Regional Conference Ornament
#128295 (A, C & D)
Issued: 1994 • Closed: 1994
Retail Price: $30

4 *Values* I $75 / ◄ $70 / † $65

The First Noël
#E2367
Issued: 1982 • Susp.: 1984
Retail Price: $9 – $10

5 *Values* I $73 / ◄ $55 / † $48

The First Noël
#E2368
Issued: 1982 • Retired: 1984
Retail Price: $9 – $10

6 *Values* ⚲ $45 / ♦ $40 / ♣ $37 / ♀♀ $35 / ▲ $32 / △ $30

Friends Never Drift Apart
#522937
Issued: 1990 • Retired: 1995
Retail Price: $17.50 – $18.50

7 *Values* ⚲ $42 / ♦ $36 / ♣ $32

Glide Through The Holidays
#521566
Issued: 1990 • Retired: 1992
Retail Price: $13.50

8 *Values* ❖ $40 / ▷ $36 / ⚲ $33 / ♦ $32

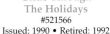

God Sent You Just In Time
#113972
Issued: 1988 • Susp.: 1991
Retail Price: $13.50 – $15

KEY						
NM Pre '81	♪ 1986	♣ 1992	† 1997
▲ 1981	♠ 1987	♀♀ 1993	ϭᴑ 1998
I 1982	❖ 1988	◄ 1994	★ 1999
◄ 1983	▷ 1989	△ 1995	◷ 2000
† 1984	⚲ 1990	♡ 1996	≜ 2001
♂ 1985	♦ 1991	UM Unmarked	

9 *Values* ♡ $26 / † $20 / ϭᴑ $20 / ★ $20 / ◷ $20 / ≜ $20

God's Precious Gift
#183881
Issued: 1996 • Open
Retail Price: $20

10 *Values* ♣ $37 / ♀♀ $32 / ◄ $30 / △ $30 / ♡ $30

Good Friends Are For Always
#524131
Issued: 1992 • Retired: 1997
Retail Price: $15 – $18.50

11 *Values* ♦ $34 / ♣ $28 / ♀♀ $25

The Good Lord Always Delivers
#527165
Issued: 1991 • Susp.: 1993
Retail Price: $15

General Ornaments

	Price Paid	Value
1.		
2.		
3.		
4.		
5.		
6.		
7.		
8.		
9.		
10.		
11.		

Totals

1

Values 🍂 $42
 🎵 $36
 ▲ $33
 ✤ $32
 ᚦ $31

Happiness Is The Lord
#15830
Issued: 1985 • Susp.: 1989
Retail Price: $10 – $13.50

2

Values 👓 $18.50
 ★ $18.50
 ⏱ $18.50
 ▰ $18.50

Happy Holidaze
#520454
Issued: 1998 • Open
Retail Price: $17.50 – $18.50

3

Values 🍶 $38
 ⚘ $36
 ⚲ $31
 ⚮ $29

Happy Trails Is Trusting Jesus
#523224
Issued: 1991 • Susp.: 1994
Retail Price: $15 – $16

4

Values 🍂 $35
 🎵 $30
 ▲ $25
 ✤ $23
 ᚦ $23
 ⚓ $23
 🍶 $23
 ⚮ $22
 ⚲ $21
 ⚱ $21
 ○ $21
 † $21
 👓 $21

Have A Heavenly Christmas
#12416
Issued: 1985 • Susp.: 1998
Retail Price: $12 – $20

5

Values ▲ $34
 ✤ $28
 ᚦ $24
 ⚓ $22
 🍶 $21
 ⚲ $20
 ⚮ $20
 ▰ $19
 ⚑ $19
 ○ $19
 † $19
 👓 $19
 ★ $19

He Cleansed My Soul
#112380
Issued: 1987 • Retired: 1999
Retail Price: $12 – $18.50

6

Values 🍂 $39
 🎵 $36
 ▲ $34
 ✤ $33
 ᚦ $33
 ⚓ $32
 🍶 $32
 ⚲ $30
 ⚮ $30

Honk If You Love Jesus
#15857
Issued: 1985 • Susp.: 1993
Retail Price: $10 – $15

General Ornaments

	Price Paid	Value
1.		
2.		
3.		
4.		
5.		
6.		
7.		
8.		
9.		
10.		
11.		
12.		
Totals		

7

Values 👓 $24.95
 ★ $24.95
 ⏱ $24.95
 ▰ $24.95

House (personalized)
#150231
Issued: 1998 • Open
Retail Price: $24.95

8

Values † $25
 👓 $25
 ★ $25
 ⏱ $25
 ▰ $25

How Can Two Work Together Except They Agree
Care-A-Van Exclusive
#456268
Issued: 1998 • Open
Retail Price: $25

9

Values ᚦ $45
 ⚓ $40
 🍶 $37
 ⚲ $35
 ⚮ $32
 ▰ $32

I Believe In The Old Rugged Cross
#522953
Issued: 1989 • Susp.: 1994
Retail Price: $15 – $16

10

Values 👓 $20

I'll Be Dog-ged It's That Season Again (Dated 1998)
#455660
Issued: 1998 • Closed: 1998
Retail Price: $18.50

11

Values ▲ $40
 ✤ $38
 ᚦ $35
 ⚓ $32

I'm A Possibility
#111120
Issued: 1987 • Susp.: 1990
Retail Price: $11 – $15

12

Values 👓 $18.50
 ★ $18.50
 ⏱ $18.50
 ▰ $18.50

I'm Just Nutty About The Holidays
#455776
Issued: 1998 • Open
Retail Price: $17.50 – $18.50

1

Values
⬆ $38
⬥ $35
D $35
▲ $32
⬧ $30
ℰ $28

I'm Sending You A
White Christmas
#112372
Issued: 1987 • Susp.: 1992
Retail Price: $11 – $15

2

Values † $63

In God's Beautiful
Garden Of Love
Century Circle Ornament
#261599
Issued: 1997 • Closed: 1997
Retail Price: $50

3

Values
⅌ $34
▲ $31
⬥ $28
D $26

It's A Perfect Boy
#102415
Issued: 1986 • Susp.: 1989
Retail Price: $10 – $13.50

4

Values
⅌ $24
⬥ $20
⬟ $19
♡ $19
† $19
6∂ $19
★ $19

It's So Uplifting To Have
A Friend Like You
#528846
Issued: 1993 • Retired: 1999
Retail Price: $16 – $18.50

5

Values
⬅ $74
† $65
⬥ $62

Jesus Is The Light
That Shines
#E0537
Issued: 1983 • Susp.: 1985
Retail Price: $9 – $10

6

Values
⬠ $24
⬥ $20
† $18.50
6∂ $18.50
★ $18.50
⊘ $18.50
⋈ $18.50

Joy From Head
To Mistletoe
#150126
Issued: 1995 • Open
Retail Price: $17 – $18.50

7

Values
† $58
⅌ $55
⅌ $51
▲ $47
⬥ $42
UM $70

Joy To The World
#E2343
Issued: 1982 • Susp.: 1988
Retail Price: $9 – $12.50

8

Values
† $50
⬥ $48
⬥ $45
▲ $43

Joy To The World
#E5388
Issued: 1984 • Retired: 1987
Retail Price: $10 – $11

General Ornaments

	Price Paid	Value
1.		
2.		
3.		
4.		
5.		
6.		
7.		
8.		
9.		
10.		
11.		
12.		

Totals

9

Values
⬠ $26
♡ $22
† $21
6∂ $21
★ $21

Joy To The World
#150320
Issued: 1995 • Retired: 1999
Retail Price: $20

10

Values
♡ $23
† $22
6∂ $22
★ $22

Joy To The World
#153338
Issued: 1996 • Retired: 1999
Retail Price: $20

11

Values
† $22
6∂ $22
★ $22

Joy To The World
#272566
Issued: 1997 • Retired: 1999
Retail Price: $20

12

Values
⬅ $58
† $50
⬥ $45
⅌ $38

Let Heaven And Nature Sing
#E0532
Issued: 1983 • Retired: 1986
Retail Price: $9 – $10

1

Values ⏾ $20
▲ $20

Let's Keep Our Eyes On The Goal
Canadian Exclusive
#802557
Issued: 2000 • Open
Retail Price: $20

2

Values ≈ $50
▲ $47
✧ $44
⊅ $40
▟ $38

Lord, Keep Me On My Toes
#102423
Issued: 1986 • Retired: 1990
Retail Price: $10 – $15

3

Values ⚘ $26
⚭ $23
⊟ $20
△ $20
♡ $18.50
† $18.50
ᗭ $18.50
★ $18.50
⏾ $18.50
▲ $18.50

Lord, Keep Me On My Toes
#525332
Issued: 1992 • Open
Retail Price: $15 – $18.50

4

Values † $38
▲ $34
≈ $33
▲ $31
✧ $31
⊅ $28

Love Is Kind
#E5391
Issued: 1984 • Susp.: 1989
Retail Price: $10 – $13.50

5

Values ⇌ $65
† $60
≈ $55
≈ $50

Love Is Patient
#E0535
Issued: 1983 • Susp.: 1986
Retail Price: $9 – $10

6

Values ⇌ $73
† $67
⚘ $63
≈ $60

Love Is Patient
#E0536
Issued: 1983 • Susp.: 1986
Retail Price: $9 – $10

KEY			
NM Pre'81	≈ 1986	⚘ 1992	† 1997
▲ 1981	▲ 1987	⚭ 1993	ᗭ 1998
✗ 1982	✧ 1988	⇌ 1994	★ 1999
⇌ 1983	⊅ 1989	△ 1995	⏾ 2000
† 1984	▲ 1990	♡ 1996	▲ 2001
⚘ 1985	▟ 1991	UM Unmarked	

7

Values ♡ $40

Love Makes The World Go 'Round (LE-1996)
Century Circle Ornament
#184209
Issued: 1996 • Closed: 1996
Retail Price: $22.50

8

Values ⊅ $30
▟ $28
▲ $25
⚘ $22
⚭ $22
⊟ $20
△ $20
♡ $20
† $20
ᗭ $20
★ $20
⏾ $20
▲ $20

Love One Another
#522929
Issued: 1989 • Open
Retail Price: $17.50 – $20

	Price Paid	Value
1.		
2.		
3.		
4.		
5.		
6.		
7.		
8.		
9.		
10.		
11.		

Totals

9

Values ≈ $28
▲ $22
✧ $20
⊅ $20
▟ $20
▟ $20
⚘ $18.50
⚭ $18.50
⊟ $18.50
△ $18.50
♡ $18.50
† $18.50
ᗭ $18.50
★ $18.50
⏾ $18.50
▲ $18.50

Love Rescued Me
#102385
Issued: 1986 • Open
Retail Price: $10 – $18.50

10

Values ⚘ $28

The Magic Starts With You (LE-1992)
Special Event Ornament
#529648
Issued: 1992 • Closed: 1992
Retail Price: $16

11

Values ⊅ $42
▟ $38
▟ $35
⚘ $33
⚭ $30
⊟ $30
△ $28
♡ $25

Make A Joyful Noise
#522910
Issued: 1989 • Susp.: 1996
Retail Price: $15 – $18.50

1

Values ☦ $39
✦ $35
♦ $34
♦ $33
♈ $30
⌐ $30

May All Your Christmases Be White
#521302
Issued: 1989 • Susp.: 1994
Retail Price: $13.50 – $16

2

Values ★ $22

May All Your Christmases Be White (LE-1999)
#521302R
Issued: 1999 • Closed: 1999
Retail Price: $20

3

Values † $36
✦ $32
♫ $32
▲ $30
✣ $28
☦ $26

May God Bless You With A Perfect Holiday Season
#E5390
Issued: 1984 • Susp.: 1989
Retail Price: $10 – $13.50

4

Variation *Values* ★ $33

May Your Christmas Be A Happy Home
(set/2, Dated 1990)
The Masterpiece Series
#523704
Issued: 1990 • Closed: 1990
Retail Price: $27.50
***Variation: Yellow shirt – *** *$60*

5

Values ✦ $43
♫ $36
▲ $34
✣ $32
☦ $30
✦ $30
♦ $30
♦ $30
♈ $30

May Your Christmas Be Delightful
#15849
Issued: 1985 • Susp.: 1993
Retail Price: $10 – $15

6

Values ★ $22

May Your Christmas Be Delightful (LE-1999)
#15849R
Issued: 1999 • Closed: 1999
Retail Price: $20

7

Values ★ $23

May Your Christmas Be Delightful (LE-1999)
#587931
Issued: 1999 • Closed: 1999
Retail Price: $20

KEY							
NM Pre'81	♫	1986	♦	1992	†	1997
▲ 1981	♣	1987	♈	1993	᚛	1998
♂ 1982	✣	1988	⌐	1994	★	1999
♙ 1983	☦	1989	⚘	1995	◐	2000
† 1984	✦	1990	♡	1996	⚑	2001
✦ 1985	♦	1991	UM	Unmarked		

General Ornaments

	Price Paid	Value
1.		
2.		
3.		
4.		
5.		
6.		
7.		
8.		
9.		
10.		
11.		

Totals

8

Values ✦ $50
♫ $45
▲ $40
✣ $40
☦ $40

May Your Christmas Be Happy
#15822
Issued: 1985 • Susp.: 1989
Retail Price: $10 – $13.50

9

Values ★ $22

May Your Wishes For Peace Take Wing (Dated 1999)
#587818
Issued: 1999 • Closed: 1999
Retail Price: $20

10

Values ⚘ $32

Merry Christmoose (LE-1995)
Special Event Ornament
#150134
Issued: 1995 • Closed: 1995
Retail Price: $17

11

Values ★ $24

Merry Giftness (LE-1999)
Distinguished Service Retailer Ornament
#532223
Issued: 1999 • Closed: 1999
Retail Price: $20

1

Values ♡ $36

The Most Precious Gift Of All (LE-1996)
#212520
Issued: 1996 • Closed: 1996
Retail Price: $20

2

Values	
🐟	$35
✝	$28
♪	$28
🌿	$25
▲	$24
✥	$24
Ð	$22
✝	$22
🔔	$22
👑	$20
☙	$20
🌿	$18.50
△	$18.50
✝	$18.50
6∂	$18.50
★	$18.50
☉	$18.50
⅍	$18.50

Mother Sew Dear
#E0514
Issued: 1983 • Open
Retail Price: $9 – $18.50

3

Values	
✗	$125
➤	$115
✝	$108

Mouse With Cheese
#E2381
Issued: 1982 • Susp.: 1984
Retail Price: $9 – $10

4

Values	
✝	$24
6∂	$24

My Love Will Keep You Warm
Catalog Ornament
#272965
Issued: 1998 • Closed: 1998
Retail Price: $20

5

Values	
✥	$40
Ð	$36
✦	$33
✦	$30

My Love Will Never Let You Go
#114006
Issued: 1988 • Susp.: 1991
Retail Price: $13.50 – $15

6

Values	
➤	$65
✝	$58
✦	$54
♪	$50

O Come, All Ye Faithful
#E0531
Issued: 1983 • Susp.: 1986
Retail Price: $9 – $10

General Ornaments

	Price Paid	Value
1.		
2.		
3.		
4.		
5.		
6.		
7.		
8.		
9.		
10.		
11.		
12.		
Totals		

7

Values	
☉	$20
⅍	$20

One Good Turn Deserves Another
#737569
Issued: 2000 • Open
Retail Price: $20

8

Values	
🌿	$23
△	$20
♡	$18.50
✝	$18.50
6∂	$18.50
★	$18.50
☉	$18.50
⅍	$18.50

Onward Christmas Soldiers
#527327
Issued: 1994 • Open
Retail Price: $16 – $18.50

9

Values	
🌿	$37
△	$32
♡	$30
✝	$30
6∂	$30
★	$30
☉	$30
⅍	$30

Ornament Enhancer
#603171
Issued: 1994 • Open
Retail Price: $30

10

Values	
✗	$58
➤	$48
✝	$42
✦	$39
♪	$37
▲	$35
✥	$35
Ð	$33
✦	$30
♦	$30

Our First Christmas Together
#E2385
Issued: 1982 • Susp.: 1991
Retail Price: $9 – $15

11

Values ♪ $35

Our First Christmas Together (Dated 1986)
#102350
Issued: 1986 • Closed: 1986
Retail Price: $10

12

Values ▲ $38

Our First Christmas Together (Dated 1987)
#112399
Issued: 1987 • Closed: 1987
Retail Price: $11

1 *Values* ❖ $26

Our First Christmas
Together (Dated 1988)
#520233
Issued: 1988 • Closed: 1988
Retail Price: $13

2 *Values* ⊕ $36

Our First Christmas
Together (Dated 1989)
#521558
Issued: 1989 • Closed: 1989
Retail Price: $17.50

3 *Values* ★ $28

Our First Christmas
Together (Dated 1990)
#525324
Issued: 1990 • Closed: 1990
Retail Price: $17.50

4 *Values* ♦ $30

Our First Christmas
Together (Dated 1991)
#522945
Issued: 1991 • Closed: 1991
Retail Price: $17.50

5 *Values* ♪ $32

Our First Christmas
Together (Dated 1992)
#528870
Issued: 1992 • Closed: 1992
Retail Price: $17.50

6 *Values* ♀ $27

Our First Christmas
Together (Dated 1993)
#530506
Issued: 1993 • Closed: 1993
Retail Price: $17.50

7 *Values* 🚂 $28

Our First Christmas
Together (Dated 1994)
#529206
Issued: 1994 • Closed: 1994
Retail Price: $18.50

8 *Values* △ $28

Our First Christmas
Together (Dated 1995)
#142700
Issued: 1995 • Closed: 1995
Retail Price: $18.50

NM	Pre'81	♫	1986	♪	1992	† 1997
▲	1981	▲	1987	♀	1993	🔆 1998
Ⅱ	1982	❖	1988	🚂	1994	★ 1999
➔	1983	⊕	1989	△	1995	⏰ 2000
†	1984	★	1990	♡	1996	🔔 2001
☘	1985	♦	1991	UM	Unmarked	

KEY

	Price Paid	Value
1.		
2.		
3.		
4.		
5.		
6.		
7.		
8.		
9.		
10.		
11.		
12.		

9 *Values* ♡ $30

Our First Christmas
Together (Dated 1996)
#183911
Issued: 1996 • Closed: 1996
Retail Price: $22.50

10 *Values* † $28

Our First Christmas
Together (Dated 1997)
#272736
Issued: 1997 • Closed: 1997
Retail Price: $20

11 *Values* 🔆 $27

Our First Christmas
Together (Dated 1998)
#455636
Issued: 1998 • Closed: 1998
Retail Price: $25

12 *Values* ★ $27

Our First Christmas
Together (Dated 1999)
#587796
Issued: 1999 • Closed: 1999
Retail Price: $25

Totals

175

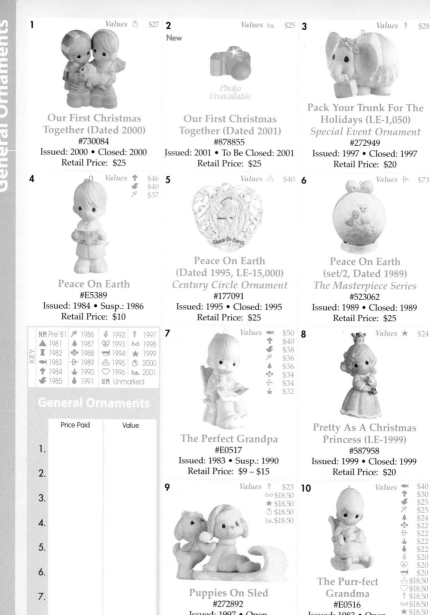

1   *Values* ⊘ $27

Our First Christmas Together (Dated 2000)
#730084
Issued: 2000 • Closed: 2000
Retail Price: $25

2   *Values* ᐟᐟ $25

New

Photo Unavailable

Our First Christmas Together (Dated 2001)
#878855
Issued: 2001 • To Be Closed: 2001
Retail Price: $25

3   *Values* ✝ $28

Pack Your Trunk For The Holidays (LE-1,050)
Special Event Ornament
#272949
Issued: 1997 • Closed: 1997
Retail Price: $20

4   *Values* ✝ $46
  ✔ $40
  ♬ $37

Peace On Earth
#E5389
Issued: 1984 • Susp.: 1986
Retail Price: $10

5   *Values* △ $40

Peace On Earth (Dated 1995, LE-15,000)
Century Circle Ornament
#177091
Issued: 1995 • Closed: 1995
Retail Price: $25

6   *Values* Đ $73

Peace On Earth (set/2, Dated 1989)
The Masterpiece Series
#523062
Issued: 1989 • Closed: 1989
Retail Price: $25

KEY					
NM	Pre'81	♬	1986	✦	1992	✝	1997
▲	1981	♠	1987	♋	1993	∂	1998
♊	1982	♣	1988	⌐	1994	★	1999
◄	1983	Đ	1989	△	1995	⊘	2000
✝	1984	✦	1990	♡	1996	ᐟᐟ	2001
✔	1985	♠	1991	�𝐔𝐌	Unmarked

7   *Values* 🐟 $50
  ✝ $40
  ♬ $38
  ♬ $36
  ♠ $36
  ◆ $34
  Đ $34
  ✦ $32

The Perfect Grandpa
#E0517
Issued: 1983 • Susp.: 1990
Retail Price: $9 – $15

8   *Values* ★ $24

Pretty As A Christmas Princess (LE-1999)
#587958
Issued: 1999 • Closed: 1999
Retail Price: $20

9   *Values* ✝ $23
  ∂ $18.50
  ★ $18.50
  ⊘ $18.50
  ᐟᐟ $18.50

Puppies On Sled
#272892
Issued: 1997 • Open
Retail Price: $18.50

10   *Values* 🐟 $40
  ✝ $30
  ♬ $25
  ♬ $25
  ♠ $24
  ◆ $22
  Đ $22
  ✦ $22
  ♠ $22
  ✦ $20
  ♋ $20
  ⌐ $20
  △ $18.50
  ♡ $18.50
  ✝ $18.50
  ∂ $18.50
  ★ $18.50
  ⊘ $18.50
  ᐟᐟ $18.50

The Purr-fect Grandma
#E0516
Issued: 1983 • Open
Retail Price: $9 – $18.50

11   *Values* ◆ $48
  Đ $44
  ✦ $40
  ♠ $36

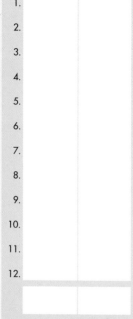

Rejoice O Earth
#113980
Issued: 1988 • Retired: 1991
Retail Price: $13.50 – $15

12   *Values* ♬ $40
  ♠ $38
  ◆ $36
  Đ $32
  ✦ $28
  ♠ $28

Rocking Horse
#102474
Issued: 1986 • Susp.: 1991
Retail Price: $10 – $15

	Price Paid	Value
1.		
2.		
3.		
4.		
5.		
6.		
7.		
8.		
9.		
10.		
11.		
12.		
Totals		

1

Photo Unavailable

A Salute To Our Stars
Local Club Chapter Convention Ornament
#549614
Issued: 1998 • Closed: 1998
Retail Price: N/A

2 *Values* ⟿ $23
△ $18.50
♡ $18.50
† $18.50
⟿ $18.50
★ $18.50
☉ $18.50
⤷ $18.50

Sending You A White Christmas
#528218
Issued: 1994 • Open
Retail Price: $16 – $18.50

3 *Values* ♪ $32
▲ $28
❖ $25

Serve With A Smile
#102431
Issued: 1986 • Susp.: 1988
Retail Price: $10 – $12.50

4 *Values* ♪ $39
▲ $35
❖ $29

Serve With A Smile
#102458
Issued: 1986 • Susp.: 1988
Retail Price: $10 – $12.50

5 *Values* ✿ $24
⟿ $20
△ $18.50
♡ $18.50
† $18.50
⟿ $18.50
★ $18.50
☉ $18.50
⤷ $18.50

Share In The Warmth Of Christmas
#527211
Issued: 1993 • Open
Retail Price: $15 – $18.50

6 *Values* ♪ $44
▲ $37
❖ $34
ᚦ $32
⚖ $32
♪ $30
⚘ $27
✿ $25

Shepherd Of Love
#102288
Issued: 1986 • Susp.: 1993
Retail Price: $10 – $15

7 *Values* ❖ $42
ᚦ $37
⚖ $34
♪ $34
⚘ $30
✿ $26

Smile Along The Way
#113964
Issued: 1988 • Susp.: 1993
Retail Price: $15 – $17.50

8 *Values* ⤷ $17.50
New

Photo Unavailable

Sno-Ball Without You (Dated 2001)
#520446
Issued: 2001 • To Be Closed: 2001
Retail Price: $17.50

KEY			
NM Pre'81	♪ 1986	⚖ 1992	† 1997
▲ 1981	▲ 1987	♪ 1993	⟿ 1998
✕ 1982	❖ 1988	⟿ 1994	★ 1999
⟿ 1983	ᚦ 1989	△ 1995	☉ 2000
† 1984	♪ 1990	♡ 1996	⤷ 2001
⟿ 1985	♪ 1991	**UM** Unmarked	

9 ▲ *Values* ♡ N/E

Sweet 16 (LE-1996)
Local Club Chapter Convention Ornament
#266841
Issued: 1996 • Closed: 1996
Retail Price: N/A

10 *Values* ⟿ $26

Take A Bow Cuz You're My Christmas Star (LE-1994)
Special Event Ornament
#520470
Issued: 1994 • Closed: 1994
Retail Price: $16

	Price Paid	Value
1.		
2.		
3.		
4.		
5.		
6.		
7.		
8.		
9.		
10.		
11.		
12.		
Totals		

11 *Values* ⟿ $65
† $60
⚓ $55
♪ $53
▲ $48
❖ $48

Tell Me The Story Of Jesus
#E0533
Issued: 1983 • Susp.: 1988
Retail Price: $9 – $12.50

12 *Values* ⟿ $59
† $57
⚓ $54
♪ $52
▲ $52
❖ $52

To A Special Dad
#E0515
Issued: 1983 • Susp.: 1988
Retail Price: $9 – $12.50

1

Values	
♣	$42
⊕	$30
★	$26
⚓	$24
⚱	$22
ஐ	$21
⊟	$21
△	$21
♡	$21
†	$21
6⋑	$21
★	$21

To My Forever Friend
#113956
Issued: 1988 • Retired: 1999
Retail Price: $16 – $20

2

Values	
⊸	$58
†	$51
⚱	$47
⋏	$45
▲	$42
⚓	$38
⊕	$34

To Thee With Love
#E0534
Issued: 1983 • Retired: 1989
Retail Price: $9 – $13.50

3

Values	
⋏	$27
▲	$25
♣	$23
⊕	$20
★	$20
⚱	$20
⚓	$18.50
ஐ	$18.50
⊟	$18.50
♡	$18.50
†	$18.50
★	$18.50
◐	$18.50
⚏	$18.50

Trust And Obey
#102377
Issued: 1986 • Open
Retail Price: $10 – $18.50

4

Values	
ⅈ	$62
†	$62
⚱	$60
⋏	$55
⋏	$53
▲	$50
⚱	$50
UM	$65

Unicorn
#E2371
Issued: 1982 • Retired: 1988
Retail Price: $9 – $13

5
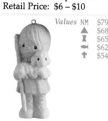

Values	
NM	$75
ⅈ	$65
ⅈ	$60
⊸	$57
†	$55
⚱	$55

Unto Us A Child Is Born
#E5630
Issued: 1981 • Susp.: 1985
Retail Price: $6 – $10

6

Values	
▲	$33
♣	$24
⊕	$22
★	$20
⚱	$20
⚓	$20
ஐ	$19
⊟	$19
△	$19
♡	$19
†	$19
6⋑	$19
★	$19

Waddle I Do Without You
#112364
Issued: 1987 • Retired: 1999
Retail Price: $11 – $18.50

General Ornaments

	Price Paid	Value
1.		
2.		
3.		
4.		
5.		
6.		
7.		
8.		
9.		
10.		
Totals		

7

Values	NM	$79
	ⅈ	$68
	ⅈ	$65
	⊸	$62
	†	$54

We Have Seen His Star
#E6120
Issued: 1981 • Retired: 1984
Retail Price: $6 – $10

8

Values	NM	$150
	▲	$145
	ⅈ	$138
	⊸	$130
	†	$125

Wee Three Kings (set/3)
#E5634
Issued: 1981 • Susp.: 1984
Retail Price: $19 – $27.50

9

Values	♡	$22
	†	$18.50
	6⋑	$18.50
	★	$18.50
	◐	$18.50
	⚏	$18.50

When The Skating's Ruff, Try Prayer
#183903
Issued: 1996 • Open
Retail Price: $18.50

10

Values	♡	$30

Wishing You A Bear-ie Merry Christmas (LE-1996)
Special Event Ornament
#531200
Issued: 1996 • Closed: 1996
Retail Price: $17.50

1  *Values* ✤ $22

You Are My Gift Come True
(Dated 1988)
#520276
Issued: 1988 • Closed: 1988
Retail Price: $12.50

2  *Values* ▲ $45
　 ✤ $40
　 ♉ $34
　 ↓ $34
　 ♦ $33
　 ♬ $33
　 ✿ $32
　 ◄ $32
　 △ $30
　 ♡ $30

You Have Touched
So Many Hearts
#112356
Issued: 1987 • Retired: 1997
Retail Price: $11 – $18.50

3  *Values* ◔ $27
　 ﹏ $27

Your Love Keeps Me
Toasty Warm
GCC Exclusive
#795577
Issued: 2000 • Closed: 2000
Retail Price: $25

4  *Values* ◔ $32

Your Love Keeps Me
Toasty Warm (Dated 2000)
#800813
Issued: 2000 • Closed: 2000
Retail Price: $30

5  *Values* △ $25
　 ♡ $20
　 † $18.50
　 ↝ $18.50
　 ★ $18.50
　 ◔ $18.50
　 ﹏ $18.50

You're "A" Number One In
My Book, Teacher
#150142
Issued: 1995 • Open
Retail Price: $17 – $18.50

KEY			
NM Pre'81	♪ 1986	♨ 1992	† 1997
▲ 1981	▲ 1987	♉ 1993	6♂ 1998
I 1982	✤ 1988	◄ 1994	★ 1999
◄ 1983	Ð 1989	△ 1995	◔ 2000
† 1984	↓ 1990	♡ 1996	﹏ 2001
✦ 1985	♦ 1991	UM Unmarked	

General Ornaments

	Price Paid	Value
1.		
2.		
3.		
4.		
5.		

Totals

179

Other PRECIOUS MOMENTS® Pieces

This section includes bells, musicals, dolls, plates, plush animals and more; all of which will help to help fill your home with the spirit of "loving, sharing and caring."

1

Values UM $215

Let The Heavens Rejoice
(Dated 1981)
#E5622
Issued: 1981 • Closed: 1981
Retail Price: $15

2

Values UM $65

I'll Play My Drum For Him
(Dated 1982)
#E2358
Issued: 1982 • Closed: 1982
Retail Price: $17

3

Values ⌁ $65
UM $70

Surrounded With Joy
(Dated 1983)
#E0522
Issued: 1983 • Closed: 1983
Retail Price: $18

4

Values † $44

Wishing You A Merry
Christmas (Dated 1984)
#E5393
Issued: 1984 • Closed: 1984
Retail Price: $19

Bells

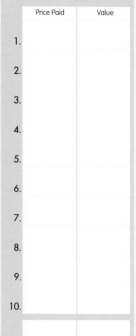

	Price Paid	Value
1.		
2.		
3.		
4.		
5.		
6.		
7.		
8.		
9.		
10.		

Totals

5

Values 🍃 $40

God Sent His Love
(Dated 1985)
#15873
Issued: 1985 • Closed: 1985
Retail Price: $19

6

Values ♨ $36

Wishing You A Cozy
Christmas (Dated 1986)
#102318
Issued: 1986 • Closed: 1986
Retail Price: $20

7

Values ▲ $44

Love Is The Best Gift Of All
(Dated 1987)
#109835
Issued: 1987 • Closed: 1987
Retail Price: $22.50

8
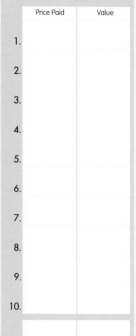
Values ⬙ $40

Time To Wish You A Merry
Christmas (Dated 1988)
#115304
Issued: 1988 • Closed: 1988
Retail Price: $25

9

Values ⅁ $38

Oh Holy Night (Dated 1989)
#522821
Issued: 1989 • Closed: 1989
Retail Price: $25

10

Values ♠ $39

Once Upon A Holy Night
(Dated 1990)
#523828
Issued: 1990 • Closed: 1990
Retail Price: $25

1 Values 🕯 $40

May Your Christmas Be Merry (Dated 1991)
#524182
Issued: 1991 • Closed: 1991
Retail Price: $25

2 Values 🕯 $36

But The Greatest Of These Is Love (Dated 1992)
#527726
Issued: 1992 • Closed: 1992
Retail Price: $25

3 Values 🕊 $40

Wishing You The Sweetest Christmas (Dated 1993)
#530174
Issued: 1993 • Closed: 1993
Retail Price: $25

4 Values 🐦 $34

You're As Pretty As A Christmas Tree (Dated 1994)
#604216
Issued: 1994 • Closed: 1994
Retail Price: $27.50

5 Values 🕆 $47
UM $52

God Understands
#E5211
Issued: 1981 • Retired: 1984
Retail Price: $15 – $19

6 Values 🕆 $46
UM $60

Jesus Is Born
#E5623
Issued: 1981 • Susp.: 1984
Retail Price: $15 – $19

7 Values 🕆 $50
🕯 $46
UM $60

Jesus Loves Me
#E5208
Issued: 1981 • Susp.: 1985
Retail Price: $15 – $19

8 Values 🕆 $55
🕯 $51
UM $60

Jesus Loves Me
#E5209
Issued: 1981 • Susp.: 1985
Retail Price: $15 – $19

KEY			
NM Pre'81	✗ 1986	🕯 1992	🕆 1997
▲ 1981	▲ 1987	🕊 1993	🔆 1998
✗ 1982	✿ 1988	1994	★ 1999
🕯 1983	⊕ 1989	△ 1995	⏀ 2000
🕆 1984	⬇ 1990	♡ 1996	🔥 2001
🕯 1985	🕯 1991	UM Unmarked	

9 Values 🕆 $40
🕯 $37
UM $46

The Lord Bless You And Keep You
#E7175
Issued: 1982 • Susp.: 1985
Retail Price: $17 – $19

10 Values 🕆 $62
🕯 $55
UM $68

The Lord Bless You And Keep You
#E7176
Issued: 1982 • Susp.: 1985
Retail Price: $17 – $19

11 Values 🕆 $65
🕯 $62
✗ $62
▲ $60
✿ $59
⊕ $57
⬇ $57
🕯 $55
🕯 $55
🕊 $55
UM $68

The Lord Bless You And Keep You
#E7179
Issued: 1982 • Susp.: 1993
Retail Price: $22.50 – $35

12 Values 🕆 $45
🕯 $42
✗ $38
▲ $36
✿ $35
UM $53

Mother Sew Dear
#E7181
Issued: 1982 • Susp.: 1988
Retail Price: $17 – $22.50

Bells

	Price Paid	Value
1.		
2.		
3.		
4.		
5.		
6.		
7.		
8.		
9.		
10.		
11.		
12.		
Totals		

1

Values † $50
      UM $60

Prayer Changes Things
#E5210
Issued: 1981 • Susp.: 1984
Retail Price: $15 – $19

2

Values † $47
      🐟 $44
      ♪ $42
      ⚓ $42
      ✚ $37
      UM $56

The Purr-fect Grandma
#E7183
Issued: 1982 • Susp.: 1988
Retail Price: $17 – $22.50

3

Values † $47
      🐟 $45
      UM $58

We Have Seen His Star
#E5620
Issued: 1981 • Susp.: 1985
Retail Price: $15 – $19

4

Values ◷ $75
      ▨ $75

**By Grace We Have
Communion With God**
#325333C
Issued: 2000 • Open
Retail Price: $75

5

Values ➼ $103
      † $98
      🐟 $95
      ♪ $90
      ⚓ $86
      ✚ $84
      UM $115

**But Love Goes On
Forever (set/2)**
#E6118
Issued: 1981 • Susp.: 1988
Retail Price: $14 – $25

6

Values † $107
      🐟 $100
      UM $125

Joy To The World (set/2)
#E2344
Issued: 1982 • Susp.: 1985
Retail Price: $20 – $22.50

Bells

	Price Paid	Value
1.		
2.		
3.		

Bible Holder

4.		

Candle Climbers

5.		
6.		

Clocks

7.		

Covered Boxes

8.		
9.		
10.		
11.		
12.		

Totals

7

Values ▨ $70

New

*Photo
Unavailable*

**It's Almost Time For Santa
(LE-2001)**
#532932
Issued: 2001 • To Be Closed: 2001
Retail Price: $70

8

Values Ⅱ $115
      ➼ $108
      † $90
      🐟 $83

Forever Friends (set/2)
#E9283
Issued: 1983 • Susp.: 1984
Retail Price: $15 – $17

9

Values ◷ $12.50
      ▨ $12.50

I'll Give You The World
#798290
Issued: 2000 • Open
Retail Price: $12.50

10

Values ➼ $53
      † $48
      🐟 $48
      ♪ $44
      ⚓ $43
      ✚ $41
      UM $60

**I'm Falling For Some
Bunny/Our Love Is
Heaven-scent (set/2)**
#E9266
Issued: 1983 • Susp.: 1988
Retail Price: $13.50 – $18.50

11

Values Ⅱ $55
      🐟 $50
      † $48
      🐟 $47

Jesus Loves Me
#E9280
Issued: 1983 • Susp.: 1985
Retail Price: $17.50 – $19

12

Values Ⅱ $72
      ➼ $68
      † $63
      🐟 $60

Jesus Loves Me
#E9281
Issued: 1983 • Susp.: 1985
Retail Price: $17.50 – $19

1
Values ⚊ $67
$63
$57
$50

**The Lord Bless You
And Keep You**
#E7167
Issued: 1982 • Susp.: 1985
Retail Price: $22.50 – $25

2
Values UM $30

Care-A-Van Truck
Care-A-Van Exclusive
#475041
Issued: 1998 • Open
Retail Price: $30

3
Values UM $30

*Photo
Unavailable*

Care-A-Van 2000 Truck
Care-A-Van Exclusive
#817546
Issued: 2000 • Open
Retail Price: $30

4
Values ⚊ $153
$142

Aaron
#12424
Issued: 1985 • Susp.: 1986
Retail Price: $135

5
Values ▲ $285

Angie, The Angel Of Mercy
(LE-12,500)
#12491
Issued: 1987 • Closed: 1987
Retail Price: $160

6
Values ⚊ $156
$156

Autumn's Praise
(LE-1990/1991)
#408808
Issued: 1990 • Closed: 1991
Retail Price: $150

7
Values ⚊ $155
$145

Bethany
#12432
Issued: 1985 • Susp.: 1986
Retail Price: $135

8
Values $280

Bong Bong (LE-12,000)
#100455
Issued: 1986 • Closed: 1986
Retail Price: $150

Covered Boxes

	Price Paid	Value
1.		

Die-Cast Trucks

2.		
3.		

Dolls

4.		
5.		
6.		
7.		
8.		
9.		
10.		
11.		
12.		

Totals

9
Values $295

Candy (LE-12,000)
#100463
Issued: 1986 • Closed: 1986
Retail Price: $150

10
Values $275

Connie (LE-7,500)
#102253
Issued: 1986 • Closed: 1986
Retail Price: $160

11
Values UM $480

Cubby (LE-5,000)
#E7267B
Issued: 1982 • Closed: 1982
Retail Price: $200

12
Values ⚊ $250
✝ $240
⚊ $235
UM $265

Debbie
#E6214G
Issued: 1981 • Susp.: 1985
Retail Price: $175 – $200

1
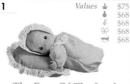

Values
⚓ $75
🔔 $68
✝ $68
💮 $68
� $68

The Eyes Of The Lord
Are Upon You
♪ "Brahms' Lullaby"
#429570
Issued: 1991 • Susp.: 1994
Retail Price: $65

2

Values
⚓ $75
🔔 $68
✝ $68
💮 $68
� $68

The Eyes Of The Lord
Are Upon You
♪ "Brahms' Lullaby"
#429589
Issued: 1991 • Susp.: 1994
Retail Price: $65

3

Values
⚓ $185
✝ $180
🍀 $180
♪ $180
▲ $180
✠ $180
UM $195

Katie Lynne
#E0539
Issued: 1983 • Susp.: 1988
Retail Price: $150 – $175

4

Values
✝ $188
🍀 $180
♪ $175
▲ $175
✠ $175
Ð $175

Kristy
#E2851
Issued: 1984 • Susp.: 1989
Retail Price: $150 – $170

5

Values
⚓ $155
🔔 $155
✝ $155

May You Have An Old
Fashioned Christmas
(LE-1991/1992)
#417785
Issued: 1991 • Closed: 1992
Retail Price: $150

6

Values
⚓ $225
✝ $220
🍀 $210
UM $255

Mikey
#E6214B
Issued: 1981 • Susp.: 1985
Retail Price: $175 – $200

Dolls

	Price Paid	Value
1.		
2.		
3.		
4.		
5.		
6.		
7.		
8.		
9.		
10.		
11.		
12.		

Totals

7

Values
✝ $360
🍀 $355
UM $355

Mother Sew Dear
#E2850
Issued: 1984 • Retired: 1985
Retail Price: $350

8

Values
🍀 $72
♪ $67
UM $75

P.D.
#12475
Issued: 1985 • Susp.: 1986
Retail Price: $50

9

Values
⚓ $155
🔔 $155

Summer's Joy (LE-1990/1991)
#408794
Issued: 1990 • Closed: 1991
Retail Price: $150

10
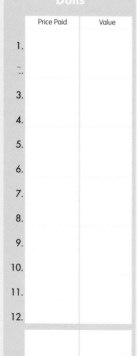

Values UM $565

Tammy (LE-5,000)
#E7267G
Issued: 1982 • Closed: 1982
Retail Price: $300

11

Values
✝ $165
🍀 $158
♪ $155
▲ $155
✠ $155
Ð $155
⚓ $155
🔔 $155

Timmy
#E5397
Issued: 1984 • Susp.: 1991
Retail Price: $125 – $150

12

Values
🍀 $82
♪ $74
UM $86

Trish
#12483
Issued: 1985 • Susp.: 1986
Retail Price: $50

1 *Values* ⚜ $155 / ♦ $155

The Voice Of Spring
(LE-1990/1991)
#408786
Issued: 1990 • Closed: 1991
Retail Price: $150

2 *Values* ⚜ $160 / ♦ $160

Winter's Song (LE-1990/1991)
#408816
Issued: 1990 • Closed: 1991
Retail Price: $150

3 *Values* ⚜ $95 / ♦ $95 / ∮ $95

You Have Touched So Many
Hearts (LE-1991/1992)
#427527
Issued: 1991 • Closed: 1992
Retail Price: $90

4 *Values* ⚜ $44 / ♦ $37

I Will Cherish The Old
Rugged Cross
(set/2, Dated 1991)
#523534
Issued: 1991 • Closed: 1991
Retail Price: $27.50

5 *Values* ∮ $38 / ✧ $32

Make A Joyful Noise
(set/2, Dated 1993)
#528617
Issued: 1993 • Closed: 1993
Retail Price: $27.50

6 *Values* ✧ $35 / ⊷ $31

A Reflection Of His Love
(set/2, Dated 1994)
#529095
Issued: 1994 • Closed: 1994
Retail Price: $27.50

7 *Values* ♦ $33 / ∮ $30

We Are God's Workmanship
(set/2, Dated 1992)
#525960
Issued: 1992 • Closed: 1992
Retail Price: $27.50

8 *Values* ◗ $55 / ✝ $50 / ✠ $48 / ⅍ $46 / ▲ $42

Blessed Are The
Pure In Heart
#E0521
Issued: 1983 • Susp.: 1987
Retail Price: $18 – $21

9 *Values* ✝ $120 / ✦ $112 / ⅍ $92 / ▲ $80

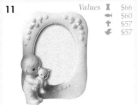

God's Precious Gift
#12033
Issued: 1985 • Susp.: 1987
Retail Price: $19 – $20

10 *Values* ✝ $68 / ✦ $65 / ⅍ $60 / ▲ $57 / ✣ $55 / ✠ $52 / ✦ $52 / ✦ $48 / ∮ $45

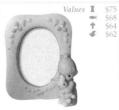

God's Precious Gift
#12041
Issued: 1985 • Susp.: 1992
Retail Price: $19 – $27.50

11 *Values* ✠ $66 / ✦ $60 / ✝ $57 / ✦ $57

Jesus Loves Me
#E7170
Issued: 1982 • Susp.: 1985
Retail Price: $17 – $19

12 *Values* ✠ $75 / ✦ $68 / ✝ $64 / ✦ $62

Jesus Loves Me
#E7171
Issued: 1982 • Susp.: 1985
Retail Price: $17 – $19

Dolls

	Price Paid	Value
1.		
2.		
3.		

Eggs

4.		
5.		
6.		
7.		

Frames

8.		
9.		
10.		
11.		
12.		

Totals

1

Values ✠ $70
🐟 $64
✝ $60
🍂 $60
▲ $56
⬧ $56
⚓ $54
☩ $54
✠ $52
🔔 $50
🕯 $48
♾ $46

The Lord Bless
You And Keep You
#E7166
Issued: 1982 • Susp.: 1993
Retail Price: $22.50 – $32.50

2

Values ✠ $55
🐟 $50
✝ $45
🍂 $45
♾ $42
▲ $40

The Lord Bless
You And Keep You
#E7177
Issued: 1982 • Susp.: 1987
Retail Price: $18 – $20

3

Values ✠ $78
🐟 $76
✝ $73
🍂 $73
♾ $71
▲ $68

The Lord Bless
You And Keep You
#E7178
Issued: 1982 • Susp.: 1987
Retail Price: $18 – $20

4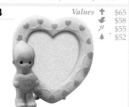

Values ✝ $65
🍂 $58
♾ $55
▲ $52

Loving You
#12017
Issued: 1985 • Susp.: 1987
Retail Price: $19 – $20

5

Values ✝ $67
🍂 $62
♾ $57
▲ $55

Loving You
#12025
Issued: 1985 • Susp.: 1987
Retail Price: $19 – $20

6

Values ✠ $59
🐟 $54
✝ $50
🍂 $46
♾ $43

Mother Sew Dear
#E7241
Issued: 1982 • Susp.: 1986
Retail Price: $18 – $19

Frames

	Price Paid	Value
1.		
2.		
3.		
4.		
5.		
6.		
7.		
8.		
9.		

Birthstone Collection Hinged Boxes

10.		
11.		
12.		

Totals

7

Values ✠ $74
🐟 $67
✝ $64

My Guardian Angel
#E7168
Issued: 1982 • Susp.: 1984
Retail Price: $18 – $19

8

Values ✠ $83
🐟 $71
✝ $68

My Guardian Angel
#E7169
Issued: 1982 • Susp.: 1984
Retail Price: $18 – $19

9

Values ✠ $55
🐟 $50
✝ $50
🍂 $50
♾ $45
▲ $43
⬧ $43

The Purr-fect Grandma
#E7242
Issued: 1982 • Susp.: 1988
Retail Price: $18 – $22.50

10

Values 👁 $25
★ $25
⏱ $25
◭ $25

Garnet – Color Of Boldness
(January)
Birthstone Collection
#335533
Issued: 1998 • Open
Retail Price: $25

11

Values 👁 $25
★ $25
⏱ $25
◭ $25

Amethyst – Color Of Faith
(February)
Birthstone Collection
#335541
Issued: 1998 • Open
Retail Price: $25

12

Values 👁 $25
★ $25
⏱ $25
◭ $25

Aquamarine – Color Of
Kindness (March)
Birthstone Collection
#335568
Issued: 1998 • Open
Retail Price: $25

1
Values 👓 $25
★ $25
🕐 $25
🐾 $25

Diamond – Color Of Purity (April)
Birthstone Collection
#335576
Issued: 1998 • Open
Retail Price: $25

2
Values 👓 $25
★ $25
🕐 $25
🐾 $25

Emerald – Color Of Patience (May)
Birthstone Collection
#335584
Issued: 1998 • Open
Retail Price: $25

3
Values 👓 $25
★ $25
🕐 $25
🐾 $25

Pearl – Color Of Love (June)
Birthstone Collection
#335592
Issued: 1998 • Open
Retail Price: $25

4
Values 👓 $25
★ $25
🕐 $25
🐾 $25

Ruby – Color Of Joy (July)
Birthstone Collection
#335606
Issued: 1998 • Open
Retail Price: $25

5
Values 👓 $25
★ $25
🕐 $25
🐾 $25

Peridot – Color Of Pride (August)
Birthstone Collection
#335614
Issued: 1998 • Open
Retail Price: $25

6
Values 👓 $25
★ $25
🕐 $25
🐾 $25

Sapphire – Color Of Confidence (September)
Birthstone Collection
#335622
Issued: 1998 • Open
Retail Price: $25

7
Values 👓 $25
★ $25
🕐 $25
🐾 $25

Opal – Color Of Happiness (October)
Birthstone Collection
#335657
Issued: 1998 • Open
Retail Price: $25

8
Values 👓 $25
★ $25
🕐 $25
🐾 $25

Topaz – Color Of Truth (November)
Birthstone Collection
#335665
Issued: 1998 • Open
Retail Price: $25

KEY			
NM Pre'81	🎃 1986	⚑ 1992	† 1997
▲ 1981	♣ 1987	🎗 1993	👓 1998
✠ 1982	✿ 1988	🍃 1994	★ 1999
◀ 1983	♫ 1989	⚜ 1995	🕐 2000
✝ 1984	✦ 1990	♡ 1996	🐾 2001
❦ 1985	✿ 1991	**UM** Unmarked	

Birthstone Collection Hinged Boxes

	Price Paid	Value
1.		
2.		
3.		
4.		
5.		
6.		
7.		
8.		
9.		

9
Values 👓 $25
★ $25
🕐 $25
🐾 $25

Turquoise – Color Of Loyalty (December)
Birthstone Collection
#335673
Issued: 1998 • Open
Retail Price: $25

10
Values 👓 $25
★ $25
🕐 $25
🐾 $25

His Burden Is Light
"Original 21" Collection
#488429
Issued: 1999 • Open
Retail Price: $25

"Original 21" Collection Hinged Boxes

10.		
11.		
12.		

11
Values 👓 $25
★ $25
🕐 $25
🐾 $25

Jesus Is The Light
"Original 21" Collection
#488437
Issued: 1999 • Open
Retail Price: $25

12
Values 👓 $25
★ $25
🕐 $25
🐾 $25

Jesus Loves Me
"Original 21" Collection
#488380
Issued: 1999 • Open
Retail Price: $25

Totals

1

Values 6ð $25
★ $25
🕐 $25
&. $25

Jesus Loves Me
"Original 21" Collection
#488399
Issued: 1999 • Open
Retail Price: $25

2

Values 6ð $25
★ $25
🕐 $25
&. $25

Love One Another
"Original 21" Collection
#488410
Issued: 1999 • Open
Retail Price: $25

3

Values 6ð $25
★ $25
🕐 $25
&. $25

Make A Joyful Noise
"Original 21" Collection
#488402
Issued: 1999 • Open
Retail Price: $25

4

Values ✦ $204
♠ $204

Autumn's Praise
(LE-1990/1991)
♪*"Autumn Leaves"*
#408751
Issued: 1990 • Closed: 1991
Retail Price: $200

5

Values ♠ $208
♦ $208

**May You Have An Old
Fashioned Christmas
(LE-1991/1992)**
♪*"Have Yourself A Merry
Little Christmas"*
#417777
Issued: 1991 • Closed: 1992
Retail Price: $200

6

Values ✦ $205
♠ $205

Summer's Joy (LE-1990/1991)
♪*"You Are My Sunshine"*
#408743
Issued: 1990 • Closed: 1991
Retail Price: $200

KEY			
NM Pre'81	♪ 1986	♣ 1992	† 1997
▲ 1981	▲ 1987	♋ 1993	6ð 1998
✠ 1982	❖ 1988	◀ 1994	★ 1999
◀ 1983	◗ 1989	△ 1995	🕐 2000
✝ 1984	✦ 1990	♡ 1996	&. 2001
✔ 1985	♠ 1991	ⅡM Unmarked	

**"Original 21" Collection
Hinged Boxes**

	Price Paid	Value
1.		
2.		
3.		

Jack-In-The-Boxes

4.		
5.		
6.		
7.		
8.		
9.		

Medallions

10.		
11.		
12.		

Totals

7

Values ✦ $205
♠ $205

**The Voice Of Spring
(LE-1990/1991)**
♪*"April Love"*
#408735
Issued: 1990 • Closed: 1991
Retail Price: $200

8

Values ✦ $208
♠ $208

Winter's Song (LE-1990/1991)
♪*"Through The Eyes
Of Love"*
#408778
Issued: 1990 • Closed: 1991
Retail Price: $200

9

Values ✦ $180
♠ $180
♦ $180

**You Have Touched So Many
Hearts (LE-1991/1992)**
♪*"Everybody Loves
Somebody"*
#422282
Issued: 1991 • Closed: 1992
Retail Price: $175

10

Values ⅡM $72

**15 Years Tweet Music
Together (LE-1993)**
*PRECIOUS MOMENTS
Collection 15th Anniversary
Convention Medallion*
#529087
Issued: 1993 • Closed: 1993
Retail Price: N/A

11

Values ⅡM $655

**Friends Never Drift Apart
(LE-1993)**
*PRECIOUS MOMENTS
Collection 15th Anniversary
Cruise Medallion*
#529079
Issued: 1993 • Closed: 1993
Retail Price: N/A

12

Values ⅡM N/E

*Photo
Unavailable*

**Make A Joyful Noise
(LE-1988)**
*Enesco Orient Tour
Medallion*
#PM030
Issued: 1988 • Closed: 1988
Retail Price: N/A

1 Values ⌂ $355

A Perfect Display Of 15 Happy Years
PRECIOUS MOMENTS Collection 15th Anniversary Convention Medallion
#177083
Issued: 1995 • Closed: 1995
Retail Price: N/A

2 Values ⊙ $50
          ⊱ $50
New

Bridal Arch
♪ *"Wedding March By Mendelssohn"*
#876151
Issued: 2001 • Open
Retail Price: $50

3 Values ⊱ $270

Bringing In The Sheaves
(LE-12,000)
Country Lane
♪ *"Bringing In The Sheaves"*
#307084
Issued: 1998 • Closed: 1998
Retail Price: $90

4 Values NM $182
          ▲ $170
          Ⅰ $160
          ◀ $157
          ✝ $150

Christmas Is A Time To Share
♪ *"Away In A Manger"*
#E2806
Issued: 1980 • Retired: 1984
Retail Price: $35 – $50

5 Values NM $162
          ▲ $145
          Ⅰ $137
          ◀ $132
          ✝ $126
          ✿ $117
          ♪♪ $115
          ▲ $115
          ⚓ $115
          ⚘ $115
          ⚓ $110
          ◉ $110
          ⚘ $110
          ♪♪ $110

Come Let Us Adore Him
♪ *"Joy To The World"*
#E2810
Issued: 1980 • Susp.: 1993
Retail Price: $60 – $100

6 Values NM $140
          ▲ $130
          Ⅰ $122
          ◀ $116
          ✝ $105

Crown Him Lord Of All
♪ *"O Come, All Ye Faithful"*
#E2807
Issued: 1980 • Susp.: 1984
Retail Price: $35 – $50

7 Values ✿ $99
          ♪♪ $92
          ◀ $88

Do Not Open 'Til Christmas
♪ *"Toyland"*
#522244
Issued: 1992 • Susp.: 1994
Retail Price: $75

8 Values ✿ $126
          ♪♪ $115
          ▲ $108
          ⚓ $102
          ✟ $100

God Sent You Just In Time
♪ *"We Wish You A Merry Christmas"*
#15504
Issued: 1985 • Retired: 1989
Retail Price: $45 – $60

KEY							
NM Pre'81	♪♪ 1986	✿ 1992	✝ 1997
▲ 1981	▲ 1987	♪♪ 1993	⊱ 1998
Ⅰ 1982	⚓ 1988	◀ 1994	★ 1999
◀ 1983	✟ 1989	⌂ 1995	⊙ 2000
✝ 1984	★ 1990	♡ 1996	⊱ 2001
✿ 1985	◉ 1991	UM Unmarked	

9 Values NM $110
          Ⅰ $91
          ◀ $80
          ✝ $75
          ✿ $68
          ▲ $65
          ⚓ $63
          ✟ $63
          ★ $62
          ◉ $62
          ♪♪ $62
          ♪♪ $60
          ▲ $60
          ⚓ $60
          ⚘ $60
          ♡ $60
          ★ $60
          ⊙ $60

The Hand That Rocks The Future
♪ *"Mozart's Lullaby"*
#E5204
Issued: 1981 • Open
Retail Price: $30 – $60

10 Values ✿ $115
          ♪♪ $92
          ▲ $85
          ⚓ $80
          ✟ $80
          ★ $80
          ◉ $77
          ⚘ $75
          ♪♪ $75

Heaven Bless You
♪ *"Brahms' Lullaby"*
#100285
Issued: 1986 • Susp.: 1993
Retail Price: $45 – $60

11 Values ⊱ $125
New

Photo Unavailable

I Give You My Love Forever True
♪ *"Pacabel's Cannon"*
#876143
Issued: 2001 • Open
Retail Price: $125

12 Values Ⅰ $210
          ◀ $200
          ✝ $180

I'll Play My Drum For Him
♪ *"The Little Drummer Boy"*
#E2355
Issued: 1982 • Susp.: 1984
Retail Price: $45 – $50

Medallions

Price Paid	Value
1.	

Musicals

2.	
3.	
4.	
5.	
6.	
7.	
8.	
9.	
10.	
11.	
12.	

Totals

1

Values	
♠	$145
✤	$132
♦	$123
⊥	$123
♦	$123
⚓	$117
∞	$113

I'm Sending You A White Christmas
♪ *"White Christmas"*
#112402
Issued: 1987 • Retired: 1993
Retail Price: $55 – $75

2

Values	
NM	$163
▲	$139
☰	$137
✤	$137
✝	$132
✦	$132

Jesus Is Born
♪ *"Hark, The Herald Angels Sing"*
#E2809
Issued: 1980 • Susp.: 1985
Retail Price: $35 – $50

3

Values	
☰	$165
✦	$155
✝	$145
✦	$137
♫	$130
▲	$130
✤	$125
♦	$125
UM	$180

Let Heaven And Nature Sing
♪ *"Joy To The World"*
#E2346
Issued: 1982 • Susp.: 1989
Retail Price: $50 – $75

4

Values	
☰	$160
✦	$135
✝	$132
✦	$132
♫	$122
UM	$170

Let The Whole World Know
♪ *"What A Friend We Have In Jesus"*
#E7186
Issued: 1982 • Susp.: 1986
Retail Price: $60 – $65

5

Values	
♫	$125
▲	$110
✤	$105
♦	$102
⊥	$98
✦	$96
♦	$93
∞	$93
☰	$91
♡	$91
✝	$91
✦	$91
★	$91

Let's Keep In Touch
♪ *"Be A Clown"*
#102520
Issued: 1986 • Retired: 1999
Retail Price: $65 – $90

6

Values	
♦	$94
⊥	$82
♦	$79
⚓	$76
∞	$74
☰	$72
♡	$72
✝	$72
∞	$71
★	$71

The Light Of The World Is Jesus
♪ *"White Christmas"*
#521507
Issued: 1989 • Retired: 1999
Retail Price: $60 – $70

KEY					
NM Pre'81	♫ 1986	♦ 1992	✝ 1997		
▲ 1981	▲ 1987	∞ 1993	∞ 1998		
☰ 1982	✤ 1988	☰ 1994	★ 1999		
✦ 1983	♦ 1989	⚓ 1995	⊙ 2000		
✝ 1984	⊥ 1990	♡ 1996	⚓ 2001		
✦ 1985	♦ 1991	UM Unmarked			

Musicals

	Price Paid	Value
1.		
2.		
3.		
4.		
5.		
6.		
7.		
8.		
9.		
10.		
11.		
12.		

Totals

7

Values	
☰	$110
✝	$106
✦	$102
♫	$95
▲	$92
✤	$90
♦	$90
♦	$88
∞	$86
☰	$86
⚓	$86
♡	$86
✝	$86
∞	$86
★	$86
⊙	$86
UM	$135

The Lord Bless You And Keep You
♪ *"Wedding March By Mendelssohn"*
#E7180
Issued: 1982 • Susp.: 2000
Retail Price: $55 – $85

8

Values	
♦	$94
⚓	$87
∞	$82

Lord, Keep My Life In Balance
♪ *"Music Box Dancer"*
#520691
Issued: 1991 • Susp.: 1993
Retail Price: $60 – $65

9

Values	
✦	$155
♫	$140
▲	$135
✤	$130
♦	$125

Lord, Keep My Life InTune (set/2)
Rejoice In The Lord Band Series
♪ *"Amazing Grace"*
#12165
Issued: 1985 • Susp.: 1989
Retail Price: $37.50 – $50

10

Values	
♫	$285
▲	$268
✤	$258
♦	$250
⊥	$230

Lord, Keep My Life InTune (set/2)
Rejoice In The Lord Band Series
♪ *"I'd Like To Teach The World To Sing"*
#12580
Issued: 1987 • Susp.: 1990
Retail Price: $37.50 – $55

11

Values	
☰	$193
✦	$180
✝	$166
✦	$160

Love Is Sharing
♪ *"School Days"*
#E7185
Issued: 1982 • Retired: 1985
Retail Price: $40 – $45

12

Values	
✝	$80
✦	$76
♫	$68
✦	$68
✤	$68
♦	$68
⊥	$68
♦	$68
∞	$68
☰	$68
⚓	$68
♡	$68
✝	$68
∞	$65
★	$65
⊙	$65
⚓	$65
UM	$105

Mother Sew Dear
♪ *"You Light Up My Life"*
#E7182
Issued: 1982 • Open
Retail Price: $35 – $65

1

Values NM $125
▲ $110
Ⅱ $100
◄ $98
† $95
♨ $92

My Guardian Angel
♪ *"Brahms' Lullaby"*
#E5205
Issued: 1981 • Susp.: 1985
Retail Price: $22.50 – $27.50

2

Values NM $122
▲ $110
Ⅱ $96
◄ $93
† $90
♨ $88
♪ $86
▲ $82
✣ $82

My Guardian Angel
♪ *"Brahms' Lullaby"*
#E5206
Issued: 1981 • Susp.: 1988
Retail Price: $22.50 – $33

3

Values Ⅱ $150
◄ $140
† $137
UM $178

O Come All Ye Faithful
♪ *"O Come, All Ye Faithful"*
#E2352
Issued: 1982 • Susp.: 1984
Retail Price: $45 – $50

4

Values ♪ $128
▲ $120
Ⅱ $115
♭ $110
★ $108
♨ $100
♬ $100

Our First
Christmas Together
♪ *"We Wish You A Merry
Christmas"*
#101702
Issued: 1986 • Retired: 1992
Retail Price: $50 – $70

5

Values NM $155
▲ $136
Ⅱ $132
◄ $125
† $120

Peace On Earth
♪ *"Jesus Loves Me"*
#E4726
Issued: 1981 • Susp.: 1984
Retail Price: $45 – $50

6

Values ▲ $165
✣ $150
♭ $150
★ $142
♨ $140
♬ $140
♔ $135

Peace On Earth
♪ *"Hark, The Herald
Angels Sing"*
#109746
Issued: 1988 • Susp.: 1993
Retail Price: $100 – $130

7

Values † $94
♨ $90
♪ $87
▲ $83
✣ $78
♭ $76
★ $70
♨ $68
♬ $66
♔ $63
UM $100

The Purr-fect Grandma
♪ *"Always In My Heart"*
#E7184
Issued: 1982 • Susp.: 1993
Retail Price: $35 – $60

8

Values NM $145
▲ $135
Ⅱ $125
◄ $115
† $110
♨ $98
♪ $95
▲ $88
✣ $85

Rejoice O Earth
♪ *"Joy To The World"*
#E5645
Issued: 1981 • Retired: 1988
Retail Price: $35 – $55

9

Values ◄ $175
† $160
♬ $152
♪ $140

Sharing Our
Season Together
♪ *"Winter Wonderland"*
#E0519
Issued: 1983 • Retired: 1986
Retail Price: $70

10

Values NM $400
▲ $390
Ⅱ $380
◄ $375
† $370
♨ $350

Silent Knight
♪ *"Silent Night"*
#E5642
Issued: 1981 • Susp.: 1985
Retail Price: $45 – $60

11

Values ♨ $112
♪ $105
▲ $97
✣ $94
♭ $90
★ $88
♨ $88
♬ $85

Silent Night
Family Christmas Series
♪ *"Silent Night"*
#15814
Issued: 1985 • Susp.: 1992
Retail Price: $37.50 – $55

12

Values ♨ $82
♬ $71
♔ $67
◄ $66
△ $65
♡ $65
† $65
◒ $65
★ $65
▲ $65
♨ $65

This Day Has Been
Made In Heaven
♪ *"Amazing Grace"*
#523682
Issued: 1992 • Open
Retail Price: $60 – $65

Musicals

	Price Paid	Value
1.		
2.		
3.		
4.		
5.		
6.		
7.		
8.		
9.		
10.		
11.		
12.		

Totals

1

Values NM $150
▲ $125
Ⅱ $117
✦ $110
✝ $105

Unto Us A Child Is Born
♪ *"Jesus Loves Me"*
#E2808
Issued: 1980 • Susp.: 1984
Retail Price: $35 – $50

2

Values ✦ $135
♪ $124
▲ $120

We Saw A Star (set/3)
♪ *"Joy To The World"*
#12408
Issued: 1985 • Susp.: 1987
Retail Price: $50 – $55

3

Values ✦ $142
✝ $136
✦ $129
♪ $122

Wee Three Kings
♪ *"We Three Kings
Of Orient Are"*
#E0520
Issued: 1983 • Susp.: 1986
Retail Price: $60

4

Values ✝ $130
✦ $122
♪ $110

**Wishing You A
Merry Christmas**
♪ *"We Wish You A
Merry Christmas"*
#E5394
Issued: 1984 • Susp.: 1986
Retail Price: $55

5

Values ᠖ $137
❀ $115
▬ $112
△ $108
♡ $105
✝ $105
6Ծ $105

Wishing You Were Here
♪ *"When You Wish
Upon A Star"*
#526916
Issued: 1993 • Susp.: 1998
Retail Price: $100

6

Values ▲ $112
✛ $106
Đ $100
✦ $96
᠖ $92
᠖ $92
❀ $90
▬ $87
△ $82
♡ $82

**You Have Touched
So Many Hearts**
♪ *"Everybody Loves
Somebody"*
#112577
Issued: 1988 • Susp.: 1996
Retail Price: $50 – $65

Musicals

	Price Paid	Value
1.		
2.		
3.		
4.		
5.		
6.		

Night Lights

7.		
8.		

Annual Plates

9.		
10.		
11.		
12.		

Totals

7

Values ✦ $125
♪ $115
✦ $110
✛ $103
Đ $99

**God Bless You
With Rainbows**
#16020
Issued: 1986 • Susp.: 1989
Retail Price: $45 – $57.50

8

Values ✝ $190
UM $255

My Guardian Angel
#E5207
Issued: 1981 • Susp.: 1984
Retail Price: $30 – $37.50

9

Values ᠖ $55

**But The Greatest Of These
Is Love** (Dated 1992)
Christmas Blessings Series
#527742
Issued: 1992 • Closed: 1992
Retail Price: $50

10

Values ❀ $55

**Wishing You The Sweetest
Christmas** (Dated 1993)
Christmas Blessings Series
#530204
Issued: 1993 • Closed: 1993
Retail Price: $50

11

Values ▬ $55

**You're As Pretty As A
Christmas Tree** (Dated 1994)
The Beauty Of Christmas Series
#530409
Issued: 1994 • Closed: 1994
Retail Price: $50

12

Values △ $58

**He Covers The Earth With
His Beauty** (Dated 1995)
The Beauty Of Christmas Series
#142670
Issued: 1995 • Closed: 1995
Retail Price: $50

1   *Values* ♡ $53

Peace On Earth . . . Anyway
(Dated 1996)
The Beauty Of Christmas Series
#183377
Issued: 1996 • Closed: 1996
Retail Price: $50

2   *Values* † $55

Cane You Join Us For A Merry Christmas
(Dated 1997)
The Beauty Of Christmas Series
#272701
Issued: 1997 • Closed: 1997
Retail Price: $50

3   *Values* ᠪᠥ $53

Photo Unavailable

I'm Sending You A Merry Christmas (Dated 1998)
#469327
Issued: 1998 • Closed: 1998
Retail Price: $50

4   *Values* ⚓ $62

Wishing You A Yummy Christmas (Dated 1990)
#523801
Issued: 1990 • Closed: 1990
Retail Price: $50

5   *Values* ◊ $55

Blessings From Me To Thee
(Dated 1991)
#523860
Issued: 1991 • Closed: 1991
Retail Price: $50

6   *Values* UM $47

Come Let Us Adore Him
(LE-15,000)
#E5646
Issued: 1981 • Closed: 1981
Retail Price: $40

7   *Values* UM $48

Let Heaven And Nature Sing (LE-15,000)
#E2347
Issued: 1982 • Closed: 1982
Retail Price: $45

8   *Values* UM $48

Wee Three Kings (LE-15,000)
#E0538
Issued: 1983 • Closed: 1983
Retail Price: $45

9   *Values* † $45   UM $50

Unto Us A Child Is Born
(LE-15,000)
#E5395
Issued: 1984 • Closed: 1984
Retail Price: $40

10   *Values* ≯ $62

I'm Sending You A White Christmas (Dated 1986)
#101834
Issued: 1986 • Closed: 1986
Retail Price: $45

11   *Values* ♠ $72

My Peace I Give Unto Thee
(Dated 1987)
#102954
Issued: 1987 • Closed: 1987
Retail Price: $45

12   *Values* ⚜ $60

Merry Christmas Deer
(Dated 1988)
#520284
Issued: 1988 • Closed: 1988
Retail Price: $50

KEY
NM Pre'81 | ≯ 1986 | ⚓ 1992 | † 1997
▲ 1981 | ♠ 1987 | ⅋ 1993 | ᠪᠥ 1998
Ⅱ 1982 | ⬩ 1988 | ★ 1994 | ★ 1999
↩ 1983 | ⅁ 1989 | △ 1995 | ⊙ 2000
† 1984 | ⚓ 1990 | ♡ 1996 | ⚏ 2001
⚜ 1985 | ◊ 1991 | UM Unmarked

Annual Plates

	Price Paid	Value
1.		
2.		
3.		

Christmas Blessings Plate Series

4.		
5.		

Christmas Collection Plate Series

6.		
7.		
8.		
9.		

Christmas Love Plate Series

10.		
11.		
12.		

Totals

193

1 Values ♦ $54

May Your Christmas Be A
Happy Home (Dated 1989)
#523003
Issued: 1989 • Closed: 1989
Retail Price: $50

2 Values † $106
♣ $92

The Voice Of Spring
(LE-1985)
#12106
Issued: 1985 • Closed: 1985
Retail Price: $40

3 Values † $87
♣ $80

Summer's Joy (LE-1985)
#12114
Issued: 1985 • Closed: 1985
Retail Price: $40

4 Values ♪ $60

Autumn's Praise (LE-1986)
#12122
Issued: 1986 • Closed: 1986
Retail Price: $40

5 Values ♣ $58
♪ $45

Winter's Song (LE-1986)
#12130
Issued: 1986 • Closed: 1986
Retail Price: $40

6 Values UM $55

Love One Another
(LE-15,000)
#E5215
Issued: 1981 • Closed: 1981
Retail Price: $40

**Christmas Love
Plate Series**

	Price Paid	Value
1.		

Four Seasons Plate Series

2.		
3.		
4.		
5.		

Inspired Thoughts Plate Series

6.		
7.		
8.		
9.		

Joy Of Christmas Plate Series

10.		
11.		
12.		

Totals

7 Values UM $45

Make A Joyful Noise
(LE-15,000)
#E7174
Issued: 1982 • Closed: 1982
Retail Price: $40

8 Values UM $40

I Believe In Miracles
(LE-15,000)
#E9257
Issued: 1983 • Closed: 1983
Retail Price: $40

9 Values ♥ $47
† $42
UM $50

Love Is Kind (LE-15,000)
#E2847
Issued: 1984 • Closed: 1984
Retail Price: $40

10 Values UM $70

I'll Play My Drum For Him
(Dated 1982)
#E2357
Issued: 1982 • Closed: 1982
Retail Price: $40

11 Values UM $78

Christmastime Is For
Sharing (Dated 1983)
#E0505
Issued: 1983 • Closed: 1983
Retail Price: $40

12 Values † $50

The Wonder Of Christmas
(Dated 1984)
#E5396
Issued: 1984 • Closed: 1984
Retail Price: $40

1 Values ✒ $80

Tell Me The Story Of Jesus
(Dated 1985)
#15237
Issued: 1985 • Closed: 1985
Retail Price: $40

2 Values ❀ $57
🍴 $52

Thinking Of You Is What I Really Like To Do
(Dated 1994)
#531766
Issued: 1994 • Closed: 1994
Retail Price: $50

3 Values △ $52

He Hath Made Every Thing Beautiful In His Time (Dated 1995)
#129151
Issued: 1995 • Closed: 1995
Retail Price: $50

④ Values ♡ $52

Of All The Mothers I Have Known There's None As Precious As My Own
(Dated 1996)
#163716
Issued: 1996 • Closed: 1996
Retail Price: $50

5 Values ⅡM $50

Mother Sew Dear
(LE-15,000)
#E5217
Issued: 1981 • Closed: 1981
Retail Price: $40

6 Values ⅡM $45

The Purr-fect Grandma
(LE-15,000)
#E7173
Issued: 1982 • Closed: 1982
Retail Price: $40

7 Values ⅡM $42

The Hand That Rocks The Future (LE-15,000)
#E9256
Issued: 1983 • Closed: 1983
Retail Price: $40

8 Values † $42

Loving Thy Neighbor
(LE-15,000)
#E2848
Issued: 1984 • Closed: 1984
Retail Price: $40

KEY					
NM Pre'81		✄ 1986		✦ 1992	† 1997
▲ 1981		♣ 1987		❀ 1993	6ↄ 1998
I 1982		✤ 1988		🍴 1994	★ 1999
◄ 1983		₱ 1989		△ 1995	⊙ 2000
✝ 1984		✦ 1990		♡ 1996	≥ 2001
✒ 1985		♨ 1991		ⅡM Unmarked	

	Price Paid	Value
1.		

Mother's Day Plate Series

2.		
3.		
4.		

Mother's Love Plate Series

5.		
6.		
7.		
8.		

General Plates

9.		
10.		
11.		
12.		

Totals

9 Values ❀ $57
🍴 $52

Bring The Little Ones To Jesus (Dated 1994)
Child Evangelism Fellowship Plate
#531359
Issued: 1994 • Closed: 1994
Retail Price: $50

10 Values ✄ $40
† $38
ⅡM $50

Jesus Loves Me
#E9275
Issued: 1983 • Susp.: 1984
Retail Price: $30

11 Values ✄ $40
† $38
ⅡM $50

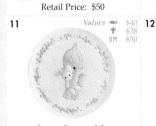

Jesus Loves Me
#E9276
Issued: 1983 • Susp.: 1984
Retail Price: $30

12 Values † $40
✄ $40
♨ $40
▲ $39
ⅡM $48

The Lord Bless You And Keep You
#E5216
Issued: 1981 • Susp.: 1987
Retail Price: $30 – $37.50

1
Values ✝ $40 🐝 $35 UM $46

Our First Christmas
Together
#E2378
Issued: 1982 • Susp.: 1985
Retail Price: $30

2
Values ✝ $35 🐝 $33 UM $40

Rejoicing With You
#E7172
Issued: 1982 • Susp.: 1985
Retail Price: $30

3
Values PE $35 OE $35

Cheers To The Leader
Hugs For The Soul
#752835
Issued: 2000 • Open
Retail Price: $35

4
Values PE $35 OE $35

Friendship Hits The Spot
Hugs For The Soul
#729167
Issued: 2000 • Open
Retail Price: $35

5
Values PE $35 OE $35

The Future Is In Our Hands
Hugs For The Soul
#752789
Issued: 2000 • Open
Retail Price: $35

6
Values PE $35 OE $35

God Loveth A
Cheerful Giver
Hugs For The Soul
#729205
Issued: 2000 • Open
Retail Price: $35

KEY:
NM Pre'81 | ⚘ 1986 | ❀ 1992 | ✝ 1997
▲ 1981 | ▲ 1987 | ✿ 1993 | ❧ 1998
I 1982 | ✤ 1988 | ➳ 1994 | ★ 1999
➦ 1983 | ➶ 1989 | ☖ 1995 | ◷ 2000
✝ 1984 | ✦ 1990 | ♡ 1996 | ➴ 2001
✦ 1985 | ◗ 1991 | UM Unmarked

General Plates

	Price Paid	Value
1.		
2.		

Plush

3.		
4.		
5.		
6.		
7.		
8.		
9.		
10.		
11.		
12.		

Totals

7
Values PE $35 OE $35

Jesus Loves Me
Hugs For The Soul
#752894
Issued: 2000 • Open
Retail Price: $35

8
Values PE $35 OE $35

Lord, Keep Me On My Toes
Hugs For The Soul
#729191
Issued: 2000 • Open
Retail Price: $35

9
Values PE $70

Photo Unavailable

Love One Another
(set/2, LE-3,500)
Century Circle Plush
Hugs For The Soul
#729213
Issued: 2000 • Open
Retail Price: $70

10
Values ES $18

Loving, Caring And
Sharing (set/3)
Special Event Piece
#822159
Issued: 2000 • Closed: 2000
Retail Price: $14.99

11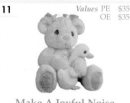
Values PE $35 OE $35

Make A Joyful Noise
Hugs For The Soul
#752762
Issued: 2000 • Open
Retail Price: $35

12
Values PE $35 OE $35

Put On A Happy Face
Hugs For The Soul
#729183
Issued: 2000 • Open
Retail Price: $35

1
Values PE $35
OE $35

Tell It To Jesus
Hugs For The Soul
#729221
Issued: 2000 • Open
Retail Price: $35

2
Values PE $35
OE $35

You Have Touched So Many Hearts
Hugs For The Soul
#729175
Issued: 2000 • Open
Retail Price: $35

3
Values 🕊 $58

God Sent His Love
(Dated 1985)
#15865
Issued: 1985 • Closed: 1985
Retail Price: $5.50

4
Values ⚘ $26

Wishing You A Cozy Christmas (Dated 1986)
#102334
Issued: 1986 • Closed: 1986
Retail Price: $5.50

5
Values ▲ $38

Love Is The Best Gift Of All (Dated 1987)
#109843
Issued: 1987 • Closed: 1987
Retail Price: $6

6
Values ✤ $55

Time To Wish You A Merry Christmas (Dated 1988)
#115312
Issued: 1988 • Closed: 1988
Retail Price: $7

7
Values Ð $26

Oh Holy Night (Dated 1989)
#522554
Issued: 1989 • Closed: 1989
Retail Price: $7.50

8
Values ✦ $24

Once Upon A Holy Night (Dated 1990)
#523844
Issued: 1990 • Closed: 1990
Retail Price: $8

9
Values ✦ $24

May Your Christmas Be Merry (Dated 1991)
#524190
Issued: 1991 • Closed: 1991
Retail Price: $8

10
Values ⚘ $22

But The Greatest Of These Is Love (Dated 1992)
#527718
Issued: 1992 • Closed: 1992
Retail Price: $8

11
Values 🕸 $18

Wishing You The Sweetest Christmas (Dated 1993)
#530182
Issued: 1993 • Closed: 1993
Retail Price: $8

12
Values ⚘ $45
▲ $40
✤ $38

Clowns (set/2)
#100668
Issued: 1986 • Susp.: 1988
Retail Price: $11 – $14

KEY							
NM	Pre'81	⚘	1986	⚓	1992	†	1997
▲	1981	▲	1987	🕸	1993	👁	1998
✠	1982	✤	1988	🍖	1994	★	1999
◄	1983	Ð	1989	△	1995	☉	2000
†	1984	✦	1990	♡	1996	⚭	2001
🕊	1985	♦	1991	UM	Unmarked		

Plush

	Price Paid	Value
1.		
2.		

Annual Christmas Thimbles

3.		
4.		
5.		
6.		
7.		
8.		
9.		
10.		
11.		

General Thimbles

12.		

Totals

1

Values ♪ $96

Four Seasons
(set/4, LE-1986)
#100641
Issued: 1986 • Closed: 1986
Retail Price: $20

2

Values	
♣	$27
♪	$22
▲	$18
✤	$16
⊅	$16

God Is Love, Dear Valentine
#100625
Issued: 1986 • Susp.: 1989
Retail Price: $5.50 – $8

3

Values	
♣	$25
♪	$25
▲	$22
✤	$20
⊅	$20
♁	$18
♦	$15

The Lord Bless You
And Keep You
#100633
Issued: 1986 • Susp.: 1991
Retail Price: $5.50 – $8

4

Values	
†	$26
♣	$22
♪	$20
▲	$18
✤	$16
⊅	$15
♁	$14
♦	$14

Love Covers All
#12254
Issued: 1985 • Susp.: 1990
Retail Price: $5.50 – $8

5

Values	
†	$21
♣	$19
♪	$18
▲	$15
✤	$15
⊅	$14
♁	$14
♦	$12
♬	$11
♞	$11
☐	$9
△	$9
♡	$9
†	$9
∞	$9
★	$9

Mother Sew Dear
#13293
Issued: 1985 • Retired: 1999
Retail Price: $5.50 – $8

6

Values	
†	$23
♣	$22
♪	$20
▲	$18
✤	$16
⊅	$15
♁	$14
♦	$13
♬	$13
♞	$12
☐	$9
△	$9
♡	$9
†	$9
∞	$9
★	$9

The Purr-fect
Grandma
#13307
Issued: 1985 • Retired: 1999
Retail Price: $5.50 – $8

General Thimbles

	Price Paid	Value
1.		
2.		
3.		
4.		
5.		
6.		

Tree Toppers

7.		
8.		

7

Values ♁ $143

Rejoice O Earth
♪ *"Hark, The Herald*
Angels Sing"
#617334
Issued: 1990 • Retired: 1991
Retail Price: $125

8

Values	
♡	$135
†	$127
∞	$127
★	$127

Sing In Excelsis Deo
#183830
Issued: 1996 • Retired: 1999
Retail Price: $125

Totals

TENDER TAILS®

The TENDER TAILS line of cuddly plush animals first joined Enesco's stable in 1997. Since then, the line has grown to include several series, as well as many special event pieces. Like their porcelain bisque counterparts, some TENDER TAILS pieces come with a production mark indicating the year they were made.

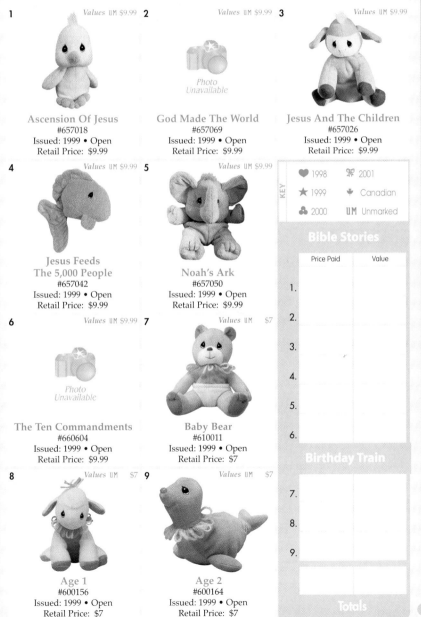

1   *Values* UM $9.99

Ascension Of Jesus
#657018
Issued: 1999 • Open
Retail Price: $9.99

2   *Values* UM $9.99

Photo Unavailable

God Made The World
#657069
Issued: 1999 • Open
Retail Price: $9.99

3   *Values* UM $9.99

Jesus And The Children
#657026
Issued: 1999 • Open
Retail Price: $9.99

4   *Values* UM $9.99

**Jesus Feeds
The 5,000 People**
#657042
Issued: 1999 • Open
Retail Price: $9.99

5   *Values* UM $9.99

Noah's Ark
#657050
Issued: 1999 • Open
Retail Price: $9.99

6   *Values* UM $9.99

Photo Unavailable

The Ten Commandments
#660604
Issued: 1999 • Open
Retail Price: $9.99

7   *Values* UM $7

Baby Bear
#610011
Issued: 1999 • Open
Retail Price: $7

8   *Values* UM $7

Age 1
#600156
Issued: 1999 • Open
Retail Price: $7

9   *Values* UM $7

Age 2
#600164
Issued: 1999 • Open
Retail Price: $7

KEY

♥ 1998		🎀 2001	
★ 1999		🍁 Canadian	
♣ 2000		UM Unmarked	

Bible Stories

	Price Paid	Value
1.		
2.		
3.		
4.		
5.		
6.		

Birthday Train

7.		
8.		
9.		

Totals

1 Values UM $7
Age 3
#600172
Issued: 1999 • Open
Retail Price: $7

2 Values UM $7
Age 4
#600180
Issued: 1999 • Open
Retail Price: $7

3 Values UM $7
Age 5
#600199
Issued: 1999 • Open
Retail Price: $7

4 Values UM $7
Age 6
#600210
Issued: 1999 • Open
Retail Price: $7

5 Values UM $10
Circus Clown
#648221
Issued: 1999 • Open
Retail Price: $10

6 Values UM $10
Display
#648213
Issued: 1999 • Open
Retail Price: $10

KEY
♥ 1998   ✿ 2001
★ 1999   ✦ Canadian
♣ 2000   UM Unmarked

Birthday Train

	Price Paid	Value
1.		
2.		
3.		
4.		
5.		
6.		

COUNTRY LANE

7.		
8.		
9.		
10.		
11.		
12.		

Totals

7 Values UM $8
Billy Goat
#476102
Issued: 1998 • Retired: 2000
Retail Price: $6.99

8 Values UM $8
Brown Cow
#540560
Issued: 1998 • Retired: 2000
Retail Price: $6.99

9 Values UM $9
Horse
#540609
Issued: 1998 • Retired: 2000
Retail Price: $6.99

10 Values UM $8
Peach Pig
#540579
Issued: 1998 • Retired: 2000
Retail Price: $6.99

11 Values UM $8
Rooster
#540617
Issued: 1998 • Retired: 2000
Retail Price: $6.99

12 Values UM $10
White Duck
#540587
Issued: 1998 • Retired: 2000
Retail Price: $6.99

1
New

Photo Unavailable

Values ♣ $6.99

Black Rhino (LE-7,500)
#799068
Issued: 2001 • Open
Retail Price: $6.99

2
New

Values ♣ $6.99

Chinchilla (LE-7,500)
#799033
Issued: 2001 • Open
Retail Price: $6.99

3
New

Values ♣ $6.99

Giant Armadillo (LE-7,500)
#799025
Issued: 2001 • Open
Retail Price: $6.99

4
New

Values ♣ $6.99

Gray Wolf (LE-7,500)
#799505
Issued: 2001 • Open
Retail Price: $6.99

5
New

Values ♣ $6.99

Grizzly Bear (LE-7,500)
#799092
Issued: 2001 • Open
Retail Price: $6.99

6
New

Values ♣ $6.99

Komodo Dragon (LE-7,500)
#799076
Issued: 2001 • Open
Retail Price: $6.99

7
New

Values ♣ $6.99

Leatherback Sea Turtle (LE-7,500)
#799051
Issued: 2001 • Open
Retail Price: $6.99

8
New

Values ♣ $6.99

Manatee-(LE 7,500)
#799084
Issued: 2001 • Open
Retail Price: $6.99

KEY		
♥ 1998	🎀 2001	
★ 1999	♣ Canadian	
♣ 2000	UM Unmarked	

9

Values UM $7

Chipmunk
#473979
Issued: 1999 • Open
Retail Price: $7

10

Values UM $7

Crow
#534285
Issued: 1999 • Open
Retail Price: $7

11

Values UM $7

Field Mouse
#547115
Issued: 1999 • Open
Retail Price: $7

12

Values UM $7

Skunk
#473960
Issued: 1999 • Open
Retail Price: $7

Endangered Tails

	Price Paid	Value
1.		
2.		
3.		
4.		
5.		
6.		
7.		
8.		

Grandma Ethel's Farm

9.		
10.		
11.		
12.		

Totals

201

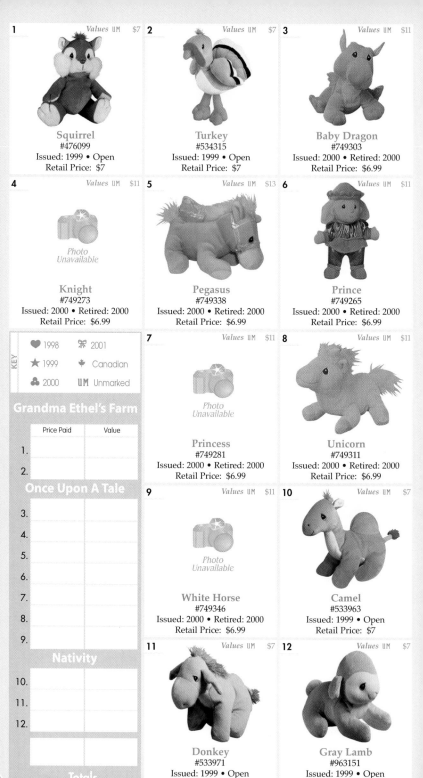

1   Values UM $7
Squirrel
#476099
Issued: 1999 • Open
Retail Price: $7

2   Values UM $7
Turkey
#534315
Issued: 1999 • Open
Retail Price: $7

3   Values UM $11
Baby Dragon
#749303
Issued: 2000 • Retired: 2000
Retail Price: $6.99

4   Values UM $11
Photo Unavailable
Knight
#749273
Issued: 2000 • Retired: 2000
Retail Price: $6.99

5   Values UM $13
Pegasus
#749338
Issued: 2000 • Retired: 2000
Retail Price: $6.99

6   Values UM $11
Prince
#749265
Issued: 2000 • Retired: 2000
Retail Price: $6.99

KEY
♥ 1998   🎀 2001
★ 1999   🍁 Canadian
♣ 2000   UM Unmarked

7   Values UM $11
Photo Unavailable
Princess
#749281
Issued: 2000 • Retired: 2000
Retail Price: $6.99

8   Values UM $11
Unicorn
#749311
Issued: 2000 • Retired: 2000
Retail Price: $6.99

9   Values UM $11
Photo Unavailable
White Horse
#749346
Issued: 2000 • Retired: 2000
Retail Price: $6.99

10   Values UM $7
Camel
#533963
Issued: 1999 • Open
Retail Price: $7

11   Values UM $7
Donkey
#533971
Issued: 1999 • Open
Retail Price: $7

12   Values UM $7
Gray Lamb
#963151
Issued: 1999 • Open
Retail Price: $7

Grandma Ethel's Farm

	Price Paid	Value
1.		
2.		

Once Upon A Tale

3.		
4.		
5.		
6.		
7.		
8.		
9.		

Nativity

10.		
11.		
12.		

Totals

1 *Values* UM $22.50

Mary/Jesus/Joseph (set/3)
#963135
Issued: 1999 • Open
Retail Price: $22.50

2 *Values* UM $7

Nativity Cow
#540668
Issued: 1999 • Open
Retail Price: $7

3 *Values* UM $10

Nativity Quilt Display
#540676
Issued: 1999 • Open
Retail Price: $10

4 *Values* UM $10

Palm Tree
#963208
Issued: 1999 • Open
Retail Price: $10

5 *Values* ♥ $8

20th Anniversary Bear
(LE-1998)
Care-A-Van Exclusive
#462829
Issued: 1998 • Closed: 1998
Retail Price: $6.99

6 *Values* ♣ $6.99

Air Force
#798983
Issued: 2000 • Open
Retail Price: $6.99

7 *Values* UM $9.99

Ant
Bug Series
#656917
Issued: 1999 • Open
Retail Price: $9.99

8 *Values* UM $6.99

Arctic Fox
#748226
Issued: 2000 • Open
Retail Price: $6.99

9 *Values* ♣ $6.99

Army
#798967
Issued: 2000 • Open
Retail Price: $6.99

10 *Values* UM $6.99

Beagle
#673226
Issued: 2000 • Open
Retail Price: $6.99

KEY		
♥ 1998	✿	2001
★ 1999	♣	Canadian
♣ 2000	UM	Unmarked

Nativity

	Price Paid	Value
1.		
2.		
3.		
4.		

General Plush

5.		
6.		
7.		
8.		
9.		
10.		

Totals

1 *Values* UM $17

Bear
#358274
Issued: 1997 • Retired: 1998
Retail Price: $6.99

2 *Values* UM $6.99

Bear
#775657
Issued: 2000 • Open
Retail Price: $6.99

3 *Values* UM $20

**Bear Couple
(w/ornament, "Our First
Christmas Together")**
#966771
Issued: 1998 • Open
Retail Price: $20

4 *Values* UM $3.99

*Photo
Unavailable*

Bear Cub
*Collect Your Own
Family Series*
#661481
Issued: 1999 • Open
Retail Price: $3.99

5 *Values* UM $10.99

Bear With Cub
*Collect Your Own
Family Series*
#661406
Issued: 1999 • Open
Retail Price: $10.99

6 *Values* ♣ $6.99
(Can.)

*Photo
Unavailable*

Beaver
Canadian Exclusive
#536369
Issued: 2000 • Open
Retail Price: $6.99 (Canadian)

KEY
♥ 1998	✿ 2001
★ 1999	♣ Canadian
♣ 2000	UM Unmarked

General Plush

	Price Paid	Value
1.		
2.		
3.		
4.		
5.		
6.		
7.		
8.		
9.		
10.		
11.		
12.		
Totals		

7 *Values* UM $8

Bee
#464295
Issued: 1999 • Retired: 2000
Retail Price: $7

8 *Values* UM $6.99

Beetle
Bug Series
#656887
Issued: 1999 • Open
Retail Price: $6.99

9 *Values* UM $6.99

Black Labrador
#704342
Issued: 2000 • Open
Retail Price: $6.99

10 *Values* UM $12

Blue Bird
#382531
Issued: 1998 • Retired: 1998
Retail Price: $6.99

11 *Values* UM $15

**Boy Bear (w/ornament,
"Baby's First Christmas")**
#966755
Issued: 1998 • Open
Retail Price: $15

12 *Values* UM $6.99

Boy Snowman
#749206
Issued: 2000 • Open
Retail Price: $6.99

1 *Values* ⅡM $6.99

Brontosaurus
#686808
Issued: 1999 • Open
Retail Price: $6.99

2 *Values* ⅡM $13

Brown Bunny
#464422
Issued: 1998 • Retired: 1999
Retail Price: $6.99

3 *Values* ⅡM $6.99

Buffalo
#748218
Issued: 2000 • Open
Retail Price: $6.99

4 *Values* ★ $12
         ♣ $12

Bunny
(6", Dated 2000)
#649120
Issued: 1999 • Closed: 2000
Retail Price: $6.99

5 *Values* ⅡM $14

Bunny
*Collect Your Own
Family Series*
#661449
Issued: 1999 • Open
Retail Price: $3.99

6 *Values* ★ $26
         ♣ $26

Bunny
(12", Dated 2000)
#670197
Issued: 1999 • Closed: 2000
Retail Price: $20

7 *Values* ⅡM $10.99

Bunny With Baby
*Collect Your Own
Family Series*
#661309
Issued: 1999 • Open
Retail Price: $10.99

8 *Values* ⅡM $9

Butterfly
#482234
Issued: 1999 • Retired: 2000
Retail Price: $7

9 *Values* ⅡM $9

Cardinal
#471909
Issued: 1998 • Retired: 1999
Retail Price: $6.99

10 *Values* ⅡM $12

Cat
#382256
Issued: 1998 • Retired: 1999
Retail Price: $6.99

11 *Values* ★ N/E

*Photo
Unavailable*

Cat
*Chapel Licensee
Show Plush*
#676497
Issued: 1999 • Closed: 1999
Retail Price: N/A

KEY	
♥ 1998	✿ 2001
★ 1999	✦ Canadian
♣ 2000	ⅡM Unmarked

General Plush

	Price Paid	Value
1.		
2.		
3.		
4.		
5.		
6.		
7.		
8.		
9.		
10.		
11.		

Totals

1 *Values* UM $10.99

Cat With Kitten
Collect Your Own Family Series
#661333
Issued: 1999 • Open
Retail Price: $10.99

2 *Values* UM $6.99

Caterpillar
Bug Series
#656941
Issued: 1999 • Open
Retail Price: $6.99

3 *Values* UM $9.99

Caveman
#686735
Issued: 1999 • Open
Retail Price: $9.99

4 *Values* UM $9.99

Cavewoman
#686743
Issued: 1999 • Open
Retail Price: $9.99

5 *Values* UM $6.99

Cocker Spaniel
#704369
Issued: 2000 • Open
Retail Price: $6.99

6 *Values* UM $12

Cow
#475890
Issued: 1998 • Retired: 1999
Retail Price: $6.99

KEY
♥ 1998 ✿ 2001
★ 1999 ✦ Canadian
♣ 2000 UM Unmarked

General Plush

	Price Paid	Value
1.		
2.		
3.		
4.		
5.		
6.		
7.		
8.		
9.		
10.		
11.		
12.		
Totals		

7 *Values* UM $6.99

Dachsund
#673293
Issued: 2000 • Open
Retail Price: $6.99

8 *Values* UM $6.99

Dalmatian
#672742
Issued: 2000 • Open
Retail Price: $6.99

9 *Values* UM $6.99

Deer
#748242
Issued: 2000 • Open
Retail Price: $6.99

10 *Values* UM $8

Diplodocus
#688061
Issued: 1999 • Retired: 1999
Retail Price: $6.99

11 *Values* UM $6.99

Dolphin
#535192
Issued: 1999 • Open
Retail Price: $6.99

12 *Values* ♣ $6.99

Photo Unavailable

Dove
Christian Bookstore Exclusive
#750158
Issued: 2000 • Open
Retail Price: $6.99

1 *Values* UM $6.99

Dove
#753491
Issued: 2000 • Open
Retail Price: $6.99

2 *Values* UM $6.99

Dragon Fly
Bug Series
#656976
Issued: 1999 • Open
Retail Price: $6.99

3 *Values* UM $11

Duck
#382515
Issued: 1998 • Retired: 1998
Retail Price: $6.99

4 *Values* UM $6.99

Eagle
*I'm Proud To Be An
American Series*
#648248
Issued: 2000 • Open
Retail Price: $6.99

5 *Values* UM $14

Elephant
#358320
Issued: 1997 • Retired: 1998
Retail Price: $6.99

6 *Values* ★ $9

Elephant
Special Event Plush
#609692
Issued: 1999 • Closed: 1999
Retail Price: $7

7 *Values* UM $15

**Girl Bear (w/ornament,
"Baby's First Christmas")**
#966763
Issued: 1998 • Open
Retail Price: $15

8 *Values* UM $6.99

Girl Snowman
#749192
Issued: 2000 • Open
Retail Price: $6.99

9 *Values* UM $9

Goose
#473952
Issued: 1999 • Retired: 2000
Retail Price: $7

10 *Values* UM N/E

Gorilla
*Local Club Chapter
Convention Plush*
#480355
Issued: 1998 • Closed: 1998
Retail Price: N/A

11 *Values* UM $8

Graduation Bear
#534595
Issued: 1999 • Closed: 2000
Retail Price: $6.99

KEY		
♥ 1998	✿ 2001	
★ 1999	♣ Canadian	
♣ 2000	UM Unmarked	

General Plush

	Price Paid	Value
1.		
2.		
3.		
4.		
5.		
6.		
7.		
8.		
9.		
10.		
11.		
Totals		

1 *Values* ★ $10
♣ $9

Graduation Bear
(Dated 2000)
#750816
Issued: 1999 • Closed: 2000
Retail Price: $6.99

2 *Values* UM $6.99

Grasshopper
Bug Series
#656933
Issued: 1999 • Open
Retail Price: $6.99

3 *Values* UM $10

Harp Seal
#382086
Issued: 1998 • Retired: 1999
Retail Price: $6.99

4 *Values* UM $9

Hippo
#475912
Issued: 1998 • Retired: 2000
Retail Price: $6.99

5 *Values* UM $6.99

Photo
Unavailable

Home Team Baseball Bear
#798932
Issued: 2000 • Open
Retail Price: $6.99

6 *Values* UM $13

Horse
#358290
Issued: 1997 • Retired: 1998
Retail Price: $6.99

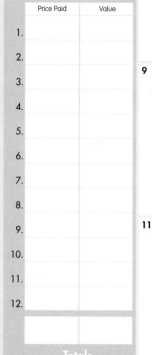

KEY

♥ 1998	✸ 2001
★ 1999	✤ Canadian
♣ 2000	UM Unmarked

General Plush

	Price Paid	Value
1.		
2.		
3.		
4.		
5.		
6.		
7.		
8.		
9.		
10.		
11.		
12.		
Totals		

7 *Values* UM $6.99

Iguariandon
#686824
Issued: 1999 • Open
Retail Price: $6.99

8 *Values* UM $6.99

I Love My Grandma
#786640
Issued: 2000 • Open
Retail Price: $6.99

9 *Values* UM $6.99

I Love My Grandma
#786659
Issued: 2000 • Open
Retail Price: $6.99

10 *Values* UM $6.99

Joy
Angel Bear Series
#749214
Issued: 2000 • Open
Retail Price: $6.99

11 *Values* UM $3.99

Kangaroo
Collect Your Own
Family Series
#661457
Issued: 1999 • Open
Retail Price: $3.99

12 *Values* UM $10.99

Kangaroo With Baby
Collect Your Own
Family Series
#661325
Issued: 1999 • Open
Retail Price: $10.99

1   *Values* UM $3.99

Kitten
*Collect Your Own
Family Series*
#661465
Issued: 1999 • Open
Retail Price: $3.99

2   *Values* ★ $12

Koala (LE-1999)
Catalog Plush
#535141
Issued: 1999 • Closed: 1999
Retail Price: $7

3   *Values* UM $15

Ladybug
#476080
Issued: 1999 • Retired: 1999
Retail Price: $7

4   *Values* UM $11

Lamb
#463299
Issued: 1998 • Retired: 1999
Retail Price: $6.99

5   *Values* UM $16

Lamb (12")
#477192
Issued: 1999 • Retired: 2000
Retail Price: $12.99

6   *Values* UM $20

Lamb (16")
#544094
Issued: 1999 • Open
Retail Price: $20

7   *Values* UM $7

Lavender Bunny
#516597
Issued: 1999 • Open
Retail Price: $7

8   *Values* UM $12

Lion
#358266
Issued: 1997 • Retired: 1998
Retail Price: $6.99

9   *Values* UM $12.49

Lion And Lamb (set/2)
#750115
Issued: 2000 • Open
Retail Price: $12.49

10   *Values* UM $6.99

Lobster
#750611
Issued: 1999 • Open
Retail Price: $6.99

11   *Values* ✦ $10 (Can.)

Loon
Canadian Exclusive
#535354
Issued: 1999 • Open
Retail Price: $10 (Canadian)

KEY
♥ 1998 ✿ 2001
★ 1999 ✦ Canadian
♣ 2000 UM Unmarked

General Plush

	Price Paid	Value
1.		
2.		
3.		
4.		
5.		
6.		
7.		
8.		
9.		
10.		
11.		
Totals		

1 — *Values* UM $6.99

Love
Angel Bear Series
#749214
Issued: 2000 • Open
Retail Price: $6.99

2 — *Values* ♣ $6.99

Marines
#798991
Issued: 2000 • Open
Retail Price: $6.99

3 — *Values* UM $10

Monkey
#475939
Issued: 1998 • Retired: 2000
Retail Price: $6.99

4 — *Values* ♥ $42

Monkey Triplets
(set/3, LE-1998)
Special Event Plush
#537977
Issued: 1998 • Closed: 1998
Retail Price: $14.99

5 — *Values* ♣ $10 (Can.)

Moose
Canadian Exclusive
#549509
Issued: 1999 • Open
Retail Price: $10 (Canadian)

6 — *Values* UM $6.99

My Grandma Loves Me
#798916
Issued: 2000 • Open
Retail Price: $6.99

KEY

♥ 1998	🎀 2001
★ 1999	♣ Canadian
♣ 2000	UM Unmarked

General Plush

	Price Paid	Value
1.		
2.		
3.		
4.		
5.		
6.		
7.		
8.		
9.		
10.		
11.		
Totals		

7 — *Values* UM $6.99

My Grandma Loves Me
#798924
Issued: 2000 • Open
Retail Price: $6.99

8 — *Values* ♣ $6.99

Navy
#798975
Issued: 2000 • Open
Retail Price: $6.99

9 — *Values* UM $6.99

Noel
Angel Bear Series
#749214
Issued: 2000 • Open
Retail Price: $6.99

10 — *Values* UM $6.99

Octopus
#750654
Issued: 1999 • Open
Retail Price: $6.99

11 — *Values* UM $6.99

Owl
#475882
Issued: 1998 • Open
Retail Price: $6.99

1
Values ♥ $15
★ $15

Panda Bear (LE-1999)
Care-A-Van Exclusive
#600873
Issued: 1999 • Closed: 1999
Retail Price: $7

2
Values ♥ $10

Parrot (LE-1999)
#480371
Issued: 1999 • Closed: 1999
Retail Price: $7

3
Values ∪M $6.99

Peace
Angel Bear Series
#749214
Issued: 2000 • Open
Retail Price: $6.99

4
Values ∪M $8

Penguin
#471917
Issued: 1998 • Retired: 2000
Retail Price: $6.99

5
Values ∪M $14

Pink Bunny
#464414
Issued: 1998 • Retired: 1999
Retail Price: $6.99

6
Values ♥ $14

Pink Flamingo (LE-1998)
#482889
Issued: 1998 • Closed: 1998
Retail Price: $6.99

7
Values ∪M $12.99

Pink Flamingo (12")
N/A
Issued: 1999 • Open
Retail Price: $12.99

8
Values ∪M $6.99

Polar Bear
#382027
Issued: 1998 • Open
Retail Price: $6.99

9
Values ∪M $6.99

Pterodactyl
#686794
Issued: 1999 • Open
Retail Price: $6.99

10
Values ∪M $6.99

Puffin
#748579
Issued: 2000 • Open
Retail Price: $6.99

KEY		
♥ 1998	✾ 2001	
★ 1999	♣ Canadian	
♣ 2000	∪M Unmarked	

General Plush

	Price Paid	Value
1.		
2.		
3.		
4.		
5.		
6.		
7.		
8.		
9.		
10.		

Totals

1 *Values* UM $7

Pumpkin (available in three colors)
#547131
Issued: 1999 • Open
Retail Price: $7

2 *Values* UM $8

Raptor
#686816
Issued: 1999 • Retired: 1999
Retail Price: $6.99

3 *Values* UM $6.99

Reindeer
#381969
Issued: 1998 • Open
Retail Price: $6.99

4 *Values* ♥ $9

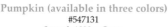

Rosie (LE-1999, available with rose, yellow, green, peach, violet or white ribbon)
Special Event Plush
#486884
Issued: 1999 • Closed: 1999
Retail Price: N/A

5 *Values* UM $6.99

Rottweiler
#703915
Issued: 2000 • Open
Retail Price: $6.99

6 *Values* UM $6.99

Seahorse
#535176
Issued: 1999 • Open
Retail Price: $6.99

7 *Values* ★ N/E

Seal (LE-1999)
Easter Seals
Commemorative Plush
N/A
Issued: 1999 • Closed: 1999
Retail Price: $7

8 *Values* UM $6.99

Shark
#750646
Issued: 1999 • Open
Retail Price: $6.99

9 *Values* ♣ $11
UM $11

Sherbert
Special Event Plush
#799262
Issued: 2000 • Closed: 2000
Retail Price: $6.99

1 *Values* UM $6.99

Snail
Bug Series
#656968
Issued: 1999 • Open
Retail Price: $6.99

2 *Values* ♣ $6.99

Special Olympics
Care-A-Van Exclusive
#798959
Issued: 2000 • Open
Retail Price: $6.99

3 *Values* UM $6.99

Photo Unavailable

Spider
(LE-1999, vibrating)
#656895E
Issued: 1999 • Closed: 1999
Retail Price: $6.99

4 *Values* UM $6.99

Starfish
#750638
Issued: 1999 • Open
Retail Price: $6.99

5 *Values* UM $6.99

Stegosaurus
#686778
Issued: 1999 • Open
Retail Price: $6.99

6 *Values* UM $6.99

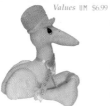

Stork
#749176
Issued: 2000 • Open
Retail Price: $6.99

7 *Values* UM $6.99

Stork
#756237
Issued: 2000 • Open
Retail Price: $6.99

8 *Values* ♥ $10

Tippy
Special Event Plush
#477869
Issued: 1999 • Closed: 1999
Retail Price: $7

9 *Values* UM $19.99

There's Snow Bunny
Like You! (16")
#750433
Issued: 2000 • Open
Retail Price: $19.99

General Plush

	Price Paid	Value
1.		
2.		
3.		
4.		
5.		
6.		
7.		
8.		
9.		
Totals		

1 *Values* UM $6.99

T-Rex
#686751
Issued: 1999 • Open
Retail Price: $6.99

2 *Values* UM $6.99

Triceratops
#686786
Issued: 1999 • Open
Retail Price: $6.99

3 *Values* UM $20

Turkey With Sign (12")
#634174
Issued: 1999 • Open
Retail Price: $20

4 *Values* UM $12

Turtle
#358339
Issued: 1997 • Retired: 1998
Retail Price: $6.99

5 *Values* ★ N/E

Turtle
*Chapel Commemorative
Plush*
#681040
Issued: 1999 • Closed: 1999
Retail Price: $6.99

6 *Values* ♥ $15

Unicorn (LE-1998)
#478180
Issued: 1998 • Closed: 1998
Retail Price: $6.99

General Plush

	Price Paid	Value
1.		
2.		
3.		
4.		
5.		
6.		
7.		
8.		
9.		
10.		
11.		

Totals

7 *Values* UM $10

Valentine Bear
#670200
Issued: 1999 • Retired: 2000
Retail Price: $6.99

8 *Values* UM $6.99

Walrus
#748234
Issued: 2000 • Open
Retail Price: $6.99

9 *Values* UM $7

Whale
#573639
Issued: 1999 • Open
Retail Price: $7

10 *Values* UM $7

Whale
#576115
Issued: 1999 • Open
Retail Price: $7

1 *Values* UM $7

Whale
#576131
Issued: 1999 • Open
Retail Price: $7

1 *Values* UM $7

Whale
#576956
Issued: 1999 • Open
Retail Price: $7

2 *Values* UM $7

Whale
#576964
Issued: 1999 • Open
Retail Price: $7

3 *Values* UM $7

Whale
#576980
Issued: 1999 • Open
Retail Price: $7

4 *Values* UM $7

Whale
#576999
Issued: 1999 • Open
Retail Price: $7

5 *Values* ♥ $8

Whale
#577006
Issued: 1999 • Retired: 1999
Retail Price: $7

6 *Values* UM N/E

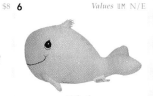

Whale
Cruise Exclusive
#795623
Issued: 2000 • Closed: 2000
Retail Price: N/A

7 *Values* UM $9

White Bunny
#382345
Issued: 1998 • Retired: 1999
Retail Price: $6.99

8 *Values* ♥ $12

White Owl (LE-1998)
Special Event Plush
#504394
Issued 1998 • Closed: 1998
Retail Price: N/A

9 *Values* ♥ $14
UM $14

White Rhino (LE-1998)
#358312
Issued: 1998 • Closed: 1998
Retail Price: $6.99

10 *Values* UM $19.99

You're Snow Beary
Special (16″)
#750468
Issued: 2000 • Open
Retail Price: $19.99

11 *Values* UM $4

Photo Unavailable

20th Anniversary Bear
#612421
Issued: 1999 • Open
Retail Price: $4

12 UM $3.99

Bear
#463256
Issued: 1998 • Open
Retail Price: $3.99

KEY
♥ 1998 | 🎋 2001
★ 1999 | 🍁 Canadian
♣ 2000 | UM Unmarked

General Plush

	Price Paid	Value
1.		
2.		
3.		
4.		
5.		
6.		
7.		
8.		
9.		
10.		

General Ornaments

11.		
12.		

Totals

1   *Values* UM $3.99

Photo Unavailable

Bear
#778109
Issued: 2000 • Open
Retail Price: $3.99

2   *Values* UM $4

Blue Bird
#478458
Issued: 1999 • Open
Retail Price: $4

3   *Values* UM $4

Bunny Mini Ornaments
(available in 6 colors)
#649112
Issued: 1999 • Open
Retail Price: $4

4   *Values* UM $3.99

Cardinal
#463264
Issued: 1998 • Open
Retail Price: $3.99

5   *Values* UM $3.99

Elephant
#463256
Issued: 1998 • Open
Retail Price: $3.99

6   *Values* UM $4

Flamingo
#612421
Issued: 1999 • Open
Retail Price: $4

General Ornaments

	Price Paid	Value
1.		
2.		
3.		
4.		
5.		
6.		
7.		
8.		
9.		
10.		
11.		
12.		
Totals		

7   *Values* UM $3.99

Harp Seal
#463264
Issued: 1998 • Open
Retail Price: $3.99

8   *Values* UM $3.99

Horse
#463256
Issued: 1998 • Open
Retail Price: $3.99

9   *Values* UM $4

Photo Unavailable

Lamb
#478458
Issued: 1999 • Open
Retail Price: $4

10   *Values* UM $3.99

Lion
#463256
Issued: 1998 • Open
Retail Price: $3.99

11   *Values* UM $4

Monkey
(available in three colors)
#612421
Issued: 1999 • Open
Retail Price: $4

12   *Values* UM $4

Owl
#612421
Issued: 1999 • Open
Retail Price: $4

1 *Values* UM $3.99

Pig
#463256
Issued: 1998 • Open
Retail Price: $3.99

2 *Values* UM $4

Pink Bunny
#478458
Issued: 1999 • Open
Retail Price: $4

3 *Values* UM $3.99

Polar Bear
#463264
Issued: 1998 • Open
Retail Price: $3.99

4 *Values* UM $3.99

Reindeer
#463264
Issued: 1998 • Open
Retail Price: $3.99

5 *Values* UM $4

Rhino
#612421
Issued: 1999 • Open
Retail Price: $4

6 *Values* UM $4

Rosie
#612421
Issued: 1999 • Open
Retail Price: $4

7 *Values* UM $4

Tippy
#612421
Issued: 1999 • Open
Retail Price: $4

8 *Values* UM $3.99

Turtle
#463256
Issued: 1998 • Open
Retail Price: $3.99

9 *Values* UM $4

Unicorn
#612421
Issued: 1999 • Open
Retail Price: $4

10 *Values* UM $4

Yellow Duck
#478458
Issued: 1999 • Open
Retail Price: $4

11 *Values* UM$12.50

Photo
Unavailable

Bear
Hugs For You
#729086
Issued: 2000 • Open
Retail Price: $12.50

12 *Values* UM$12.50

Photo
Unavailable

Bird
Hugs For You
#729094
Issued: 2000 • Open
Retail Price: $12.50

KEY		
♥ 1998	✿ 2001	
★ 1999	✦ Canadian	
♣ 2000	UM Unmarked	

General Ornaments

	Price Paid	Value
1.		
2.		
3.		
4.		
5.		
6.		
7.		
8.		
9.		
10.		

Other Collectibles

11.		
12.		

Totals

217

1 *Values* UM$12.50

*Photo
Unavailable*
Bunny
Hugs For You
#729116
Issued: 2000 • Open
Retail Price: $12.50

2 *Values* UM$12.50

*Photo
Unavailable*
Cat
Hugs For You
#729051
Issued: 2000 • Open
Retail Price: $12.50

3 *Values* UM$12.50

*Photo
Unavailable*
Cow
Hugs For You
#729132
Issued: 2000 • Open
Retail Price: $12.50

4 *Values* UM$12.50

Dog
Hugs For You
#729078
Issued: 2000 • Open
Retail Price: $12.50

5 *Values* UM$12.50

Elephant
Hugs For You
#729159
Issued: 2000 • Open
Retail Price: $12.50

6 *Values* UM$12.50

*Photo
Unavailable*
Lion
Hugs For You
#729140
Issued: 2000 • Open
Retail Price: $12.50

KEY	
♥ 1998	✿ 2001
★ 1999	✦ Canadian
♣ 2000	UM Unmarked

Other Collectibles

	Price Paid	Value
1.		
2.		
3.		
4.		
5.		
6.		
7.		
8.		

Totals

7 *Values* UM$12.50

Monkey
Hugs For You
#729124
Issued: 2000 • Open
Retail Price: $12.50

8 *Values* UM$12.50

Pig
Hugs For You
#729108
Issued: 2000 • Open
Retail Price: $12.50

Chapel Exclusives

In this section, you will find both figurines and ornaments that were exclusively for sale through The PRECIOUS MOMENTS Chapel. The Chapel is located in Carthage, Missouri, but, for collectors who can't make it there, pieces are also available through the Chapel's web site and its catalog.

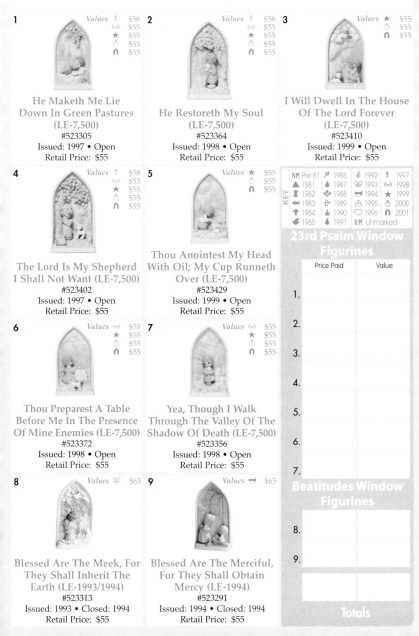

1
Values † $58
ᵭ $55
★ $55
◷ $55
ᴖ $55

He Maketh Me Lie
Down In Green Pastures
(LE-7,500)
#523305
Issued: 1997 • Open
Retail Price: $55

2
Values † $58
ᵭ $55
★ $55
◷ $55
ᴖ $55

He Restoreth My Soul
(LE-7,500)
#523364
Issued: 1998 • Open
Retail Price: $55

3
Values ★ $55
◷ $55
ᴖ $55

I Will Dwell In The House
Of The Lord Forever
(LE-7,500)
#523410
Issued: 1999 • Open
Retail Price: $55

4
Values † $58
ᵭ $55
★ $55
◷ $55
ᴖ $55

The Lord Is My Shepherd
I Shall Not Want (LE-7,500)
#523402
Issued: 1997 • Open
Retail Price: $55

5
Values ★ $55
◷ $55
ᴖ $55

Thou Anointest My Head
With Oil; My Cup Runneth
Over (LE-7,500)
#523429
Issued: 1999 • Open
Retail Price: $55

KEY							
NM Pre'81	♫ 1986	♦ 1992	† 1997
▲ 1981	♠ 1987	♋ 1993	ᵭ 1998
Ⅱ 1982	♣ 1988	⊷ 1994	★ 1999
⊷ 1983	♭ 1989	⚖ 1995	◷ 2000
✝ 1984	⚓ 1990	♡ 1996	ᴖ 2001
⚘ 1985	♪ 1991	UM Unmarked	

23rd Psalm Window Figurines

	Price Paid	Value
1.		
2.		
3.		
4.		
5.		
6.		
7.		

6
Values ᵭ $55
★ $55
◷ $55
ᴖ $55

Thou Preparest A Table
Before Me In The Presence
Of Mine Enemies (LE-7,500)
#523372
Issued: 1998 • Open
Retail Price: $55

7
Values ᵭ $55
★ $55
◷ $55
ᴖ $55

Yea, Though I Walk
Through The Valley Of The
Shadow Of Death (LE-7,500)
#523356
Issued: 1998 • Open
Retail Price: $55

8
Values ♋ $63

Blessed Are The Meek, For
They Shall Inherit The
Earth (LE-1993/1994)
#523313
Issued: 1993 • Closed: 1994
Retail Price: $55

9
Values ⊷ $65

Blessed Are The Merciful,
For They Shall Obtain
Mercy (LE-1994)
#523291
Issued: 1994 • Closed: 1994
Retail Price: $55

Beatitudes Window Figurines

8.	
9.	

Totals

1 Values 🪶 $75

Blessed Are The
Peacemakers, For They
Shall Be Called The
Children Of God (LE-1995)
#523348
Issued: 1995 • Closed: 1995
Retail Price: $55

2 Values ♻ $70

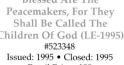

Blessed Are The Poor In
Spirit, For Theirs Is The
Kingdom Of Heaven
(LE-1992)
#523437
Issued: 1992 • Closed: 1992
Retail Price: $55

3 Values 🪶 $70

Blessed Are The Pure In
Heart, For They Shall See
God (LE-1994/1995)
#523399
Issued: 1994 • Closed: 1995
Retail Price: $55

4 Values ♐ $65

Blessed Are They That
Hunger And Thirst After
Righteousness, For They
Shall Be Filled (LE-1993)
#523321
Issued: 1993 • Closed: 1993
Retail Price: $55

5 Values ♻ $70

Blessed Are They That
Mourn, For They Shall Be
Comforted (LE-1992)
#523380
Issued: 1992 • Closed: 1992
Retail Price: $55

6 Values
† $32.50
👓 $32.50
★ $32.50
🕐 $32.50
∩ $32.50
UM $38

Coleenia
#204889
Issued: 1996 • Open
Retail Price: $32.50

KEY			
NM Pre'81	🎗 1986	♻ 1992	† 1997
▲ 1981	♣ 1987	♐ 1993	👓 1998
✕ 1982	♦ 1988	➡ 1994	★ 1999
➡ 1983	� 1989	⟁ 1995	🕐 2000
✝ 1984	✦ 1990	♡ 1996	∩ 2001
➳ 1985	♨ 1991	UM Unmarked	

Beatitudes Window Figurines

	Price Paid	Value
1.		
2.		
3.		
4.		
5.		

General Figurines

6.		
7.		
8.		
9.		
10.		
11.		

Totals

7 Values
† $35
👓 $35
★ $35
🕐 $35
∩ $35
UM $42

Crown Him Lord Of All
#261602
Issued: 1997 • Open
Retail Price: $35

8 Values
🪶 $34
⟁ $32
♡ $30
† $30
👓 $30
★ $30
🕐 $30
∩ $30
UM $45

Death Can't Keep Him
In The Ground
#531928
Issued: 1994 • Open
Retail Price: $30

9 Values
👓 $67.50
★ $67.50
🕐 $67.50
∩ $67.50

Feed My Lambs
#453722
Issued: 1998 • Open
Retail Price: $67.50

10 Values
★ $45
🕐 $45
∩ $45
UM $45

Fountain Of Angels
#384844
Issued: 1998 • Open
Retail Price: $45

11 Values
∩ $45
UM $45

Good Night, Sleep Tight
#542636
Issued: 1999 • Open
Retail Price: $45

1
Values ⏱ $50
☊ $50
UM $50

Gone But Never Forgotten
#135976
Issued: 2000 • Open
Retail Price: $50

2
Values ⏚ $125
♡ $125
† $105
6∂ $100
★ $100
⏱ $100
☊ $100

Grandpa's Island
#129259
Issued: 1995 • Open
Retail Price: $100

3
Values UM N/E

Happy 10th Anniversary
10th Anniversary
Commemorative Figurine
#540013
Issued: 1999 • Closed: 1999
Retail Price: $45

4
Values ☊ $95
UM $95

He Is My Inspiration
#523038
Issued: 1991 • Open
Retail Price: $60

5
Variation

> HE IS NOT HERE
> FOR HE IS RISEN
> AS HE SAID.
> MATH 28:6

Values ⫪ $68
⏚ $63
♡ $60
† $60
6∂ $60
★ $60
⏱ $60
☊ $60
UM $100

He Is Not Here For He Is Risen As He Said
#527106
Issued: 1993 • Open
Retail Price: $60
Variation: Inscription reads "Math" – $105

6
Values ☊ $30
UM $30

He Is The Bright Morning Star
#588067
Issued: 1999 • Open
Retail Price: $30

7
Values † $45
6∂ $45
★ $45
⏱ $45
☊ $45
UM $60

Heaven Must Have Sent You
#135992
Issued: 1996 • Open
Retail Price: $45

KEY			
NM Pre'81	⌡ 1986	⧢ 1992	† 1997
▲ 1981	▲ 1987	♉ 1993	6∂ 1998
⏃ 1982	⧉ 1988	⫟ 1994	★ 1999
⬡ 1983	⧩ 1989	⬠ 1995	⏱ 2000
† 1984	⟟ 1990	♡ 1996	☊ 2001
⬞ 1985	⬥ 1991	UM Unmarked	

General Figurines

	Price Paid	Value
1.		
2.		
3.		
4.		
5.		
6.		
7.		
8.		
9.		
10.		
11.		
Totals		

8
Values ♡ $28
† $28
6∂ $28

His Presence Is Felt In The Chapel
#163872
Issued: 1996 • Retired: 1998
Retail Price: $25

9
Values ☊ $50
UM $50

I'm Gonna Let It Shine
#349852
Issued: 1999 • Open
Retail Price: $50

10
Values UM $45

A King Is Born
#604151
Issued: 1994 • Retired: 1995
Retail Price: $25

11
Values ⏱ $32.50
☊ $32.50
UM $32.50

Let Earth Receive Her King
#748382
Issued: 2000 • Open
Retail Price: $32.50

1

Values △ $45
♡ $36
† $36
∞ $36

Lighting The Way To A Happy Holiday
#129267
Issued: 1995 • Retired: 1998
Retail Price: $30

2

Values ∩ $50
UM $50

The Lord Is Our Chief Inspiration
#204862
Issued: 1996 • Open
Retail Price: $45

3

Values UM $285

The Lord Is Our Chief Inspiration
(9", LE-1996/1997)
#204870
Issued: 1996 • Closed: 1997
Retail Price: $250

4

Values ∩ $32.50
UM $32.50

On Our Way To The Chapel
#795518
Issued: 2000 • Open
Retail Price: $32.50

5

Values ♡ $52
† $50
∞ $50
UM $85

On The Hill Overlooking The Quiet Blue Stream
#603503
Issued: 1994 • Retired: 1998
Retail Price: $45

6

Values ∩ $30
UM $30

Our Loss Is Heaven's Gain
#731676
Issued: 2000 • Open
Retail Price: $30

KEY					
NM Pre'81	♪ 1986	ℰ 1992	† 1997
▲ 1981	♠ 1987	❀ 1993	∞ 1998
✕ 1982	✤ 1988	➤ 1994	★ 1999
✚ 1983	✣ 1989	△ 1995	○ 2000
✚ 1984	✦ 1990	♡ 1996	∩ 2001
✦ 1985	♦ 1991	UM Unmarked	

General Figurines

	Price Paid	Value
1.		
2.		
3.		
4.		
5.		
6.	30 ₀₀	
7.		
8.		
9.		
10.		

Totals

7

Values UM $90

Our Love Will Flow Eternal
#588059
Issued: 1999 • Open
Retail Price: $90

8

Values ∩ $35
UM $35

Mary Had A Little Lamb
#850969
Issued: 2000 • Open
Retail Price: $35

9

Values ★ $45
○ $45
∩ $45
UM $45

A Prayer Warrior's Faith Can Move Mountains
#354406
Issued: 1998 • Open
Retail Price: $45

10

Values ∞ $262
★ $262

A Prayer Warrior's Faith Can Move Mountains
(9", LE-1998)
#354414
Issued: 1998 • Closed: 1998
Retail Price: $250

1 Values ∩ $50
UM $50

Precious Moments Chapel
Lilliput Lane® Figurine
#L2258
Issued: 1999 • Open
Retail Price: $50

2 Values 6ð $32
★ $30
Ⓒ $30
UM $46

Seeds Of Love From
The Chapel
#271586
Issued: 1997 • Susp.: 1999
Retail Price: $30

3 Values ⌐ $35
△ $33
♡ $30
† $30
6ð $30
★ $30
Ⓒ $30
∩ $30
UM $56

Surrounded With Joy
#531677
Issued: 1993 • Open
Retail Price: $30

4 Values ∩ $75
UM $75

There Shall Be Fountains
Of Blessings
#731668
Issued: 2000 • Open
Retail Price: $75

5

Variation Values ♦ $70
⚲ $64
⌐ $60
△ $58
UM $105

There's A Christian Welcome Here
#523011
Issued: 1989 • Susp.: 1995
Retail Price: $45
Variation: Missing right eyebrow – $125

6 Values † $87
6ð $87
★ $87
Ⓒ $87
UM $95

This World Is Not My
Home (I'm Just A
Passing Thru)
#212547
Issued: 1997 • Retired: 1999
Retail Price: $85

7 Values 6ð $40
★ $40
Ⓒ $40
∩ $40

Toy Maker
#475092
Issued: 1998 • Open
Retail Price: $40

KEY						
NM Pre'81	✿ 1986	♠ 1992	† 1997
▲ 1981	▲ 1987	♋ 1993	6ð 1998
✕ 1982	✤ 1988	⌐ 1994	★ 1999
◄ 1983	↵ 1989	△ 1995	Ⓒ 2000
† 1984	★ 1990	♡ 1996	∩ 2001
✿ 1985	♦ 1991	UM Unmarked	

General Figurines

	Price Paid	Value
1.		
2.		
3.		
4.		
5.		
6.		
7.		
8.		
9.		

8 Values ∩ $85
UM $85

Victorious In Jesus
#850942
Issued: 2000 • Open
Retail Price: $85

9 Values ∩ $30
UM $30

You Color Our World With
Loving, Caring And
Sharing
#644463
Issued: 2000 • Open
Retail Price: $30

10 Values † $27
6ð $25
★ $25
Ⓒ $25
∩ $25
UM $35

Crown Him Lord Of All
#261610
Issued: 1997 • Open
Retail Price: $25

11 Values UM N/E

*Photo
Unavailable*

Happy 10th Anniversary
*10th Anniversary
Commemorative Figurine*
#588040
Issued: 1999 • Closed: 1999
Retail Price: $20

General Ornaments

10.		
11.		

Totals

1

Values † $23
6∂ $23
 UM $28

His Presence Is Felt
In The Chapel
#163880
Issued: 1996 • Susp.: 1998
Retail Price: $17.50

2

Values ∩ $20
UM $20

Photo Unavailable

He Is The Bright
Morning Star
#588075
Issued: 1999 • Open
Retail Price: $20

3

Values UM $45

A King Is Born
#532088
Issued: 1994 • Retired: 1995
Retail Price: $17.50

4

Values ∩ $25
UM $25

Let Earth Receive Her King
#748390
Issued: 2000 • Open
Retail Price: $25

5

Values △ $32
♡ $25
† $20
6∂ $20
★ $20

Lighting The Way To A
Happy Holiday
#129275
Issued: 1995 • Susp.: 1999
Retail Price: $20

6

Values ⊣ $22
△ $20
♡$17.50
†$17.50
6∂$17.50
★$17.50
⊙$17.50
∩$17.50
UM $39

Surrounded With Joy
#531685
Issued: 1993 • Open
Retail Price: $17.50

7

Values ℗ $27
⊣ $24
△ $24
♡$22.50
†$22.50
6∂$22.50
★$22.50
⊙$22.50
∩$22.50
UM $35

There's A Christian
Welcome Here
#528021
Issued: 1992 • Open
Retail Price: $22.50

8

Values 6∂ $20
★ $20
⊙ $20
∩ $20

Toy Maker
#475106
Issued: 1998 • Open
Retail Price: $20

KEY			
NM Pre'81	⫗ 1986	₰ 1992	† 1997
▲ 1981	▲ 1987	℗ 1993	6∂ 1998
✕ 1982	⬧ 1988	⊣ 1994	★ 1999
⬅ 1983	⭗ 1989	△ 1995	⊙ 2000
✝ 1984	⚘ 1990	♡ 1996	∩ 2001
⚜ 1985	♦ 1991	UM Unmarked	

General Ornaments

	Price Paid	Value
1.		
2.		
3.		
4.		
5.		
6.		
7.		
8.		

Totals

Collectors' Club

This section contains pieces that have been made available only to members of Enesco's PRECIOUS MOMENTS clubs. Since the inception of the line, there have been three different clubs.

1

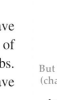

Values NM $195
▲ $163
I $160

But Love Goes On Forever
(charter member figurine)
#E0001
Issued: 1981 • Closed: 1981
Retail Price: N/A

2

Values ▲ $90
I $76
UM $130

But Love Goes On Forever
(charter member plaque)
#E0102
Issued: 1982 • Closed: 1982
Retail Price: N/A

3

Values ▲ $82
I $70
Variation UM $120

But Love Goes On Forever
#E0202
Issued: 1982 • Closed: 1982
Retail Price: N/A
Variation: 🍂 *(mistakenly produced and sent to Canada) – $130*

4

Values I $72
🍂 $62

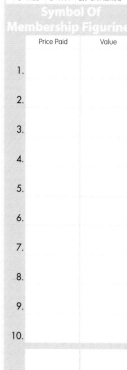

Let Us Call The Club
To Order
(charter member figurine)
#E0103
Issued: 1983 • Closed: 1983
Retail Price: N/A

5

Values I $66
🍂 $58
✝ $55

Let Us Call The Club
To Order
#E0303
Issued: 1983 • Closed: 1983
Retail Price: N/A

6

Values 🍂 $66
✝ $54

Join In On The Blessings
(charter member figurine)
#E0104
Issued: 1984 • Closed: 1984
Retail Price: N/A

KEY	NM Pre'81	🌿 1986	🦋 1992	✝ 1997
	▲ 1981	🔺 1987	♀♀ 1993	🔗 1998
	I 1982	⚘ 1988	🌾 1994	★ 1999
	🍂 1983	⅁ 1989	△ 1995	⊘ 2000
	✝ 1984	✦ 1990	♡ 1996	≈ 2001
	🍂 1985	🍂 1991	UM	Unmarked

7

Values 🍂 $58
✝ $46

Join In On The Blessings
#E0404
Issued: 1984 • Closed: 1984
Retail Price: N/A

8

Values ✝ $52
🍂 $47

Seek And Ye Shall Find
#E0005
Issued: 1985 • Closed: 1985
Retail Price: N/A

9

Values ✝ $62
🍂 $50

Seek And Ye Shall Find
(charter member figurine)
#E0105
Issued: 1985 • Closed: 1985
Retail Price: N/A

10

Values 🍂 $47
🌿 $42

Birds Of A Feather
Collect Together
#E0006
Issued: 1986 • Closed: 1986
Retail Price: N/A

Symbol Of
Membership Figurines

	Price Paid	Value
1.		
2.		
3.		
4.		
5.		
6.		
7.		
8.		
9.		
10.		

Totals

1 Values 🍃 $52
🍐 $48

**Birds Of A Feather
Collect Together**
(charter member figurine)
#E0106
Issued: 1986 • Closed: 1986
Retail Price: N/A

2  Values 🍐 $48
🌲 $36

Sharing Is Universal
#E0007
Issued: 1987 • Closed: 1987
Retail Price: N/A

3 Values 🍐 $53
🌲 $48

Sharing Is Universal
(charter member figurine)
#E0107
Issued: 1987 • Closed: 1987
Retail Price: N/A

4  Values 🌲 $44
⚜ $32

A Growing Love
#E0008
Issued: 1988 • Closed: 1988
Retail Price: N/A

5  Values 🌲 $53
⚜ $47

A Growing Love
(charter member figurine)
#E0108
Issued: 1988 • Closed: 1988
Retail Price: N/A

6 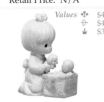 Values ⚜ $46
🔔 $41
🌷 $37

**Always Room For
One More**
#C0009
Issued: 1989 • Closed: 1989
Retail Price: N/A

KEY			
NM Pre'81	🍃 1986	🍐 1992	✝ 1997
▲ 1981	🔔 1987	🕊 1993	🔆 1998
𝕀 1982	⚜ 1988	🍷 1994	★ 1999
🔚 1983	🔔 1989	🍦 1995	🌐 2000
✝ 1984	🌷 1990	♡ 1996	🔨 2001
🍃 1985	🔔 1991	UM Unmarked	

Symbol Of Membership Figurines

	Price Paid	Value
1.		
2.		
3.		
4.		
5.		
6.		
7.		
8.		
9.		
10.		
11.		
12.		
Totals		

7  Values ⚜ $54
🔔 $50

**Always Room For
One More**
(charter member figurine)
#C0109
Issued: 1989 • Closed: 1989
Retail Price: N/A

8  Values 🔔 $42
🌷 $32

My Happiness
#C0010
Issued: 1990 • Closed: 1990
Retail Price: N/A

9  Values 🔔 $55
🌷 $45

My Happiness
(charter member figurine)
#C0110
Issued: 1990 • Closed: 1990
Retail Price: N/A

10  Values 🌷 $44
🔔 $34

**Sharing The
Good News Together**
#C0011
Issued: 1991 • Closed: 1991
Retail Price: N/A

11  Values 🌷 $50
🔔 $43

**Sharing The
Good News Together**
(charter member figurine)
#C0111
Issued: 1991 • Closed: 1991
Retail Price: N/A

12 Values 🔔 $46
🍐 $38

**The Club That's Out
Of This World**
#C0012
Issued: 1992 • Closed: 1992
Retail Price: N/A

1   *Values* 🔔 $50
           🔔 $44

The Club That's Out
Of This World
(charter member figurine)
#C0112
Issued: 1992 • Closed: 1992
Retail Price: N/A

2   *Values* 🔔 $44
           🔔 $38

Loving, Caring, And
Sharing Along The Way
#C0013
Issued: 1993 • Closed: 1993
Retail Price: N/A

3   *Values* 🔔 $52
           🔔 $46

Loving, Caring, And
Sharing Along The Way
(charter member figurine)
#C0113
Issued: 1993 • Closed: 1993
Retail Price: N/A

4   *Values* 🔔 $40
           🔔 $30

You Are The End
Of My Rainbow
#C0014
Issued: 1994 • Closed: 1994
Retail Price: N/A

5   *Values* 🔔 $50
           🔔 $45

You Are The End
Of My Rainbow
(charter member figurine)
#C0114
Issued: 1994 • Closed: 1994
Retail Price: N/A

6   *Values* 🔔 $40
           🔔 $39

You're The Sweetest
Cookie In The Batch
#C0015
Issued: 1995 • Closed: 1995
Retail Price: N/A

7   *Values* 🔔 $46
           🔔 $35

You're The Sweetest
Cookie In The Batch
(charter member figurine)
#C0115
Issued: 1995 • Closed: 1995
Retail Price: N/A

8   *Values* 🔔 $33
           ♡ $28

You're As Pretty As A Picture
#C0016
Issued: 1996 • Closed: 1996
Retail Price: N/A

9   *Values* 🔔 $38
           ♡ $30

You're As Pretty As A Picture
(charter member figurine)
#C0116
Issued: 1996 • Closed: 1996
Retail Price: N/A

10   *Values* ♡ $38
           † $35

A Special Toast To
Precious Moments
#C0017
Issued: 1997 • Closed: 1997
Retail Price: N/A

11   *Values* ♡ $40
           † $34

A Special Toast To
Precious Moments
(charter member figurine)
#C0117
Issued: 1997 • Closed: 1997
Retail Price: N/A

12   *Values* † $35
           6∂ $27

Focusing In On Those
Precious Moments
#C0018
Issued: 1998 • Closed: 1998
Retail Price: N/A

NM Pre'81	🦋 1986	🔔 1992	† 1997
▲ 1981	♣ 1987	♀♀ 1993	6∂ 1998
I 1982	✤ 1988	🔔 1994	★ 1999
◄ 1983	Ð 1989	△ 1995	◐ 2000
† 1984	↓ 1990	♡ 1996	≜ 2001
◆ 1985	🔔 1991	UM Unmarked	

**Symbol Of
Membership Figurines**

	Price Paid	Value
1.		
2.		
3.		
4.		
5.		
6.		
7.		
8.		
9.		
10.		
11.		
12.		

Totals

1 Values † $35
63 $27

**Focusing In On Those
Precious Moments
(charter member figurine)**
#C0118
Issued: 1998 • Closed: 1998
Retail Price: N/A

2 Values 63 $45
★ $45

**Wishing You A
World Of Peace**
#C0019
Issued: 1999 • Closed: 1999
Retail Price: N/A

3 Values 63 $45
★ $45

**Wishing You A
World Of Peace
(charter member figurine)**
#C0119
Issued: 1999 • Closed: 1999
Retail Price: N/A

4 Values ★ N/E
○ N/E

Thanks A Bunch
#C0020
Issued: 2000 • Closed: 2000
Retail Price: N/A

5 Values ★ N/E
○ N/E

**Thanks A Bunch
(charter member figurine)**
#C0020
Issued: 2000 • Closed: 2000
Retail Price: N/A

6 Values ○ N/E
☙ N/E
New

**Friends Write From
The Start**
#C0021
Issued: 2001 • To Be Closed: 2001
Retail Price: N/A

KEY			
NM Pre'81	✐ 1986	⚓ 1992	† 1997
▲ 1981	♠ 1987	♋ 1993	63 1998
✠ 1982	✤ 1988	⌘ 1994	★ 1999
◄ 1983	✛ 1989	△ 1995	○ 2000
✝ 1984	✦ 1990	♡ 1996	☙ 2001
✿ 1985	✦ 1991	UM Unmarked	

**Symbol Of
Membership Figurines**

	Price Paid	Value
1.		
2.		
3.		
4.		
5.		
6.		
7.		

Members Only Figurines

8.		
9.		
10.		
11.		
12.		

Totals

7 Values ○ N/E
☙ N/E
New

**Friends Write From
The Start
(charter member figurine)**
#C0021
Issued: 2001 • To Be Closed: 2001
Retail Price: N/A

8 Values ▲ $455
✠ $440

Hello, Lord, It's Me Again
#PM811
Issued: 1981 • Closed: 1981
Retail Price: $25

9 Values ✠ $205
◄ $190

Smile, God Loves You
#PM821
Issued: 1982 • Closed: 1982
Retail Price: $25

10 Values ✠ $225
◄ $200
† $195

Put On A Happy Face
#PM822
Issued: 1983 • Closed: 1983
Retail Price: $25

11 Values ◄ $76
† $70

Dawn's Early Light
#PM831
Issued: 1983 • Closed: 1983
Retail Price: $27.50

12 Values ◄ $95
† $60
✿ $50

God's Ray Of Mercy
#PM841
Issued: 1984 • Closed: 1984
Retail Price: $25

1   Values † $66
     $60

**Trust In The Lord To
The Finish**
#PM842
Issued: 1984 • Closed: 1984
Retail Price: $25

2   Values ◆ $82

The Lord Is My Shepherd
#PM851
Issued: 1985 • Closed: 1985
Retail Price: $25

3   Values ◆ $68
     ♪ $62

I Love To Tell The Story
#PM852
Issued: 1985 • Closed: 1985
Retail Price: $27.50

4   Values ◆ $300

God Bless Our Years Together
*5th Anniversary
Commerative Figurine*
#12440
Issued: 1985 • Closed: 1985
Retail Price: $175

5   Values ◆ $92
     ♪ $80
     ▲ $76

Grandma's Prayer
#PM861
Issued: 1986 • Closed: 1986
Retail Price: $25

6   Values ♪ $88

I'm Following Jesus
#PM862
Issued: 1986 • Closed: 1986
Retail Price: $25

7   Values ♪ $92
     ▲ $65
     ✤ $58

Feed My Sheep
#PM871
Issued: 1987 • Closed: 1987
Retail Price: $25

8   Values ♪ $66
     ▲ $58
     ✤ $55

In His Time
#PM872
Issued: 1987 • Closed: 1987
Retail Price: $25

KEY			
NM Pre'81	♫ 1986	◢ 1992	† 1997
▲ 1981	♠ 1987	♋ 1993	6✦ 1998
✗ 1982	✤ 1988	◄ 1994	★ 1999
◄ 1983	✛ 1989	◬ 1995	◷ 2000
† 1984	✦ 1990	♡ 1996	◔ 2001
◆ 1985	♦ 1991	UM Unmarked	

**Members Only
Figurines**

	Price Paid	Value
1.		
2.		
3.		
4.		
5.		
6.		
7.		
8.		
9.		
10.		
11.		
12.		

Totals

9   Values ♪ $49
     ▲ $43
     ✤ $41

Loving You Dear Valentine
#PM873
Issued: 1987 • Closed: 1987
Retail Price: $25

10   Values ♪ $52
     ▲ $47
     ✤ $42

Loving You Dear Valentine
#PM874
Issued: 1987 • Closed: 1987
Retail Price: $25

11   Values ▲ $68
     ✤ $57
     ✛ $50

**God Bless You For
Touching My Life**
#PM881
Issued: 1988 • Closed: 1988
Retail Price: $27.50

12   Values ✤ $56
     ✛ $50

**You Just Cannot Chuck A
Good Friendship**
#PM882
Issued: 1988 • Closed: 1988
Retail Price: $27.50

1 *Values* ✝ $50 ☀ $44

You Will Always Be My Choice
#PM891
Issued: 1989 • Closed: 1989
Retail Price: $27.50

2 *Values* ✝ $63 ☀ $56

Mow Power To Ya
#PM892
Issued: 1989 • Closed: 1989
Retail Price: $27.50

3 *Values* ☀ $54 ☀ $50

Ten Years And Still Going Strong
#PM901
Issued: 1990 • Closed: 1990
Retail Price: $30

4 *Values* ☀ $63 ☀ $55

You Are A Blessing To Me
#PM902
Issued: 1990 • Closed: 1990
Retail Price: $27.50

5 *Values* ☀ $60 ⚓ $52

One Step At A Time
#PM911
Issued: 1991 • Closed: 1991
Retail Price: $33

6 *Values* ☀ $64 ⚓ $57

Lord, Keep Me In Teepee Top Shape
#PM912
Issued: 1991 • Closed: 1991
Retail Price: $27.50

KEY			
NM Pre'81	⚘ 1986	⚓ 1992	✝ 1997
▲ 1981	▲ 1987	⚲ 1993	ᵇ 1998
✕ 1982	⬥ 1988	➯ 1994	★ 1999
➥ 1983	✝ 1989	△ 1995	◷ 2000
✝ 1984	☀ 1990	♡ 1996	⚬ 2001
⚘ 1985	♦ 1991	UM Unmarked	

Members Only Figurines

	Price Paid	Value
1.		
2.		
3.		
4.		
5.		
6.		
7.		
8.		
9.		
10.		
11.		
12.		
Totals		

7 *Values* ⚓ $68 ⚲ $62

Only Love Can Make A Home
#PM921
Issued: 1992 • Closed: 1992
Retail Price: $30

8 *Values* ⚓ $44 ⚲ $38

Sowing The Seeds Of Love
#PM922
Issued: 1992 • Closed: 1992
Retail Price: $30

9 *Values* ⚓ $390

This Land Is Our Land (LE-1992)
#527386
Issued: 1992 • Closed: 1992
Retail Price: $350

10 *Values* ⚲ $50 ➯ $46

His Little Treasure
#PM931
Issued: 1993 • Closed: 1993
Retail Price: $30

11 *Values* ⚲ $76 ➯ $70

Loving
#PM932
Issued: 1993 • Closed: 1993
Retail Price: $30

12 *Values* ➯ $62 △ $58

Caring
#PM941
Issued: 1994 • Closed: 1994
Retail Price: $35

1 *Values* 🍽 $62 △ $58

Sharing
#PM942
Issued: 1994 • Closed: 1994
Retail Price: $35

2 *Values* 🍽 $85

You Fill The Pages Of My
Life (w/book, stock number
for figurine is #530980)
#PMB034
Issued: 1994 • Closed: 1995
Retail Price: $67.50

3 *Values* △ $45

You're One In A
Million To Me
#PM951
Issued: 1995 • Closed: 1995
Retail Price: $35

4 *Values* △ $56

Always Take Time To Pray
#PM952
Issued: 1995 • Closed: 1995
Retail Price: $35

5 *Values* △ $145

A Perfect Display Of
Fifteen Happy Years
*15th Anniversary
Commemorative Figurine*
#127817
Issued: 1995 • Closed: 1995
Retail Price: $100

6 *Values* △ $60 ♡ $52

Teach Us To Love
One Another
#PM961
Issued: 1996 • Closed: 1996
Retail Price: $40

7 *Values* ♡ $60

Our Club Is Soda-licious
#PM962
Issued: 1996 • Closed: 1996
Retail Price: $35

8 *Values* † $56

You Will Always Be A
Treasure To Me
#PM971
Issued: 1997 • Closed: 1997
Retail Price: $50

KEY					
NM Pre'81	✔ 1986	✔ 1992	† 1997
▲ 1981	▲ 1987	✔ 1993	✔ 1998
✗ 1982	✔ 1988	✔ 1994	★ 1999
✔ 1983	✔ 1989	△ 1995	✔ 2000
† 1984	✔ 1990	♡ 1996	✔ 2001
✔ 1985	✔ 1991	UM Unmarked	

Members Only Figurines

	Price Paid	Value
1.		
2.		
3.		
4.		
5.		
6.		
7.		
8.		
9.		
10.		
11.		
12.		
Totals		

9 *Values* † $49

Blessed Are The Merciful
#PM972
Issued: 1997 • Closed: 1997
Retail Price: $40

10 *Values* † $53 ✔ $52

Happy Trails
#PM981
Issued: 1998 • Closed: 1998
Retail Price: $50

11 *Values* † $47 ✔ $47

Lord, Please Don't Put
Me On Hold
#PM982
Issued: 1998 • Closed: 1998
Retail Price: $40

12 *Values* ✔ N/E

How Can Two Work
Together Except They Agree
*20th Anniversary
Commemorative Figurine*
#PM983
Issued: 1998 • Closed: 1998
Retail Price: $125

231

1   *Values* ★ $34

Jumping For Joy
#PM991
Issued: 1999 • Closed: 1999
Retail Price: $30

2   *Values* ★ $33

God Speed
#PM992
Issued: 1999 • Closed: 1999
Retail Price: $30

3   *Values* ★ N/E

He Watches Over Us All
Millennium Figurine
#PM993
Issued: 1999 • Closed: 1999
Retail Price: $225

4   *Values* ◔ $110

**Collecting Friends
Along The Way**
PMA002
Issued: 2000 • Closed: 2000
Retail Price: $100

5   *Values* ◔ $31

My Collection
PM001
Issued: 2000 • Closed: 2000
Retail Price: $28

6   *Values* ◔ N/E
    ☙ N/E

**Thank You For
Your Membership**
5 Year Membership Piece
#635243
Issued: 2000 • Open
Retail Price: $30

KEY							
NM Pre'81	🦋 1986	💠 1992	✝ 1997
▲ 1981	♠ 1987	∞ 1993	👓 1998
Ⅱ 1982	⬦ 1988	⬏ 1994	★ 1999
➡ 1983	➗ 1989	🔺 1995	◔ 2000
✝ 1984	✛ 1990	♡ 1996	☙ 2001
🐚 1985	♦ 1991	UM Unmarked	

**Members Only
Figurines**

	Price Paid	Value
1.		
2.		
3.		
4.		
5.		
6.		
7.		
8.		
9.		
10.		
Totals		

7   *Values* ◔ N/E
    ☙ N/E

**A Club Where Friendship
Is Made**
10 Year Membership Piece
#635251
Issued: 2000 • Open
Retail Price: $40

8   *Values* ◔ N/E
    ☙ N/E

**A Club Where
Fellowship Reigns**
15 Year Membership Piece
#635278
Issued: 2000 • Open
Retail Price: $50

9   *Values* ◔ N/E
    ☙ N/E

**Companionship Happens
In Our Club**
20 Year Membership Piece
#635286
Issued: 2000 • Open
Retail Price: $60

10   *Values* ☙ $50
New

**Calling To Say
You're Special**
#PM011
Issued: 2001 • To Be Closed: 2001
Retail Price: $50

1

Values ᴬ $35

New

You're A Computie Cutie
#PM0012
Issued: 2001 • To Be Closed: 2001
Retail Price: $35

2

Values UM $20

Blessed Are The Meek, For
They Shall Inherit The Earth
#PM390
Issued: 1990 • Closed: 1990
Retail Price: $15

3

Values UM $20

Blessed Are The Merciful,
For They Shall Obtain Mercy
#PM590
Issued: 1990 • Closed: 1990
Retail Price: $15

4

Values UM $20

Blessed Are The
Peacemakers, For They Shall
Be Called Sons Of God
#PM790
Issued: 1990 • Closed: 1990
Retail Price: $15

5

Values UM $20

Blessed Are The Poor In
Spirit, For Theirs Is The
Kingdom Of Heaven
#PM190
Issued: 1990 • Closed: 1990
Retail Price: $15

6

Values UM $20

Blessed Are The Pure
In Heart, For They
Shall See God
#PM690
Issued: 1990 • Closed: 1990
Retail Price: $15

7

Values UM $20

Blessed Are They That
Hunger And Thirst, For
They Shall Be Filled
#PM490
Issued: 1990 • Closed: 1990
Retail Price: $15

8

Values UM $20

Blessed Are They That
Mourn, For They Shall
Be Comforted
#PM290
Issued: 1990 • Closed: 1990
Retail Price: $15

9

Values UM $140

Members' Only Ornaments (set/7)
#PM890
Issued: 1990 • Closed: 1990
Retail Price: $105

KEY			
NM Pre'81	1986	1992	1997
1981	1987	1993	1998
1982	1988	1994	1999
1983	1989	1995	2000
1984	1990	1996	2001
1985	1991	UM Unmarked	

Members Only Figurines

	Price Paid	Value
1.		

Members Only Ornaments

2.
3.
4.
5.
6.
7.
8.
9.

Totals

233

Collectors' Club

1 *Values* ⅡM $12

Celebrating A Decade Of Loving, Caring, And Sharing (Dated 1990)
10th Anniversary Commemorative Ornament
#227986
Issued: 1990 • Closed: 1990
Retail Price: $7

2 *Values* ♀♀ $38

Loving, Caring, And Sharing Along The Way
#PM040
Issued: 1993 • Closed: 1993
Retail Price: $15

3 *Values* ⟆ $37

You Are The End Of My Rainbow
#PM041
Issued: 1994 • Closed: 1994
Retail Price: $15

4 *Values* ⅡM $20

Giraffe (LE-1998, gift application exclusive, TENDER TAILS)
#358304
Issued: 1998 • Closed: 1998
Retail Price: N/A

5 *Values* 6ᗡ N/E

God Loveth A Cheerful Giver (early renewal gift, hinged box)
#495891
Issued: 1998 • Closed: 1998
Retail Price: N/A

6 *Values* ⅡM N/E

Pig (early renewal gift, also available in stores, TENDER TAILS)
#358258
Issued: 1998 • Retired: 1998
Retail Price: N/A

KEY					
NM Pre'81	⅍ 1986	৶ 1992	✝ 1997
▲ 1981	▲ 1987	♀♀ 1993	6ᗡ 1998
Ⅰ 1982	✧ 1988	⟆ 1994	★ 1999
◄ 1983	⧫ 1989	⚏ 1995	⊘ 2000
✝ 1984	✦ 1990	♡ 1996	৶ 2001
◄ 1985	♦ 1991	ⅡM Unmarked	

Members Only Ornaments

	Price Paid	Value
1.		
2.		
3.		

Members Gifts

4.		
5.		
6.		
7.		

Precious Rewards Figurines

8.		
9.		
10.		
11.		

Sharing Season Gifts

12.		

Totals

7 *Values* ⅡM $7.50

Twinkle (TENDER TAILS)
#646237
Issued: 1999 • Closed: 2000
Retail Price: $6.99

8 *Values* ✝ $85
6ᗡ $85

Faith Is The Victory
#283592
Issued: 1997 • Closed: 1998
Retail Price: N/A

9 *Values* ✝ $68
6ᗡ $68

God Bless You With Bouquets Of Victory
#283584
Issued: 1997 • Closed: 1998
Retail Price: N/A

10 *Values* ⅡM N/E

Photo Unavailable

Lord, It's Hard To Be Humble
N/A
Issued: 1998 • Closed: 1998
Retail Price: N/A

11 *Values* ✝ $45
6ᗡ $45

Rejoice In The Victory
#283541
Issued: 1997 • Closed: 1998
Retail Price: N/A

12 *Values* ✝ $115

Precious Moments Last Forever (medallion)
#12246
Issued: 1984 • Closed: 1984
Retail Price: N/A

1 *Values* ℣ $175

Birds Of A Feather Collect Together (ornament)
#PM864
Issued: 1986 • Closed: 1986
Retail Price: N/A

2 *Values* ✣ $70

A Growing Love (ornament)
#520349
Issued: 1988 • Closed: 1988
Retail Price: N/A

3 *Values* ⅁ $98

Always Room For One More (ornament)
#522961
Issued: 1989 • Closed: 1989
Retail Price: N/A

4 *Values* ★ $88

My Happiness (ornament)
#PM904
Issued: 1990 • Closed: 1990
Retail Price: N/A

5 *Values* ♦ $80

Sharing The Good News Together (ornament)
#PM037
Issued: 1991 • Closed: 1991
Retail Price: N/A

6 *Values* ♒ $76

The Club That's Out Of This World (ornament)
#PM038
Issued: 1992 • Closed: 1992
Retail Price: N/A

7 *Values* ◀ $93
             ℣ $82
             ▲ $80

Our Club Can't Be Beat
#B0001
Issued: 1986 • Closed: 1986
Retail Price: N/A

8 *Values* ℣ $74
             ▲ $68
             ✣ $60

A Smile's The Cymbal Of Joy
#B0002
Issued: 1987 • Closed: 1987
Retail Price: N/A

9 *Values* ℣ $80
             ▲ $75

Variation

Photo Unavailable

A Smile's The Cymbal Of Joy (charter member figurine)
#B0102
Issued: 1987 • Closed: 1987
Retail Price: N/A
Variation: "A Smile's The <u>Symbol</u> Of Joy" – $92

10 *Values* ✣ $48
              ⅁ $43

The Sweetest Club Around
#B0003
Issued: 1988 • Closed: 1988
Retail Price: N/A

11 *Values* ✣ $53
              ⅁ $46

The Sweetest Club Around (charter member figurine)
#B0103
Issued: 1988 • Closed: 1988
Retail Price: N/A

KEY			
NM Pre'81	℣ 1986	♒ 1992	† 1997
▲ 1981	▲ 1987	❀ 1993	⊶ 1998
✕ 1982	✣ 1988	➡ 1994	★ 1999
◀ 1983	⅁ 1989	⚖ 1995	◎ 2000
✝ 1984	★ 1990	♡ 1996	⬛ 2001
◀ 1985	♦ 1991	UM Unmarked	

Sharing Season Gifts

	Price Paid	Value
1.		
2.		
3.		
4.		
5.		
6.		

Symbol Of Membership Figurines

7.		
8.		
9.		
10.		
11.		

Totals

235

1 *Values* ⏁ $38
⚖ $32

**Have A Beary
Special Birthday**
#B0004
Issued: 1989 • Closed: 1989
Retail Price: N/A

2 *Values* ♣ $50
⏁ $37
⚖ $32

**Have A Beary
Special Birthday
(charter member figurine)**
#B0104
Issued: 1989 • Closed: 1989
Retail Price: N/A

3 *Values* ⚖ $37
🔔 $33

**Our Club Is A Tough
Act To Follow**
#B0005
Issued: 1990 • Closed: 1990
Retail Price: N/A

4 *Values* ⚖ $40
🔔 $35

**Our Club Is A Tough
Act To Follow
(charter member figurine)**
#B0105
Issued: 1990 • Closed: 1990
Retail Price: N/A

5 *Values* 🔔 $37
𝄢 $33

**Jest To Let You Know
You're Tops**
#B0006
Issued: 1991 • Closed: 1991
Retail Price: N/A

6 *Values* 🔔 $40
𝄢 $34

**Jest To Let You Know
You're Tops
(charter member figurine)**
#B0106
Issued: 1991 • Closed: 1991
Retail Price: N/A

KEY			
NM Pre'81	⚘ 1986	𝄢 1992	✝ 1997
▲ 1981	♣ 1987	� 1993	👓 1998
⚔ 1982	⬥ 1988	⚑ 1994	★ 1999
⇆ 1983	⏁ 1989	△ 1995	◷ 2000
✝ 1984	⚖ 1990	♡ 1996	⚓ 2001
◆ 1985	🔔 1991	⭢	�) Unmarked

Symbol Of Membership Figurines

	Price Paid	Value
1.		
2.		
3.		
4.		
5.		
6.		
7.		
8.		
9.		
10.		
11.		
12.		
Totals		

7 *Values* 𝄢 $39
� $33

**All Aboard For
Birthday Club Fun**
#B0007
Issued: 1992 • Closed: 1992
Retail Price: N/A

8 *Values* 𝄢 $42
� $35

**All Aboard For
Birthday Club Fun
(charter member figurine)**
#B0107
Issued: 1992 • Closed: 1992
Retail Price: N/A

9 *Values* � $32
⛝ $28

Happiness Is Belonging
#B0008
Issued: 1993 • Closed: 1993
Retail Price: N/A

10 *Values* � $32
⛝ $28

**Happiness Is Belonging
(charter member figurine)**
#B0108
Issued: 1993 • Closed: 1993
Retail Price: N/A

11 *Values* ⭢ $33
△ $29

**Can't Get Enough
Of Our Club**
#B0009
Issued: 1994 • Closed: 1995
Retail Price: N/A

12 *Values* ⭢ $38
△ $33

**Can't Get Enough
Of Our Club
(charter member figurine)**
#B0109
Issued: 1994 • Closed: 1995
Retail Price: N/A

1 Values ⏃ $34 ♡ $29

Hoppy Birthday
#B0010
Issued: 1995 • Closed: 1996
Retail Price: N/A

2 Values ⏃ $40 ♡ $34

Hoppy Birthday
(charter member figurine)
#B0110
Issued: 1995 • Closed: 1996
Retail Price: N/A

3 Values ♡ $33 † $28

Scootin' By Just To Say Hi!
#B0011
Issued: 1996 • Closed: 1997
Retail Price: N/A

4 Values ♡ $36 † $29

Scootin' By Just To Say Hi!
(charter member figurine)
#B0111
Issued: 1996 • Closed: 1997
Retail Price: N/A

5 Values † $26 ◠◠ $24

The Fun Starts Here
#B0012
Issued: 1997 • Closed: 1998
Retail Price: N/A

6 Values † $32 ◠◠ $26

The Fun Starts Here
(charter member figurine)
#B0112
Issued: 1997 • Closed: 1998
Retail Price: N/A

7 Values ⌀ $140 ▲ $126

Fishing For Friends
#BC861
Issued: 1986 • Closed: 1986
Retail Price: $10

8 Values ▲ $110 ✤ $97 ⅌ $90

Hi Sugar
#BC871
Issued: 1987 • Closed: 1987
Retail Price: $11

KEY			
NM Pre'81	⌀ 1986	✦ 1992	† 1997
▲ 1981	▲ 1987	◈ 1993	◠◠ 1998
✕ 1982	✤ 1988	▭ 1994	★ 1999
◀ 1983	⅌ 1989	⏃ 1995	◔ 2000
✝ 1984	✦ 1990	♡ 1996	≜ 2001
✦ 1985	♠ 1991	ⅡM Unmarked	

Symbol Of Membership Figurines

	Price Paid	Value
1.		
2.		
3.		
4.		
5.		
6.		

Members Only Figurines

7.		
8.		
9.		
10.		
11.		
12.		

9 Values ✤ $63 ⅌ $53

Somebunny Cares
#BC881
Issued: 1988 • Closed: 1988
Retail Price: $13.50

10 Values ⅌ $58 ✦ $52 ♠ $49

Can't Beehive Myself
Without You
#BC891
Issued: 1989 • Closed: 1989
Retail Price: $13.50

11 Values ✦ $38 ♠ $34

Collecting Makes
Good Scents
#BC901
Issued: 1990 • Closed: 1990
Retail Price: $15

12 Values ✦ $38 ♠ $33

I'm Nuts Over
My Collection
#BC902
Issued: 1990 • Closed: 1990
Retail Price: $15

Totals

1 Values ⚫ $42 ⚫ $38

Love Pacifies
#BC911
Issued: 1991 • Closed: 1991
Retail Price: $15

2 Values ⚫ $45 ⚫ $40

True Blue Friends
#BC912
Issued: 1991 • Closed: 1991
Retail Price: $15

3 Values ⚫ $39 ⚫ $34

Every Man's House
Is His Castle
#BC921
Issued: 1992 • Closed: 1992
Retail Price: $16.50

4 Values ⚫ $40 ⚫ $34

I Got You Under My Skin
#BC922
Issued: 1992 • Closed: 1992
Retail Price: $16

5 Values ⚫ $25 ⚫ $22

Put A Little Punch
In Your Birthday
#BC931
Issued: 1993 • Closed: 1993
Retail Price: $15

6 Values ⚫ $32 ⚫ $28

Owl Always Be Your Friend
#BC932
Issued: 1993 • Closed: 1993
Retail Price: $16

KEY			
NM Pre'81	✐ 1986	⚫ 1992	✝ 1997
▲ 1981	♣ 1987	✿ 1993	6⊃ 1998
Ⅱ 1982	✤ 1988	☜ 1994	★ 1999
⬤ 1983	✢ 1989	△ 1995	◓ 2000
✝ 1984	✦ 1990	♡ 1996	⚫ 2001
✦ 1985	⚫ 1991	UM Unmarked	

Members Only Figurines

	Price Paid	Value
1.		
2.		
3.		
4.		
5.		
6.		
7.		
8.		
9.		
10.		
11.		
12.		
Totals		

7 Values ☜ $39 △ $32

God Bless Our Home
#BC941
Issued: 1994 • Closed: 1994
Retail Price: $16

8 Values ☜ $33 △ $27

You're A Pel-I-Can Count On
#BC942
Issued: 1994 • Closed: 1994
Retail Price: $16

9 Values △ $36

Making A Point To Say
You're Special
#BC951
Issued: 1995 • Closed: 1995
Retail Price: $15

10 Values △ $68

10 Wonderful Years
Of Wishes
#BC952
Issued: 1995 • Closed: 1995
Retail Price: $50

11 Values ♡ $25

There's A Spot In
My Heart For You
#BC961
Issued: 1996 • Closed: 1996
Retail Price: $15

12 Values ♡ $28 ✝ $23

You're First In My Heart
#BC962
Issued: 1996 • Closed: 1996
Retail Price: $15

1   *Values* † $22   **2**   *Values* † $22   **3**   *Values* 6ə $19
                                                                                    ★ $19

Hare's To The
Birthday Club
#BC971
Issued: 1997 • Closed: 1997
Retail Price: $16

Holy Tweet
#BC972
Issued: 1997 • Closed: 1997
Retail Price: $18.50

Slide Into The Celebration
(LE-1999)
#BC981
Issued: 1998 • Closed: 1999
Retail Price: $15

4   *Values* 6ə $22   **5**   *Values* 6ə $32   **6**   *Values* ★ N/E
          ★ N/E   ★ N/E   ⓞ N/E

You Are My Mane
Inspiration
(charter member figurine)
#B0014
Issued: 1999 • Closed: 1999
Retail Price: N/A

You Are My Mane
Inspiration (double
charter member figurine)
#B0114
Issued: 1999 • Closed: 1999
Retail Price: N/A

Don't Fret, We'll
Get There Yet
N/A
Issued: 2000 • Closed: 2000
Retail Price: N/A

7   *Values* ★ N/E   **8**   *Values* ⓞ N/E
         ⓞ N/E   New   ๒ɑ. N/E

Don't Fret, We'll
Get There Yet
(charter member figurine)
N/A
Issued: 2000 • Closed: 2000
Retail Price: N/A

True Friendship Is A
Precious Treasure
#F0003
Issued: 2001 • To Be Closed: 2001
Retail Price: N/A

NM Pre'81	ⵊ 1986	⚘ 1992	† 1997
▲ 1981	♠ 1987	ꝙ 1993	6ə 1998
Ⲏ 1982	✦ 1988	⚘ 1994	★ 1999
◄ 1983	⅁ 1989	⚖ 1995	ⓞ 2000
✝ 1984	✦ 1990	♡ 1996	๒ɑ. 2001
ⲁ 1985	♠ 1991	UM Unmarked	

Members Only Figurines

	Price Paid	Value
1.		
2.		
3.		

Symbol Of Membership Figurines

4.		
5.		
6.		
7.		
8.		
9.		

9   *Values* ⓞ N/E   **10**   *Values* UM $11
New   ๒ɑ. N/E

True Friendship Is A
Precious Treasure
(charter member figurine)
#F0103
Issued: 2001 • To Be Closed: 2001
Retail Price: N/A

Chester (TENDER TAILS)
#BC992
Issued: 1999 • Closed: 1999
Retail Price: $7

Members Only Pieces

10.		
11.		
12.		

11   *Values* ★ $18   **12**   *Values* ⓞ N/E

Ewe Are So Special To Me
#BC991
Issued: 1999 • Closed: 1999
Retail Price: $15

Hold On To The Moment
#FC003
Issued: 2000 • Closed: 2000
Retail Price: N/A

Totals

1 *Values* UM N/E

**Reed The Centipede
(TENDER TAILS)**
#FC002
Issued: 2000 • Closed: 2000
Retail Price: N/A

2 *Values* UM N/E

**Ronnie The Rhino Beetle
(TENDER TAILS)**
#FC001
Issued: 2000 • Closed: 2000
Retail Price: N/A

3 *Values* UM $11

Chippie (TENDER TAILS)
#BC993
Issued: 1999 • Closed: 1999
Retail Price: $7

4 *Values* N/E
New

**I'm Always Happy When
You're A-Long**
#FC011
Issued: 2001 • To Be Closed: 2001
Retail Price: $18.50

5 *Values* UM N/E
New

**Chris The Crocodile
(TENDER TAILS)**
#FC012
Issued: 2001 • To Be Closed: 2001
Retail Price: $6.99

6 *Values* UM N/E
New

**Monty The Mandrill
(TENDER TAILS)**
#FC013
Issued: 2001 • To Be Closed: 2001
Retail Price: $6.99

KEY		
NM Pre'81	𝄞 1986	𝄞 1992 † 1997
▲ 1981	▲ 1987	♉ 1993 ☙ 1998
☰ 1982	♧ 1988	☳ 1994 ★ 1999
◄ 1983	☋ 1989	△ 1995 ☉ 2000
✝ 1984	✚ 1990	♡ 1996 ☄ 2001
✿ 1985	♂ 1991	UM Unmarked

Members Only Pieces

	Price Paid	Value
1.		
2.		
3.		
4.		
5.		
6.		

Members Gifts

7.		
8.		
9.		
10.		
11.		

Club Kit Pieces

12.		

Totals

7 *Values* UM $30

**Gorilla (early renewal gift,
TENDER TAILS)**
#602361
Issued: 1999 • Closed: 1999
Retail Price: N/A

8 *Values* UM $12

**Toucan (LE-1999, gift
application club exclusive,
TENDER TAILS)**
#612413
Issued: 1999 • Closed: 1999
Retail Price: N/A

9 *Values* UM $30

Peacock (TENDER TAILS)
N/A
Issued: 2000 • Closed: 2000
Retail Price: N/A

10 *Values* UM N/E
New

**Wade (early renewal gift,
TENDER TAILS)**
N/A
Issued: 2001 • To Be Closed: 2001
Retail Price: N/A

11 *Values* UM N/E
New

Zelda (TENDER TAILS)
N/A
Issued: 2001 • To Be Closed: 2001
Retail Price: N/A

12 *Values* UM $20

**Iris (TENDER TAILS,
transforming animal)**
N/A
Issued: 2000 • Closed: 2000
Retail Price: N/A

Future Releases

Check our web site, *CollectorsQuest.com*, for new product releases and record the information here.

PRECIOUS MOMENTS®	Item #	Production Mark	Price Paid	Market Value
Infant Son	848816	2000	20°°	
Infant Daughter	880906	2000	20°°	
Family Dog	848824	2000	20°°	
Grandfather	529574	1500 1992	15°°	
Stork w/ Baby Sam (Retired)	LE1994 529788	1994	22.50	
Pg 71 Baby Boy & Girl				
Pg 72 Babies First ...				
Pg 74 & 75				
Pg 77 #7				
Pg 116 my love will never let you go	103497			
Pg 130 Tell Me a Story				
Pg 156 World's Best Series				
Pg 152 Mexican Boy				

	Price Paid	Market Value
Page Totals:		

Future Releases

Check our web site, *CollectorsQuest.com*, for new product releases and record the information here.

PRECIOUS MOMENTS®	Item #	Production Mark	Price Paid	Market Value

Page Totals:	Price Paid	Market Value

Total Value Of My Collection

Record your collection here by adding the totals from
the bottom of each Value Guide page.

PRECIOUS MOMENTS®

Page Number	Price Paid	Market Value
Page 31		
Page 32		
Page 33		
Page 34		
Page 35		
Page 36		
Page 37		
Page 38		
Page 39		
Page 40		
Page 41		
Page 42		
Page 43		
Page 44		
Page 45		
Page 46		
Page 47		
Page 48		
Page 49		
Page 50		
Page 51		
Page 52		
Subtotal		

PRECIOUS MOMENTS®

Page Number	Price Paid	Market Value
Page 53		
Page 54		
Page 55		
Page 56		
Page 57		
Page 58		
Page 59		
Page 60		
Page 61		
Page 62		
Page 63		
Page 64		
Page 65		
Page 66		
Page 67		
Page 68		
Page 69		
Page 70		
Page 71		
Page 72		
Page 73		
Page 74		
Subtotal		

Page Totals:	Price Paid	Market Value

Total Value Of My Collection

Record your collection here by adding the totals from
the bottom of each Value Guide page.

PRECIOUS MOMENTS®			PRECIOUS MOMENTS®		
Page Number	Price Paid	Market Value	Page Number	Price Paid	Market Value
Page 75			Page 97		
Page 76			Page 98		
Page 77			Page 99		
Page 78			Page 100		
Page 79			Page 101		
Page 80			Page 102		
Page 81			Page 103		
Page 82			Page 104		
Page 83			Page 105		
Page 84			Page 106		
Page 85			Page 107		
Page 86			Page 108		
Page 87			Page 109		
Page 88			Page 110		
Page 89			Page 111		
Page 90			Page 112		
Page 91			Page 113		
Page 92			Page 114		
Page 93			Page 115		
Page 94			Page 116		
Page 95			Page 117		
Page 96			Page 118		
Subtotal			Subtotal		

Page Totals:	Price Paid	Market Value

Total Value Of My Collection

Record your collection here by adding the totals from
the bottom of each Value Guide page.

PRECIOUS MOMENTS®			PRECIOUS MOMENTS®		
Page Number	Price Paid	Market Value	Page Number	Price Paid	Market Value
Page 119			Page 141		
Page 120			Page 142		
Page 121			Page 143		
Page 122			Page 144		
Page 123			Page 145		
Page 124			Page 146		
Page 125			Page 147		
Page 126			Page 148		
Page 127			Page 149		
Page 128			Page 150		
Page 129			Page 151		
Page 130			Page 152		
Page 131			Page 153		
Page 132			Page 154		
Page 133			Page 155		
Page 134			Page 156		
Page 135			Page 157		
Page 136			Page 158		
Page 137			Page 159		
Page 138			Page 160		
Page 139			Page 161		
Page 140			Page 162		
Subtotal			Subtotal		

	Price Paid	Market Value
Page Totals:		

Total Value Of My Collection

Record your collection here by adding the totals from
the bottom of each Value Guide page.

PRECIOUS MOMENTS®			PRECIOUS MOMENTS®		
Page Number	Price Paid	Market Value	Page Number	Price Paid	Market Value
Page 163			Page 185		
Page 164			Page 186		
Page 165			Page 187		
Page 166			Page 188		
Page 167			Page 189		
Page 168			Page 190		
Page 169			Page 191		
Page 170			Page 192		
Page 171			Page 193		
Page 172			Page 194		
Page 173			Page 195		
Page 174			Page 196		
Page 175			Page 197		
Page 176			Page 198		
Page 177			Page 199		
Page 178			Page 200		
Page 179			Page 201		
Page 180			Page 202		
Page 181			Page 203		
Page 182			Page 204		
Page 183			Page 205		
Page 184			Page 206		
Subtotal			Subtotal		

Page Totals:	Price Paid	Market Value

Total Value Of My Collection

Record your collection here by adding the totals from
the bottom of each Value Guide page.

PRECIOUS MOMENTS®			PRECIOUS MOMENTS®		
Page Number	Price Paid	Market Value	Page Number	Price Paid	Market Value
Page 207			Page 229		
Page 208			Page 230		
Page 209			Page 231		
Page 210			Page 232		
Page 211			Page 233		
Page 212			Page 234		
Page 213			Page 235		
Page 214			Page 236		
Page 215			Page 237		
Page 216			Page 238		
Page 217			Page 239		
Page 218			Page 240		
Page 219			Page 241		
Page 220			Page 242		
Page 221			Subtotal		
Page 222					
Page 223					
Page 224					
Page 225					
Page 226					
Page 227					
Page 228					
Subtotal					

	Price Paid	Market Value
Page Totals:		

How To Shop The Secondary Market

Since Enesco has been producing PRECIOUS MOMENTS pieces since 1978, you probably would like to know how to obtain some of the older pieces that you've only heard about. But where do you begin searching for a figurine that's been out of production for many years? While it may be difficult to find certain pieces, it just may be that someone, somewhere is looking to sell the exact figurine that you need to complete your collection. The secondary market is the key place to begin searching for retired, suspended or closed PRECIOUS MOMENTS figurines.

What Is The Secondary Market?

A secondary market is formed when a piece is no longer available at retail price, such as when a retirement occurs. For

PRECIOUS MOMENTS, production of a piece stops when it is retired, and once stores sell out of that figurine, it will sometimes become difficult to purchase at retail again. Therefore, once a piece is out of production, it becomes more valuable on the secondary market and collectors are typically willing to pay more than its original worth, increasing the value of the figurine.

Retired, Suspended And Closed Pieces

There are three methods that Enesco uses to end production of a piece. When a piece is retired, the mold is broken and the piece can never be created again. Enesco rarely announces that a piece will be retired, usually they retire pieces with no warning. After a piece is out of production, collectors have only a small amount of time to find the piece and buy it before it will never be seen again.

A pile of retired molds that were collected to be destroyed.

Other PRECIOUS MOMENTS pieces are suspended, meaning that their production ends temporarily, and the molds for the figurines remain in tact. Suspended pieces can be re-introduced at a later time. Nonetheless, they are sometimes brought back for a short time or a special event with some change in color, which makes both the re-designed piece and the original piece valuable to collectors and unique in their own way.

Closed pieces are usually dated pieces or figurines that are known to have a limited production run. Frequently only produced for a certain year, or limited to a pre-specified quantity, closed pieces (otherwise known as limited edition pieces) tend to have higher secondary market values.

Getting The Most Out Of The Secondary Market

If you're looking to sell, trade or buy pieces off the secondary market, keep the condition of the piece in mind. Traditionally, pieces purchased for the first time at a retail price have seen a minimal amount of wear and tear on both the figurine and the packaging, but those pieces that have been out of production for a while run a greater risk of having slight damage that may deter you from purchasing the hard-to-find piece.

When buying a piece off the secondary market, first examine the figurine for damage, including, but not limited to, chips, scratches, paint smudges or water damage. If a piece does have some flaws, you can expect to pay slightly less for it, but there is no right or wrong amount to pay. It is up to you to decide how much a piece is worth.

Packaging also makes a difference in the value of the piece. Boxes are necessary for safe storage and many collectors consider a piece without its packaging incomplete. When you purchase a piece at retail, be sure to store the box in a cool, dry place just in case you ever decide to sell it. That way, you will be sure to get the true value of the figurine on the secondary market.

Many PRECIOUS MOMENTS pieces have been produced over multiple years! So it stands to reason that the piece that was  produced in 1983 is likely worth more than its counterpart produced in the early 1990s. Thanks to the production marks on most figurines manufactured after 1981, it is easy for collectors to tell which year their piece was produced. (See page 29 for details on production marks).

Ready, Set, Trade!

Now that you've taken a crash course in secondary market basics, you're ready to go out there and explore! There are many avenues to try, one of which may be as close as your computer. The Internet is the largest and fastest growing source of secondary market locations. Through specific dealer web sites and on-line stores and auction houses, you can quickly access hundreds of dealers and collectors across the country.

But don't forget the traditional routes, such as secondary market exchanges. Exchange services provide listings of dealers who may have what you're looking for, but be informed – there may be a subscription fee involved, and some services charge a commission fee on pieces sold through their service.

And don't forget to consult your local newspaper's "Swap and Sell" section in the classified ads. Whether you're looking to sell a piece or locate one, you might be able to find someone to swap with or sell to right in your own backyard!

Variations

Variations usually occur for one of two reasons: either Enesco is not completely satisfied with a design and, after its initial production, decides to rework it; or, at some time during the production process human error comes into play. In most cases, no matter what the reason for the change, variations that are sought after by collectors generally consist of dramatic color changes, changes to the actual design of the piece or changes in the text that appears on the figurine.

Variations With Value

The following is a list of variations that have shown significant increases in value on the secondary market. Each variation and its value can be found in the Value Guide section.

Baby's First Christmas (#E2362): Two variations have been noted on this ornament. In one, the girl's straight hair appears curly, while in the second, the girl with curly hair is missing the decal on the bottom of the piece.

Be Not Weary In Well Doing (#E3111): In some of these pieces the inspiration was printed as "Be Not Weary **And** Well Doing."

But Love Goes On Forever (#E0202): After production on this piece ended, some were mistakenly reproduced and shipped to Canada. Variations can be identified by the "dove" year mark.

Clown Figurines (set/4, #12238): The decal on the variation was incorrectly printed as "C**r**owns."

Come Let Us Adore Him (set/11, #E2395): When this set debuted it contained a boy holding a lamb. At some point, the boy was replaced by a shepherd wearing a turban.

Faith Takes The Plunge (#111155): In the first year this figurine was produced, some of the figurines had a smile as opposed to a frown.

Friendship Hits The Spot (#520748): This piece has two variations. In one variation, the decal has the misspelling "Fr**ei**ndship Hits The Spot," while in the other, the table between the two girls is missing.

The Future Is In Our Hands (#730068): In limited numbers of this figurine, the girl is holding a cardinal instead of a blue bird.

God Blessed Our Year Together With So Much Love And Happiness (#E2854): Some of the decals were mislabeled "God Blessed Our Year**s** Together With So Much Love And Happiness."

Groom (#E2837): This piece was produced from two different molds: one with the boy's hands visible and one with his hands hidden by his sleeves.

He Is Not Here For He Is Risen As He Said (#527106): This Chapel Exclusive piece contains a misprint on the sign outside the tomb which reads "Mat**h**" instead of "Matt."

I Believe In Miracles (#E7156R): The variation for this piece can be identified by the lack of the inscribed "Sam B." signature which appears on the bottom of every PRECIOUS MOMENTS piece. Also, the little boy's head is slightly smaller than normal.

Let The Heavens Rejoice (#E5679): This ornament can be found missing the PRECIOUS MOMENTS decal.

May Your Christmas Be A Happy Home (set/2, #523704): The boy on this ornament was painted wearing both a yellow and a blue shirt. The version with the boy in the yellow shirt is considered to be the variation.

My Days Are Blue Without You (#520802): Similar to the piece "Faith Takes The Plunge," this figurine was made with both a smile and a frown.

Nobody's Perfect (#E9268): As with the previous variation, this also features a boy smiling instead of wearing a frown.

Prayer Changes Things (#E5214): The words "Holy Bible" on this piece were, in some instances, accidentally placed on the back of the book.

A Smile's The Cymbal Of Joy (#B0102): This Charter Member Figurine can be found mislabeled as "A Smile's The **Symbol** Of Joy."

There's A Christian Welcome Here (#523011): The angel's right eyebrow is sometimes hidden from view by his hair on the variation of this Chapel Exclusive piece.

You Are My Main Event (#115231): The balloons on this figurine sometimes have pink strings as opposed to white strings.

Other Known Variations

The following is a list of variations that, though they are well-known, have yet to achieve significant secondary market value.

Baby's First Christmas (#E2372): When this piece first came out it did not come with an inspiration. However, before it was suspended, an inspiration was added. As the piece without the caption was available for a shorter period of time, it is considered to be the variation.

Dropping In For The Holidays (#531952): The cup that holds the little angel in this ornament was painted both pink and blue.

He Careth For You (#E1377B) and ***He Leadeth Me (#E1377A):*** The inspirations which were to appear on these two pieces were often swapped so that they had the wrong name.

I'm Falling For Somebunny/Our Love Is Heaven-scent (#E9266): These two pieces were both produced with the inspiration "Somebunny Cares."

Isn't He Precious (#E5379): This piece has been seen completely devoid of paint, which is very rare.

O Worship The Lord (#102229): Through the years, many collectors have found versions of this piece missing the "O" in the title "O Worship The Lord."

Praise The Lord Anyhow (#E1374B): In some versions of this piece the dog has a black nose, while in others, the pup's nose is brown.

Rejoicing With You (#E4724): In this figurine, the letter "e" in the word "Bible" is sometimes covered by the girl's hand.

Sending My Love Your Way (#528609): The kite the little girl is holding in this figurine has appeared missing its stripes, while in other pieces, the kitten who should be sitting at her feet was left off the figurine entirely.

Smile, God Loves You (#E1373B): The boy in this piece was to have a black eye, though variations have surfaced where the eye was shaded brown.

Twenty Years And The Vision's Still The Same (#306843): On a limited number of these commemorative figurines both the "sword" and the "eyeglass" year marks appear at once.

Wishing You A Season Filled With Joy (#E2805): Pieces with the "dove" year mark have shown the dog with both of its eyes painted black as opposed to the intended one single painted eye.

"Loving, Caring And Sharing" For Your Collection

Keeping your PRECIOUS MOMENTS pieces in tip-top shape is of the utmost importance to most collectors, so here are a few tips on how to keep your figurines looking their very best:

One of the key factors in caring for your collection is to keep each of the pieces someplace safe. Try to place your figurines in an area where they will not be at risk of breaking or collecting dust. And it's also best to keep pieces in a smoke-free environment, so that they will not get dingy from smoke in the air. Also, you may want to keep your pieces out of the path of direct sunlight, which has been known to fade the hand-painted collectibles. However, no matter how hard you try, at some point you may notice that your collection could use a little 'tlc.'

PRECIOUS MOMENTS figurine manufacturer Enesco recommends hand-washing your figurines and TENDER TAILS. Using warm water and mild soap, wipe your figurine with a damp cloth. Be sure to place a towel or pillow over your work area in case the piece happens to slip and fall. Once clean, gently wipe the piece off with a soft towel and let it air dry.

If you plan on selling your pieces in the future, remember that it is important to keep them in mint condition and that it is always better to have the figurine's original packaging. Figurines that are sold with their original packaging tend to command a higher price on the secondary market and help to guarantee authenticity.

Protecting Your Investment

In addition to the proper cleaning and maintenance of your PRECIOUS MOMENTS collection, you should also make sure that your collection is adequately insured in the event of theft, flood, fire or other unforeseen circumstances. Insuring your collection is a wise move, and it doesn't have to be costly or difficult.

1. Assess the value of your collection. If your collection is extensive, you may want to have it professionally appraised. However, you can determine the value of your collection yourself by consulting a reputable price guide such as the Collector's Value Guide™.

2. Determine the amount of coverage you need. Collectibles are often covered under homeowner's or renter's insurance, but ask your agent if your policy covers all possibilities, including damage due to routine handling. Also, find out if your policy covers claims at "current replacement value" – the amount that it

would cost you to replace items if they were damaged, lost or stolen. You may want to consider adding a Personal Articles Floater or a Fine Arts Floater ("rider") to your policy if your insurance does not adequately cover your collection.

3. Keep documentation of your collectibles and their values. Save all your receipts and photograph each item, taking special care to show variations, artist signatures and other special features. Be sure to keep all of your documentation in a safe place, such as a safe deposit box, or make two copies and give one to a friend or relative for safekeeping.

From Paper To Porcelain –
How A Figurine Is Created

The PRECIOUS MOMENTS production process begins when artist Sam Butcher commits a drawing to paper. Once he is satisfied with it, the drawing is photographed and sent to a design studio in Nagoya, Japan, where Master Sculptor Yasuhei Fujioka oversees its transformation into a figurine.

First, one of the skilled artisans at the design studio shapes a model out of clay based on the illustration. Once the model is completed, it goes through the first of many inspections to ensure Enesco's high standards of quality.

It is easier to work with

A prototype is molded out of clay.

smaller pieces, so the model is then disassembled and molds are made from the individual pieces. When the molds are complete, wet clay (called "slip") is poured into the molds and allowed to dry for a short time. The result is a solid piece of porcelain known as "greenware."

Molds are made using the original clay sculpture.

Once this step is complete, the individual pieces are joined together with slip and the seams are smoothed out by the artisans. The fully assembled piece is left to air dry, and then is baked in the kiln at 2,300° F for 14 hours.

When the figure is taken out of the kiln, it is then immersed in a bath of pumice and water to give the figurine its smooth texture. The piece is then polished and painted. The signature "teardrop" eyes are the most difficult to paint. It can take an artisan up to three years to master them!

Finally, the piece goes into the kiln for four more hours so that the paint will adhere to the porcelain. After a final inspection, it is ready to make its debut in stores across the country.

The piece is dipped in a pumice bath before being painted.

COLLECTOR'S
VALUE GUIDE

Collectors' Club News

It's hard to believe that 20 years have gone by, but it was back in 1981 that the Enesco PRECIOUS MOMENTS *Collectors' Club* celebrated its inaugural year. We've now entered a new millennium, and we're still celebrating all those "precious moments" with the *Collectors' Club*.

Back in 1981, Enesco hoped to enroll 10,000 members by the end of the year. They did – and then some! By the end of that year, there were nearly 70,000 members of the PRECIOUS MOMENTS *Collectors' Club*. Today, it is one of the largest collectors' clubs in the country, and has even been named "Collectors' Club of the Year" by NALED.

A one-year club membership costs only $28 and runs from January 1 to December 31 each year. Members who join in 2001 will receive a special *Symbol of Membership* figurine titled "Friends Write From The Start," depicting a girl writing a letter to a friend. The membership kit also includes a desktop stationery set, two Pentel® gel roller pens and exclusive *Collectors' Club* stationery and envelopes all packaged in a decorative box suitable for display. Club membership also entitles collectors to a free subscription to the "GOODNEWSLETTER," the club's official quarterly publication. The "GOODNEWSLETTER" is filled with collector's stories, information on new releases, exclusives and special events, and other interesting and informative articles about the line and the company.

Along with their free membership gifts, collectors can purchase the figurine, "Friends Write From the Start" when they join the Collectors' Club in 2001.

Additionally, club members have the opportunity to purchase two *Members' Only Figurines* – "Calling To Say You're Special" and "You're A Computie Cutie." Membership also includes access to the club's exclusive web site and special mailings throughout the year.

The PRECIOUS MOMENTS *Fun Club* is a simple and perfect way to get the whole family to collect PRECIOUS MOMENTS. The *Fun Club*, which replaced the *Birthday Club*, provides contests, family activities, arts and crafts ideas, stories for children and much more!

Membership for 2001 is only $22.50 and runs from January 1 to December 31, 2001. The 2001 *Fun Club* Membership Kit includes the 2001 *Symbol of Membership Figurine,* "True Friendship Is A Precious Treasure," featuring an

The 2001 *Fun Club* Membership Kit has many great surprises!

adorable zebra and its mouse pal. It also comes with a zany TENDER TAILS zebra named "Zelda," a TENDER TAILS attachable of "Zelda" with glow-in-the-dark features and an exciting game.

This holiday *Fun Club* issue from 2000 has great suggestions for celebrating the season!

Membership in the *Fun Club* also includes a free subscription to the quarterly *Fun Club* newsletter which contains games, recipes, contests, ways for kids to "care and share" and stories about people and animals from around the world! Members also have the opportunity to purchase special *Members' Only* exclusive pieces throughout the year. And if all that isn't enough, *Fun Club* members also have access to the club's exclusive web site, which is full of games and activities that the whole family can enjoy together.

If you'd like to join in all the fun, contact your local retailer for information on how to join the Enesco PRECIOUS MOMENTS *Collectors' Club* or the PRECIOUS MOMENTS *Fun Club*, or visit the Enesco web site at ***www.enescoclubs.com.***

The PRECIOUS MOMENTS® Chapel

In 1989, artist Sam Butcher realized his dream of building a place where he could share the love and peace of the Lord with all who visit. The PRECIOUS MOMENTS Chapel, located in Carthage, Missouri, is host to hundreds of thousands of visitors per year for general visits and special events.

The Chapel

The PRECIOUS MOMENTS Chapel is considered by many to be an architectural masterpiece. Inspired by the beauty of other

chapels, such as the Sistine Chapel in Rome, Sam Butcher has decorated the chapel with over 80 stained-glass windows and murals that depict stories from the Bible and other inspirational themes. Along with his understudy, Nelson Lete, Butcher designed elaborately carved wooden doors, bronze details and marble floors which decorate the chapel and make it an awesome sight to behold.

Visitors gaze at the murals in the chapel.

The Fountain Of Angels®

In 1997, after years of planning and building, The Fountain of Angels was opened to the public. Today, all who enter the massive amphitheater are treated to a heavenly display of water, lights and sound. The exciting show features over 250 bronze sculptures of the famed teardrop-eyed children and a water and light

The Fountain Of Angels is a heavenly site to behold!

display. The performance is choreographed to music by members of the London Philharmonic Symphony Orchestra. The fountain is one of the greatest attractions on The Chapel's 3,000 acre campus.

Wedding Island

One of the many nooks on the sprawling Chapel Complex is the Wedding Island. Both the Victorian mansion and chapel are well-suited to wedding ceremonies. In fact, couples come from miles around to recite their vows on this romantic island. In 2000, PRECIOUS MOMENTS, Inc. introduced a service where brides-to-be can receive

The PRECIOUS MOMENTS Wedding Island is the perfect site for special ceremonies.

wedding planning advice for creating a PRECIOUS MOMENTS-style ceremony and reception from wedding planners via The PRECIOUS MOMENTS Chapel web site, *www.preciousmoments.com.*

Visitor's Center

These life-sized PRECIOUS MOMENTS characters are always happy to meet collectors!

The European village recreated on the grounds of The Chapel serves as the Visitor's Center. Complete with a gift shop, costumed characters, a moat and a waterfall, the Visitor's Center is a great place to get acquainted with The Chapel grounds and find those exclusive collectibles you've been searching for!

Visitors can choose from two types of accommodations – Cubby Bear's® RV Park or the Best Western PRECIOUS MOMENTS® Hotel. Admission to The Chapel is free to the public, though there is a fee for tours of the Wedding Island and The Fountain of Angels.

Helping Others Is Care-A-Van-Tastic

The 2000 Care-A-Van visited military bases and
Special Olympics events throughout the year.

It's bright blue, has 18 wheels, is full of porcelain and stuffed treasures and brings big, toothy smiles everywhere it goes. What is it? The Enesco **PRECIOUS MOMENTS** Care-A-Van, of course! The Care-A-Van (which debuted at the International Collectible Exposition in 1998) began its 2000 tour around the country with a few special places in mind. Stopping at military bases and Special Olympics events across the United States, the Care-A-Van, a museum on wheels, shared the inspirational message of "loving, caring and sharing" with both **PRECIOUS MOMENTS** collectors and members of the armed forces. They also cheered on Special Olympics athletes to victory at five Special Olympics events around the United States!

As part of the Care-A-Van tradition, **PRECIOUS MOMENTS** offered two exclusive figurines to those who visited the museum. Some of the proceeds from the exclusive, "A Winning Spirit Comes From Within," benefit the Special Olympics and the re-release "Believe The Impossible," offered at military bases and select retailers, underwent a few color changes and is back from suspension. And don't miss out on your chance to add a die-cast reproduction of the Care-A-Van to your collection. The 2000 edition is the second die-cast truck made to commemorate the Care-A-Van.

Stay tuned to *www.CollectorsQuest.com* throughout the year to find out if the Care-A-Van will be coming to a town near you!

The Year In Review

Each year, Enesco and PRECIOUS MOMENTS, Inc. (PMI) thrill collectors with a myriad of special events and get-togethers where all who love the line can share their collections and heart-warming stories. These events are also perfect for acquiring the hottest new exclusive figurines, and the first year of the new millennium was certainly no exception!

Around The World With PRECIOUS MOMENTS®

★ The PRECIOUS MOMENTS Alaskan Cruise kicked off the summer of 2000. Collectors were awed by the beauty of the Alaskan wildlife and landscape. Back on the ship, the travelers found loads of PRECIOUS MOMENTS-style fun! Along with the fun and games

came the excitement of collecting "PM Bucks" which featured the well-known faces of such Enesco and PMI employees as Gene Freedman, Sam Butcher and Rachel Perkal, and having figurines signed by Sam Butcher, himself! Collectors returned with the Cruise Exclusive figurine "Whale Have Oceans Of Fun" and the TENDER TAIL "Whale," both of which are sure to spark memories of good times with new friends and old pals!

★ Just days after the Alaskan Cruise returned to harbor, the International Collectible Exposition in Rosemont, Illinois began.

With just enough time to unpack, collectors lined up for a glimpse of the new 2001 introductions and to meet and greet their favorite Enesco associates. Collectors received a warm welcome in the Enesco Hospitality Room where *Collectors' Club* members were presented with special gifts as a thank you for their continuing support! The show's exclusive piece was "You Have A Special Place In My Heart," which is likely a mutual sentiment between PRECIOUS

MOMENTS collectors and those who bring them their favorite collectible line.

★ The holiday season is always celebrated with much fanfare in Carthage, Missouri, especially since the Collectors' Christmas Weekend has become an annual event at the PRECIOUS MOMENTS Chapel. Beginning on November 30th, The Chapel received thousands of collectors and shared the spirit of the Christmas season. Collectors enjoyed tours of the

A youngster hides behind a child-sized PRECIOUS MOMENTS sculpture.

grounds, stood awed at the beauty of Sam Butcher's famed labor of love, The Fountain of Angels, and listened in on seminars that addressed collector's questions and other topics of interest. Collectors were delighted to receive the weekend's exclusive, "Ready In The Nick Of Time," which featured a little boy sweeping his chimney in preparation for a Christmas Eve visit!

Events Worth Waiting For

★ On October 29, 2000, "A Toast To 2000" was held at over 4,000 PRECIOUS MOMENTS retail locations throughout the United

States. Previously, an exclusive piece had been sealed in a time capsule which was opened during the retail event. Many happy collectors witnessed the unveiling of "He Shall Lead The World Into The 21st Century," a figurine depicting Jesus surrounded by children from around the world.

★ In keeping with the tradition of "loving, caring and sharing," Enesco teamed up with NABCO, The National Alliance of Breast Cancer Organizations, in 2000 to help fund breast cancer awareness and treatment. The benefit piece, titled "Life Is Worth Fighting For," features a young girl wearing boxing gloves and a pink ribbon, the symbol of breast cancer awareness.

★ Sam Butcher's favorite piece is "To God Be The Glory." Originally suspended in 1987, the piece was re-released with some

modifications at a special event held from November 17 – 19, 2000. Packaged with the new figurine was a hand-numbered collector's card and some fortunate collectors found a scrap of Sam Butcher's painting shirt tucked inside the box. For years, collectors have known that Sam would be willing to give them the shirt off his back and now he's gone and done it!

★ "We're Serving Others" was a PRECIOUS MOMENTS Distinguished Service Retailer and Century Circle Retailer event held on August 12th and 13th. An exquisite exclusive was featured – "Scoopin' Up Some Love," which portrays a girl holding two ice cream cones. And to add to the excitement, the figurine has a variation – 2,000 figurines were produced with a rainbow sherbet cone!

★ For one week in July, a figurine featuring Enesco's Master Sculptor was made available. "Mr. Fujioka" was a free gift with the purchase of select figurines at the "We're Making A Joyful Noise, Thank You!" event.

Saminals: A Breed Apart

Animal lovers have a reason to rejoice with the introduction of a new collection from the PRECIOUS MOMENTS line. These very special wild animals, which made their debut in 2000, will take you on a jungle safari and capture your heart, as well.

Called "Saminals" (because they're "Sam's animals," of course), these 10 jungle animals from artist Sam Butcher feature his trade-mark teardrop-shaped eyes and expressive faces. Each special figurine comes with a puzzle piece showing which part of the world that animal inhabits. And when you've collected all 10 animals, you can put the pieces together to complete the jungle puzzle scene! It's like getting two collectibles for the price of one!

The inaugural collection contains a variety of adorable animals including a warthog, hippo, monkey, elephant, giraffe, gorilla, lion, meerkat, rhino and zebra. With all these guys hanging around, you'll soon have your own miniature zoo!

Each tiny resin figurine is depicted in an adorable pose – they just can't resist "monkeying around" – and features a letter somewhere on the piece. And when all the letters are placed together, they spell out the message "Jungle Love." Future additions to the line will spell out different messages.

So strap on your safari hat and get ready for a "puzzling" jungle adventure – you just never know where the adventurous Sam Butcher and PRECIOUS MOMENTS will take you next!

More PRECIOUS MOMENTS®

Do you want to have a PRECIOUS MOMENTS-themed birthday party or send a PRECIOUS MOMENTS greeting card? Whatever your desire, there is probably a PRECIOUS MOMENTS licensee which produces a product to suit your needs. There are more than 60 licensees of the PRECIOUS MOMENTS line, each of which is carefully regulated by PRECIOUS MOMENTS Inc., the company established to make sure that only the finest quality goods are manufactured bearing PRECIOUS MOMENTS images. From crafts to candles, whatever you're looking for is sure to be out there. Here is a listing of some licensed PRECIOUS MOMENTS goods.

Books – Inspirational books, Bibles, prayer books and Bible stories can be found in retail stores for those who take comfort in PRECIOUS MOMENTS' messages. For youngsters, children's Bibles, in addition to story, coloring and activity books are available from various companies.

Children's Items – Your precious ones can be surrounded by their favorite PRECIOUS MOMENTS images! Baby-care products are available to gently care for your little ones, and mobiles, musical pull toys and soft cloth characters will keep them entertained for hours (when you're not wheeling them around in their PRECIOUS MOMENTS stroller).

For preschool-aged children, be sure to look for PRECIOUS MOMENTS-themed board games, boxed activity products and videos. PRECIOUS MOMENTS characters can watch over them as they sleep, too, when you decorate their room with themed bedding, curtains and pillows.

Clothing – Share your love of PRECIOUS MOMENTS with the world when you wear T-shirts, sweatshirts, footwear, sleepwear, swimwear and even medical uniforms decorated with PRECIOUS MOMENTS images. Many of these products are available for both the young and the young at heart. Watches and jewelry are also available, as are backpacks and handbags.

Crafts – Sewing enthusiasts can visit their local craft store where they will most likely find a wide variety of PRECIOUS MOMENTS embroidery cards and cross stitch books, kits and pamphlets. Or, if you're looking for a project for the entire

family, record of all of your "precious moments" in a scrapbooking kit, or use rubber stamps and stamp pads to create cards and decorations featuring your favorite designs.

Dolls – One of the most popular products on the market are vinyl dolls licensed through the PRECIOUS MOMENTS Company. These dolls are collectibles in their own right, with limited editions, retirements and suspensions, just like in the figurine line. Additionally, porcelain dolls are available through direct mail from the Ashton-Drake Galleries.

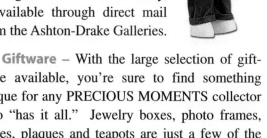

Giftware – With the large selection of giftware available, you're sure to find something unique for any PRECIOUS MOMENTS collector who "has it all." Jewelry boxes, photo frames, plates, plaques and teapots are just a few of the items that are sure to appeal to the collector in your life. And don't forget to wrap the gift in PRECIOUS MOMENTS wrapping paper!

Home Decor – Make your home a PRECIOUS MOMENTS oasis with the home decor items currently on the market. Woven blankets, posters, prints, wall coverings and borders all make tasteful and decorative home accents. Displaying your collection has never been easier with a themed curio cabinet. Even yard products such as garden statues and planters can create a unique and inspirational atmosphere.

Party Goods – Make your next big event an affair to remember with festive PRECIOUS MOMENTS decorations, tableware and accessories. Several companies offer gift wrapping goods, while others provide wedding invitations and announcements, as well as holiday and birthday invitations. Wedding accessories and cake toppers will delight the bride and groom on their big day, while edible cake decorations will turn any cake into a work of art. Don't forget balloons to inflate the excitement!

Personal Care – Perfumes, shampoo and bath oils will relax you when you manage to grab some *precious moments* for yourself!

Your car can sport PRECIOUS MOMENTS gear, too, with baby auto shades, license plate frames and decals! But how will you pay for it all? Just whip out your PRECIOUS MOMENTS checks (held, of course, in your PRECIOUS MOMENTS checkbook cover).

There's no end to the wonderful products available from PRECIOUS MOMENTS licensees, and there will surely be many new products to come! And once you have all these goodies, there are plenty of ways to have fun with your vast collection of

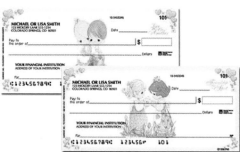

PRECIOUS MOMENTS products. See the following section on "Making Memories With PRECIOUS MOMENTS" for some ideas!

Making Memories With PRECIOUS MOMENTS®

Collecting PRECIOUS MOMENTS figurines is fun, but decorating, crafting and gift-giving with PRECIOUS MOMENTS is even better! There are so many exciting and easy ways to integrate PRECIOUS MOMENTS into your life! In the next few pages, we'll give you a few tips to get started.

Crafting

If you'd like to share your love of PRECIOUS MOMENTS with others and give a gift treasured for years to come, cross stitching and embroidering with PRECIOUS MOMENTS patterns is the perfect project for you. Designs by Gloria & Pat, Inc. offers a multitude of PRECIOUS MOMENTS cross stitching books and leaflets for craft mavens and beginners, alike. Many of the books, which can be found at craft stores across the country, are themed, such as one which offers sports based on PRECIOUS MOMENTS figurines. If there's a budding sports star in your life, create a personalized design for them using one of these patterns. Maybe your mother has passed along her love of sewing to you. If so, why not create a special cross stitch design for her and give it to her next Mother's Day along with the "Mother Sew Dear" figurine?

Scrapbooking is a great way to capture memories and moments for a lifetime and many PRECIOUS MOMENTS accessories are available to help you customize your book. Start a scrapbook for your child, or for another special person in your life. You can use PRECIOUS MOMENTS rubber stamps and stickers to decorate and personalize the album and give them as gifts.

Next time you throw a baby shower, why not give each guest a page of a scrapbook to decorate with the materials you have provided. When everyone has finished, collect all of the pages and affix photos from the shower to each one. Present it to the mother-to-be along with a PRECIOUS MOMENTS figurine such as "A Love Like No Other."

Party Planning And Gift Giving

Make festive occasions even more special by incorporating PRECIOUS MOMENTS into your decorating scheme. Pull out the rubber stamps again and use them to decorate your invitations and envelopes. Choose invitations in soft pastel colors and affix PRECIOUS MOMENTS address labels in the upper left-hand corner of the envelopes to expand on the PRECIOUS MOMENTS theme.

When you're ready to decorate, bunches of PRECIOUS MOMENTS balloons can be tied to chairs or even affixed outside the house to let everyone know where the party is. Guests can each take a balloon home with them at the end of the get-together as a keepsake. Consider using PRECIOUS MOMENTS figurines among flowers as centerpieces or giving away figurines that match the theme of your party as door prizes. And don't forget PRECIOUS MOMENTS decorations and tableware to complete the perfect party look!

Whether it be for a birthday, holiday or other special occasions, PRECIOUS MOMENTS make great gifts. There are also anniversary figurines, holiday pieces, Mother's Day and special birthday figurines. Additionally, with over 1,600 pieces to choose from, there are a great many figurines that are wonderful to give "just because."

PRECIOUS MOMENTS baby and wedding albums are great ways to preserve precious memories forever. Developed by the PRECIOUS MOMENTS Company and Hallmark, these albums make great gifts for new parents and newlyweds. Consider giving them in a gift basket along with appropriate figurines and other goodies. For example, a new mother might enjoy receiving a basket containing TENDER TAILS or *Hugs For The Soul* plush animals along with a pretty pastel receiving blanket, rattles, bottles and other small baby items.

For a daughter or son cramming for finals at college, why not make them a "care package" containing home-baked goodies, an encouraging letter and a figurine such as "Just A Line To Wish You A Happy Day."

Seasonal Celebrations

Decorating for the holidays is so much more fun with PRECIOUS MOMENTS! Besides the regular line's supply of ornaments and holiday pieces, many companies offer licensed holiday items. For almost every holiday occasion, you can find appropriate PRECIOUS MOMENTS pieces with which to decorate your home.

Christmas is a particularly appropriate season to decorate with PRECIOUS MOMENTS. Why not have a PRECIOUS MOMENTS-themed tree? You can decorate it with PRECIOUS MOMENTS ornaments (including special dated ornaments), TENDER TAILS ornaments and a PRECIOUS MOMENTS tree topper. Start a family tradition by buying ornaments for each member of the family annually. Start with pieces like "Baby's First Christmas" or "Our First Christmas Together" and go from there! Soon, you'll have a tree full of wonderful memories!

A great project the whole family can enjoy is making your own PRECIOUS MOMENTS ornaments. Stencil the outline of a PRECIOUS MOMENTS image onto a thin piece of cardboard. Paint it in pretty pastels (or Christmas colors). When the paint is dry, cut out the shape. Punch a hole through the top and tie a pretty ribbon through it so that the ornament can be hung on the tree.

Make a holiday display by using the PRECIOUS MOMENTS *Nativity* series. Arrange the pieces to your liking, add a stable and some hay, and you'll have a beautiful Nativity scene to remind you of the true meaning of Christmas.

Easter is another holiday which lends itself perfectly to PRECIOUS MOMENTS displays. Place fake grass on a table or shelf and incorporate your favorite pieces, colored Easter eggs and pretty spring flowers into the display. And Easter baskets are a sure way to delight your friends and relatives who love to collect PRECIOUS MOMENTS Fill a basket with fake grass, candy and add a PRECIOUS MOMENTS figurine such as "Bunnies" from the *Two By Two* series or a TENDER TAILS bunny.

We hope that you have found these ideas exciting and easy to use! To share your ideas on how you enjoy displaying with other collectors, be sure to add a posting to our PRECIOUS MOMENTS bulletin board at *www.CollectorsQuest.com*.

Alphabetical Index

– Key –

All PRECIOUS MOMENTS pieces are listed below in alphabetical order. Following each piece in parentheses is an abbreviation for the type of item (see key) and the stock number. The first number in the page and picture column refers to the piece's location within the Value Guide section and the second to the box in which it is pictured on that page.

ABBREVIATION KEY

A	Accessories
B	Bells
BH	Bible Holders
C	Clocks
CB	Covered Boxes
CC	Candle Climbers
DI	Displays
DM	Die-Cast Metal
DO	Dolls
E	Eggs
F	Figurines
FR	Frames
H	TENDER TAILS Hugs For You
HB	Hinged Boxes
J	Jack-In-The-Boxes
LM . . .	LITTLE MOMENTS
ME	Medallions
MU	Musicals
N	Night Lights
O	Ornaments
P	Plates
PL	Plush
TH	Thimbles
TR	Tree Toppers
TO	TENDER TAILS Ornaments
TT	TENDER TAILS

	Pg.	Pic.

Alphabetical Index

Alphabetical Index

289

Alphabetical Index

Numerical Index

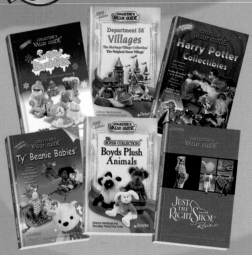